Contents

5 • SPEND LIKE A MISER, LIVE LIKE A KING

6 • FABULOUS HEALTH AFTER 50

1

Money Secrets of Multimillionaires

The Automatic Millionaire's Very Simple Get-Rich Secret

Sticking to a budget means depriving yourself today for the sake of your future well-being. Few of us have the discipline that this requires—we dine at expensive restaurants...buy new cars every few years...and spend $3.50 for a cup of coffee. Result? Even people with decent incomes live from paycheck to paycheck.

To save steadily, most people need to put savings on autopilot. Arrange for a certain percentage of each paycheck to be tucked away. This takes little discipline or effort. You can arrange for your bank or mutual fund firm to automatically take money out of your bank account every month.

HOW MUCH TO SET ASIDE

Start out small. Save 1% of your salary. Soon, you can bump that up to 3%. Your goal should be to save at least 10%. Those with grander objectives should save 15% to 20%. You will be amazed by how little sacrifice is involved.

Say you now buy lunch at the office every day. By brown-bagging it (at a cost of $1 per day instead of $8), you can save $35 a week, or about $150 a month. If you earn a 7% annual return, that savings would grow to $73,791 in 20 years.

The best way to save is with a 401(k) or other tax-advantaged plan. If you save after-tax dollars, the federal government alone takes about $3 of every $10 you earn. When you put $10 into a retirement plan, the entire sum goes to work and won't be taxed until withdrawal.

PAY DOWN YOUR MORTGAGE

Making regular mortgage payments is a form of forced savings.

To accelerate the process, see if your bank will allow you to pay off your mortgage early,

---

David Bach, founder and CEO of FinishRich, Inc., financial advisers and educators, New York City. *www.finishrich.com*. He is author of *Smart Couples Finish Rich, Smart Women Finish Rich* and *The Automatic Millionaire* (all published by Broadway Books).

perhaps by making one payment every two weeks instead of one a month. By following this system, you will make 26 half payments, or the equivalent of 13 monthly payments each year. You could pay off a 30-year mortgage in about 23 years.

Consider that a $250,000 30-year mortgage with an interest rate of 6% will cost you $289,595 in interest. By paying biweekly, you will pay $60,972 less.

Are You a Savvy Consumer?

Elisabeth Leamy, Emmy Award–winning television investigative reporter, Washington, DC. She is author of *The Savvy Consumer: How to Avoid Scams and Rip-Offs that Cost You Time and Money* (Capital). For more quizzes, visit *www.thesavvyconsumer.com*.

As a TV investigative reporter, I see even smart people getting ripped off for thousands of dollars every day.

To avoid being a target, be the hunter, *not* the hunted. Ignore any company that pursues you too aggressively—the contractor who knocks on your door claiming to be working on other houses in the neighborhood...the broker who cold-calls you with must-own stocks...the carpet cleaner who sends you a coupon offering steep discounts. Always conduct your own research first, then hire someone that you have sought out.

To test just how knowledgeable you are as a consumer, take my quiz. *Answer true or false...*

- **When you buy a new car, federal law allows you three days to change your mind and return it.**

False. All car sales are final. Consumers frequently make this mistake because they believe automobiles fall under the Federal Trade Commission's "cooling-off rule." This regulation allows you 72 hours to cancel the purchase of a product—but only if it was sold to you at your home or away from the seller's normal place of business, such as at a hotel or convention center.

The only way you can return a new car is if it qualifies as a lemon under state law. Lemon laws apply only to new cars and vary by state. Typically, you have to prove that the car has had the same problem repeatedly and can't be fixed, or that it has been in a repair shop for a total of more than 30 days within the first 12 months or 12,000 miles. For help in getting the manufacturer to comply with lemon laws, contact your state consumer protection office or use the Better Business Bureau's Auto Line, a free program that helps car owners resolve disputes about defects (800-955-5100, *www.bbb.org/us/auto-line-lemon-law*).

- **If your home-improvement contractor rips you off or does shoddy work, some states will pay you back.**

True. Many states have "construction recovery" or "contractor's guaranty" funds that reimburse consumers for as much as $50,000 or more. The fund covers general contractors, plumbers, electricians, etc. Check with the state board of contractors or department of licensing to see if such a fund is available.

Important: To be eligible for reimbursement, you must have hired a contractor who is licensed in your state. (Thirty-six states require contractors to be licensed, and nearly all states license plumbers and electricians.)

You can present your case yourself at a formal hearing and be reimbursed by your state in as little as 60 days.

Helpful evidence: Photos of shoddy work and an inspector's report.

To avoid unlicensed contractors, know the warning signs...

- An unmarked vehicle. Most states require license numbers to appear on vehicles, estimates and advertising.
- The only contact information for him/her is through a post office box, a pager or an answering service, instead of a permanent street address.
- He has a "business" or "occupancy" license, not a contractor's license. A business license is not proof of competency and requires no testing or apprenticeships. An occupancy license is for zoning—it simply grants permission to conduct a certain type of business at a particular address.

• If you receive unsolicited merchandise in the mail, you are legally obligated to send back the product or pay for it.

False. Federal law makes it illegal for companies to send you something that you didn't order and then bill you for it. You're allowed to keep the item as a gift, give it away or throw it out. *Other steps to take...*

• Send a certified letter to the company notifying it that you have received unwanted merchandise and will not be burdened with the time and expense of returning it. You are not required by law to send such a letter, but you will establish a paper trail in case the company ever tries to come after you with collection notices.

• If it appears that you received an item through an honest error—such as a customer mix-up at a legitimate merchant—you can write or E-mail the seller saying that you're giving it a reasonable amount of time (15 to 30 days) to send a courier to pick up the product or else you reserve the right to keep the item. If you receive a bill, contact your local US Postal Inspector's office to report the company.

• A coupon to clean four rooms of carpeting for $29.95 is a good deal.

False. Based on my investigations of carpet cleaners, initial low prices with these common come-ons always are followed by hefty "upcharges." Typically, you'll be charged extra for pretreatment solutions, deodorizers and protective spray...moving furniture...and cleaning carpeting in closets.

To avoid rip-offs...

• Use a reputable carpet cleaner. These companies tend to charge by the square foot, not the room. You may also want to hire a cleaning contractor that uses truck-mounted equipment, which is more powerful than the self-contained equipment used by cut-rate carpet cleaners.

• To find a reputable cleaner in your area, contact the Institute of Inspection, Cleaning and Restoration Certification (800-835-4624, *www.iicrc.org*).

• Your chances of winning a publisher's sweepstakes increase if you buy a magazine.

False. More than half of American adults entered a sweepstakes in the past year. What many don't realize is that, by law, sweepstakes mail offers must give you an equal chance of winning, even if you buy nothing.

Know these rules...

• When representatives for legitimate sweep stakes promotions call, they cannot describe the prize before making their sales pitch.

• After the sales pitch, they must reveal the retail value of all prizes and disclose your odds of winning, when the prizes will be awarded and how to get a list of winners.

• They cannot claim that you have won a prize unless you really have. Winning a "free vacation offer" is not the same thing.

Important: Don't make up-front payments. Promoters of legitimate sweepstakes never ask for money to cover taxes and processing, judging or entry fees.

If you suspect fraud, contact your state's attorney general or secretary of state.

• When you get an unwanted telemarketing pitch, you should say, "Take me off your list."

False. That request has no legal teeth. *Better...*

• Ask the telemarketer to put you on the company's "do-not-call" list. Laws require telemarketers to maintain and honor such lists.

• Have your home phone number put on three do-not-call lists—the Direct Marketing Association list, 212-768-7277, *www.the-dma.org*... your state's "Do-Not-Call" Registry (contact your state consumer protection agency office to find out if your state has one)...and the Federal Trade Commission's National Registry, 888-382-1222, *www.donotcall.gov.* It is not necessary to include cell phone numbers—telemarketing to them has always been illegal—but they can be registered.

• Parking garage time clocks are accurate.

False. When I investigated parking garages around Washington, DC, I discovered that 75% of them skewed their clocks in their favor by at least six minutes.

Typical result: A customer checks in, returning just before an hour has elapsed, only to be charged for some or all of the second hour.

To avoid rip-offs...

• Make a note of the time on your own watch as you enter and exit, and show the attendant. What matters is the time that has elapsed.

• If there is a discrepancy, complain and threaten to contact the department of consumer affairs in your city or town. Most garages will back down rather than risk having an official complaint lodged against them.

• **You can improve or repair your credit score within 24 to 72 hours.**

True. While the credit repair industry is riddled with scams, "rapid rescoring" is a legitimate service offered by local credit bureaus when you apply for a home loan.

How it works: Rescorers work directly with the three major credit bureaus. Not only do they correct errors on your credit report, they restructure your debt in ways that boost your credit score.

Cost: About $200. This might seem high, but by raising your credit score, you can often qualify for a lower mortgage rate and save thousands of dollars.

How it might work: A rescorer notices that you have three credit cards. One is near its limit, while you hardly use the other two at all. By transferring some debt to the underused cards, you improve your score by 5%. Why would this be? Scoring models are biased against consumers who are near any of their credit limits.

If you want assistance from a rapid rescorer, ask your mortgage broker or lender to refer you to one—rapid rescoring firms don't work directly with consumers. If you get an unsolicited offer for overnight credit repair, it's a scam.

What to Do with Reward Points

Pay your American Express bill with reward points. American Express will accept its own membership rewards points for bill payment, at the rate of 20,000 points for a $100 credit. Consider the Amex offer if you have more reward points than you can use, can't get a free ticket to a preferred destination or don't plan to travel by plane. (A total of 20,000 to 25,000 points earns an airline ticket worth much more than $100.)

Tim Winship, editor, FrequentFlier.com, a Web site that provides frequent-flier program information and advice, Los Angeles.

Painless Ways to Save

Mary Hunt, founder and publisher of the newsletter *Debt-Proof Living*. She is author of *Live Your Life for Half the Price (Without Sacrificing the Life You Love)* (DPL Press).

For those people who are trying to stretch their cash, here are some easy suggestions on how to cut costs...

HOLIDAY TURKEYS

Frozen turkeys are much fresher than fresh turkeys. How is that possible?

Modern equipment flash freezes the turkey within minutes of processing.

Freezing does not change the taste or quality. And buying a frozen bird during "turkey season" saves you 50% to 75% of the cost of a fresh turkey.

Never pay for a "name brand." While there are many major brands of turkey, most are processed at one of the five major turkey processing plants in the United States.

GASOLINE

You can earn free gasoline when you go grocery shopping. Large supermarket chains, such as Save Mart Supermarkets, S-Mart Foods and Lucky.

How it works: Visit participating retailers to get your rewards card. Scan your card when you check out and earn Fuel Rewards on qualified purchases.

Recent examples: Buy two candy bars and get four cents-per-gallon off your next fuel purchase. Buy $10 worth of merchandise and get five cents-per-gallon off your next fuel purchase.

Note: The actual products will vary. Different stores have different items at different times.

For more information: *www.fuelrewards.com.*

BOOKS

• **Booksfree.com.** Instead of paying retail or getting on long waiting lists for books at public libraries, you can choose from this pay library's great selection of books. Includes over 250,000 titles (fiction, nonfiction, audio and children's books) for a monthly fee depending on how many books you rent. Each book can be purchased for up to 30% off list price.

How it works: You can receive two to 15 books at a time through Media Mail. There are no due dates, late fees or shipping costs.

When you finish, return the books in a prepaid mailer. You can cancel your membership at any time without paying a penalty. *www.booksfree.com.*

Alternative: Buy new and used titles at Half.com, a division of eBay, for 50% to 90% less than retail stores. *www.half.ebay.com.*

TELEPHONE

• **Cheap overseas calls.** Onesuite.com, *www.onesuite.com* (1.8 cents/minute to Australia, 3.2 cents/minute to Germany)…Kallcents.com, *www.kallcents.com* (6 cents/minute to Hong Kong). You buy minutes in advance and receive a toll-free access phone number.

ENERGY/UTILITIES

• **Use less hot water.** Set your soap dispenser or soap dish on the left side of the sink in your kitchen and bathroom, as close to the hot-water handle as possible.

You, family members and visitors will reach for the cold faucet handle automatically. Cool water is just as effective for cleaning your hands as hot water.

AUTOMOBILES

• **Rent out your garage.** If parking spaces are at a premium in your neighborhood, you could collect $100 or more per month just for parking your own car on the street or in your driveway.

Specify that the arrangement is "for storage only"—no work can be done on the car there. Post a sign on your lawn or place an ad in your local newspaper.

• **Get the most from insurance claims.** If a driver damages your car, you may be able to file a claim for "diminution of value" against his/her insurance company. You might have to provide photos, *Blue Book* values, appraisals, etc. Check with your insurance agent.

Reason: Even though your car was repaired adequately, it has diminished resale value, for which you may be compensated.

Easy Ways to Cut Your Expenses

Jonathan D. Pond, president, Jonathan D. Pond, LLC, One Gateway Center, 300 Washington St., Newton, Massachusetts. He is author of *Your Money Matters* (Putnam) and *1,001 Ways to Cut Your Expenses* (Dell).

In virtually every part of our lives, we can find easy ways to reduce the cost of living. Housing, clothes, cars and leisure activities all take a large portion of our paychecks. Even our pets cost money to feed and keep healthy.

A little forethought can help us cut our expenses significantly without depriving us of anything we really need. And don't think cutting out the small things won't help save money. Small savings actually compound over the years to produce big savings.

Proven ways to cut costs and get the most for the money you must spend…

HOUSING EXPENSES

• **Don't buy the most expensive home in the neighborhood if you're relocating.** And—don't improve your home so much that it becomes the fanciest one on the block.

Money-saver: Buy a multifamily dwelling and rent out the other units. That way, other people will be paying part—or all—of your mortgage costs.

Alternative: Take in a boarder.

• **If you purchase a condo, do not choose one in a brand-new condominium community.** The maintenance fee won't be predictable. It could go way up.

• **Obtain several bids on home-repair and improvement projects.** After seeing the best offer, ask the other bidders if they can do better—and even after deciding, try to negotiate a still better price with the chosen contractor.

BREAKDOWNS AND CRISES

• **Learn to make emergency repairs yourself.** That way, if a water pipe suddenly bursts or your power fails, you will be able to take swift action to prevent the problem from becoming worse—and more expensive to fix. Buy the necessary fix-it books, tools and supplies.

• **Make an inventory of all your household possessions.** And—save receipts for all major purchases. Keep copies in your safe-deposit box or office. If disaster strikes, you will be able to show the insurance company what you owned and how much it cost.

• **Never assume that a broken appliance must be replaced by a new model.** If you can't get it repaired under the warranty, spend a little to discover exactly what is wrong and how much it will cost to make it usable. And if it can't be fixed, consider doing without it.

Money- and time-saver: Keep all your warranties and owner's manuals in one file.

CLOTHING EXPENSES

• **Find a good tailor who can alter garments that you can no longer wear** because they are out of style or your size has changed...a good shoe repair person who can extend the life of your shoes...and buy clothes that do not require dry-cleaning.

• **Time your purchases.** Before buying any clothes, ask the salesperson if and when they will be going on sale.

SHOPPING EXPENSES

• **Make a shopping list.** Set a spending budget before you go shopping for anything...and stick to it.

• **Check classified ads and thrift stores for used furniture.** The best buys are likely to be found in upper-class neighborhoods.

Other furniture money-savers: Visit several discount furniture showrooms...consider buying brand-name furniture by mail or over the Internet where some great bargains are available.

• **Shop for major appliances near the end of the month, quarter or year.** That is when sellers are most anxious to push merchandise out the door to meet sales quotas or win awards.

• **Don't buy service contracts.** The seller expects to make money on them, so premiums are set higher than the average purchaser is likely to spend on repairs.

CAR EXPENSES

• **Buy a good used car instead of an expensive new car.** Keep the car until it costs more to keep it running than to replace it.

Money-saver: If you want a near-new model, ask the dealer about a demonstrator car with a new-car guarantee...or a low-mileage vehicle from a rental agency.

• **If you must buy a new car, be sure to do your homework.** Research all the incentives available on different models that meet your needs. Shop around among different dealers, and consider using an auto brokerage service to get the very best deal available.

Money-saver: The best time to buy is at the end of the model year...or at the beginning of the next model year, when the dealer is even more desperate to get rid of his/her old stock.

• **Keep your car in good shape so that it lasts longer.** Check the level of oil and other fluids weekly...change oil according to the manufacturer's specifications (or even more often)...and check tire pressure and condition frequently.

• **Choose the highest deductible you can live with on your auto insurance.** Reduce your premium further by buying antitheft devices ...inquiring about discounts for low annual mileage or for taking a defensive driving course...or asking about discounts for student drivers with good grades or who are away at college.

Money-saver: If your car is worth less than $2,000, drop the collision and/or comprehensive coverage.

LEISURE AND ENTERTAINMENT

• **Eat at home instead of going out.** If you crave a change in diet, buy inexpensive take-out food. If you must go to a restaurant, choose an inexpensive one. Check the price range before you go.

• **When you eat out, don't order more food than you can eat.** If you do, take it home. Don't order the most expensive dishes on the menu.

Money-saver: Split the dessert.

Better still: Eat dessert at home.

• **Drop your memberships in clubs**—social, country or athletic—you don't visit frequently.

• **Watch out for book and music clubs.** Don't join clubs that offer you 10 items for a dollar—or even a penny—if you have to agree to buy more books at the club's regular prices. If you figure out the average price of all the required purchases, including postage and handling, it is likely to be higher than you would pay at a discount store. Instead, borrow books and music from your local public library—for free.

PETS

• **Adopt a companion from an animal shelter** instead of buying one at a pet shop.

• **Choose a smaller animal.** It requires less food than a bigger one. Buy generic pet food rather than expensive brand-name food.

Five Reasons to Splurge On a New Car

Eric Peters, Washington, DC–based automotive columnist and author of *Automotive Atrocities: The Cars We Love to Hate* (MotorBooks.com).

From a strictly financial standpoint, it pays for most people to buy used cars. *But five engineering improvements might make it worthwhile for you to consider a new model...*

• **Safer brakes.** Today, even many economy cars have four-wheel disc brakes, and antilock brake systems are becoming common. *Brake Assist*—a new feature that further reduces stopping distances during emergency braking—is also being featured in family cars from Toyota, Volvo and others. Brake Assist automatically applies full pressure to the system during an emergency stop if the driver fails to depress the brake pedal fully. This slows the car more quickly.

• **Intelligent navigation systems.** The latest in-car satellite navigation systems can direct you around traffic jams and help you find the best route to your destination. Real-time data about traffic conditions is uploaded into the system automatically every few minutes via the car's onboard satellite radio hookup. That data is compared against your planned route in the global positioning satellite (GPS) navigation computer. If there's a bottleneck ahead, an alternate route is displayed.

• **Bodies that don't rust—and paint jobs that last.** Today's cars are so well-protected against rust by multiple coats of protective undercoating and chip-resistant primers that body rot is becoming as rare a sight as a wood-paneled Pacer.

• **Engines that don't pollute.** At least 95% of the combustion by-products of any newer model-year car is harmless water vapor and carbon dioxide. Several models from Ford, General Motors, Honda, Toyota and Volvo qualify as ultra-low emissions vehicles (ULEVs), with virtually no harmful emissions.

• **Decent gas mileage.** Even the worst offender two-ton V8 sport-utility vehicle can get mileage per gallon (mpg) in the mid-teens on the highway. And American drivers no longer have to cram themselves into microsized subcompacts to get 30 mpg.

Vastly improved fuel economy with little difference in size, power or performance can be credited to electronic fuel injection and the widespread use of overdrive transmissions. Both reduce engine operating speeds (and thus fuel consumption) once a vehicle has reached road speed. Seven-speed automatics (BMW and Mercedes-Benz) and continuously variable transmissions (CVTs) hold the promise of further mileage improvements. CVTs deliver the fuel economy of a manual transmission with the ease of an automatic.

How to Travel Free

Robert William Kirk, author of *You Can Travel Free* (Pelican Publishing Co.).

There are hundreds of budget guides that tell you how to cut costs on trips. Many of these books contain low-cost travel tips, but they don't give you the ultimate scoop on *no-cost* travel. Instead of traveling cheap, you could be traveling free—from transportation by air or sea to lodgings, meals and entertainment. Most free travel requires no special skills, credentials or contacts. And it can be just as luxurious—and often more pleasurable—than the most expensive paid vacation.

COMPLIMENTARY CRUISES

Cruise lines generally offer a free passage to anyone who recruits 10 to 15 paying passengers. (Many airlines offer similar deals.) If you can't lure that many customers, you can get a prorated reduction on your fare.

You can also cruise free as an expert in a pertinent subject. Historians, anthropologists, naturalists and ornithologists are in especially high demand. Your job on the cruise would be to present a series of lectures and to be available for informal questioning. It helps to have a PhD (or at least a master's degree) and to have published articles on the subject, but an affable personality and a willingness to share your knowledge with others can stretch your credentials.

After your first cruise in this capacity, a good reference will ease the way at other lines.

Free cruises are also available to doctors and nurses who are willing to be on 24-hour call (here a salary is an added inducement)...to athletic directors and coaches who can help organize recreational activities...to musicians and entertainers willing to perform...to cosmetologists who can barter their services for a ride.

There is also a strong demand for "hosts"—distinguished single gentlemen who are usually age 55 and older. They serve by dining and dancing with the many unattached older women taking these vacation cruises. Besides free room and board, hosts are encouraged to make use of an unlimited bar tab available for themselves and their new female friends.

FREE FOREIGN TOURS

Enlist enough people and get a whole trip—long or short—free. Some travel agencies recruit teachers, who receive a free trip if they bring six students. With 12 students, the teacher's spouse also travels free.

The same deal is available to anyone willing to organize a special-interest tour. An auto racing fan might lead a group to Le Mans...an opera aficionado might arrange a trip to La Scala in Milan. Similar trips focus on photography, architecture, theater, music, golf or wine tasting. The group leader sets the itinerary, chooses lodgings and arranges for side trips. Travel experience and linguistic skills are usually helpful, but not essential.

Travel Savings

Tom Parsons, editor of *Bestfares.com*, a clearinghouse of hidden travel deals, 1301 S. Bowen Rd., Suite 490, Arlington, Texas 76013. 800-880-1234. He travels about 100 days a year.

Traveling can be expensive. *Following are a few suggestions on how to save money when booking a hotel and reserving a rental car...*

HOTELS

• **Book your reservation after joining a discount club.** Many hotels list as many as 10 to 12 different rates *per room.* Calling the hotel directly gives you a better chance to get a lower rate than the one offered through the hotel's 800 number.

And even better than calling the hotel is joining a discount club. These clubs are run by national hotel chains and offer members hotel-room discounts of up to *50% below most other rates.* Call several national hotel chains to determine their club fees, benefits and restrictions.

• **Save up to 50% by going through a hotel broker.** Hotel brokers book rooms in hundreds of hotels around the country. Because of the volume they handle, hotels give them steep discounts on rooms. *Examples...*

• Central Reservations Service, 800-894-0680, *www.crshotels.com.*

• Hotels.com, 800-246-8357, *www.hotels.com.*

• Quikbook, 800-789-9887, *www.quikbook.com.*

RENTAL CARS

• **Check the rates offered by all of your frequent-flier accounts.** Not all airline frequent-flier plans offer the same car discounts at the same time.

Example: One company's daily rate at Washington's National Airport recently was $36/day if you belonged to one airline's frequent-flier plan. The same car was $20/day for another airline's frequent-flier plan members.

Make a list of your frequent-flier programs. Then call the car rental firm's main number, and make a list of the different plans' discounts.

• **Use the Internet to reserve rental cars.** Like airlines, rental car companies are eager to promote their Web sites. Many rental-car sites offer great discounts or free upgrades if you book over the Internet.

Example: One aggressive rental-car agency on the Web recently offered discounts of up to 40% off list rates.

Secrets to Predicting The Stock Market

Jeffrey Hirsch, president of The Hirsch Organization, an investment research firm, 184 Central Ave., Old Tappan, New Jersey 07675. He and his father, Yale Hirsch, edit *Stock Trader's Almanac* (John Wiley & Sons). They also publish *Almanac Investor Newsletter.* Their Web site is *www.stocktradersalmanac.com.*

Stock market gyrations aren't entirely random. For nearly 44 years, *Stock Trader's Almanac* has offered amazingly reliable indicators of market performance.

Consult a financial adviser if you have questions or if trends seem contradictory to you. You still need to analyze individual stocks before you start investing in them.

THE JANUARY BAROMETER

The stock market usually sets its direction for the whole year in January.

The S&P 500 Index has reflected this tendency 92.3% of the time since 1950. Eleven bear markets out of 17 began with a poor January.

BEST SIX MONTHS FOR INVESTING

Since 1950, the stock market has performed best from November through April and worst from May through October.

Only three times since 1950 has the Dow posted a double-digit loss during the November-through-April period—in 1970, during the invasion of Cambodia, in 1973, during the OPEC oil embargo, and in 2008 during the global credit crisis.

DECEMBER'S FREE LUNCH AND THE SANTA CLAUS RALLY

Investors typically dump losing stocks in December in order to realize tax losses. By late December, many stocks have been hammered down to bargain levels.

The New York Stock Exchange stocks selling at their 52-week lows near the end of December usually outperform the market by February. Over 29 years, these stocks have averaged a 13.9% increase in that short span, compared with the NYSE Composite, which gained 4.2% over the same period.

A short but robust rally during the last five days of December and the first two days of January—the Santa Claus rally—comes to Wall Street most years.

Since 1969, the gain from this rally has averaged 1.7% over just those few days. There have been 25 Santa Claus rallies in the last 33 years.

Beware of Santa's claws: When there's no Santa Claus rally, trouble often is ahead. Hence the couplet—*If Santa Claus should fail to call, bears may come to Broad and Wall* (where the New York Stock Exchange is located).

There was no Santa Claus rally in 1999. The bear market began on January 14, 2000.

PRE–ST. PATRICK'S DAY RALLY

Experienced traders know that the market often rallies before major legal holidays. People are about to get time off, so they feel upbeat. Most traders don't realize how strong the market is the day before St. Patrick's Day—which isn't a legal holiday but is celebrated by many.

Going back to 1953, the S&P 500 has gained an average of 0.33% on that day—equal to a 30-point advance for the Dow at today's levels.

I view this indicator just for fun, but some people do make money by following it.

DOWN FRIDAY AND MONDAY

Trouble often looms when stock prices are down sharply on both a Friday and the following Monday—six times out of seven, the market will go lower within five days.

In 1987, the Dow lost 108 points on Friday, October 16, and 508 points the following Monday.

Insider Trading Alert

Beware of insider trading if you work for—or have access to information on—a public company. To avoid this illegal act, ask anyone who gives you a stock tip where he/she got the information. Make sure the information is either publicly available or is the result of independent research and that there is no agreement to keep the information confidential. Never give inside information to anyone, even your spouse. Don't encourage family members to buy or sell stock in your company—the transactions may look suspicious even if they are innocent. Learn your company's trading policies when you buy or sell stock shares.

Dan Brecher, attorney specializing in claims against stockbrokers, New York City.

Another Financial Meltdown Is Headed Our Way—How to Protect Yourself *and* Profit

Robert A. Wiedemer, CEO and president of The Foresight Group, Herndon, Virginia, an economic forecasting and risk-assessment firm that advises large hedge funds and businesses. He is managing partner of the Business Valuation Center, which advises the US Small Business Administration's venture capital division. He is coauthor of *America's Bubble Economy: Profit When It Pops* and *Aftershock: Protect Yourself and Profit in the Next Global Financial Meltdown* (both by Wiley). *www.bvcvalue.com*

Many economic forecasters say that the worst is over. The stock market has largely rebounded from its 2008 meltdown…the recession is past…and depressed housing markets are starting to improve.

But a few forecasters see a darker outlook. There are more economic bubbles about to burst, they say, and the fallout will do much more damage.

Among these pessimistic forecasters is Robert A. Wiedemer—and he has been right before. In 2006, Wiedemer and his associates were among the very few forecasters who accurately identified the signs of a looming recession, which hit hard in 2008. He predicted the bursting of bubbles in housing, private debt and the stock market. Now he says that the federal government's mounting debt is dangerous enough that investors should consider paring back their US stock investments drastically.

We asked him to tell us more about what's ahead and what we can do to prepare…

THE DEBT DANGER

The total debt held by the US government was approaching $17 trillion in the early part of 2013, bloated by the economic stimulus plans and the wars. Unfortunately, the more we spend and borrow, the less each dollar is worth. At some point, our creditors—mostly Asian and European investors—will have had enough of our fiscal irresponsibility and the ultralow interest rates that we pay to borrow from them. Once a few major foreign investors, such as China, decide to invest less in the US, there will be a stampede for the exits.

It's hard to believe that the US, the de facto leader of the world for so long, could ever reach the end of its credit limit, but our debt is so staggering and out of control that I think this will happen within the next three to five years, and the harmful effects will last for years. The bond and stock markets will tumble hard, and I expect unemployment, inflation and interest rates to all rise into the double digits.

Getting by will be even tougher than it is now, and our lifestyle will take a bigger hit. Like a family without credit cards, the government will be forced to live within the constraints of its actual income, the money that it takes in from taxes. That means the US will resort to big tax increases and severe budget cuts to deal with the situation.

BET AGAINST THE US DOLLAR

You don't have to panic or make big changes in your portfolio or lifestyle immediately. The US has a big credit limit, so the debt bubble may not pop until 2014. *But shrewd investors will start making these moves now…*

• **Reduce your stock holdings.** Even with no net gains over the past decade, the Dow Jones Industrial Average is still up tenfold over the past 30 years without an equal rise in corporate earnings.

Best: Start with small changes to your portfolio, then expand them as the economy grows worse. For example, one of my clients has been selling off 2% of his stock holdings every week.

Instead of investing in stocks…

• **Buy gold.** I am not a "gold bug," but as many other types of assets decline in value, gold will see a big increase in investment demand. The government of India recently made the single largest gold purchase by a central bank in the past 30 years as a way to diversify its assets away from the US dollar. I expect gold to rise to $3,000 or more an ounce in three to five years. I have advised my clients to put 20% of their portfolios in gold but to wait for at least a 20% pullback from its recent peak prices first.

ALTER YOUR BOND STRATEGY

• **Sell bonds that have long- and medium-term maturities.** Interest rates will rise prior to the government debt bubble popping and again very dramatically afterward. That will absolutely devastate the value of your longer-term bonds. Since the yields on these bonds currently are substantial, hang on to longer-term bonds for the moment, but be ready to pull the trigger quickly, as soon as rates start to rise in the next 12 to 24 months.

Plan to move into short-term bonds and/or Treasury Inflation-Protected Securities (TIPS).

OTHER SMART MOVES

• **Don't get a new whole-life insurance policy, the kind that includes an investment account.** It's a poor investment because if the value of the assets supporting these policies drops substantially, it is hard to guarantee a return rate. Holding term-life insurance is fine, but buy an inflation rider so that the value of your payoff isn't greatly reduced.

• **Stay away from adjustable-rate debt.** All adjustable-rate loans, including credit cards and mortgages, will become treacherous when the government debt bubble bursts. Interest rates will soar, and so will your mortgage and other payments if you don't get out of them. On the other hand, if you have a low-rate mortgage or home-equity loan, don't hurry to pay it off. Your fixed-rate payments will look cheap relative to what other home owners or renters have to pay, and you will have a good, cheap place to live for as long as you wish.

• **Be cautious about real estate purchases.** Buying a vacation condo in places such as Florida may look like a bargain now, but prices will go even lower. Even if some markets rebound after a dip, any real estate recovery will likely be short-lived. We are nowhere near a bottom in real estate values. If you are planning to sell your house to move or retire in the near future, do it now. Don't expect home values to keep rising in the near future.

How Good Is Your Broker? Watch Out For These Red Flags

Daniel R. Solin, JD, attorney in New York City who has won judgments on behalf of investors against some of Wall Street's most prestigious brokerage firms. He is author of *Does Your Broker Owe You Money?* (Perigee). *www.smartestinvestmentbook.com*

There are many possible danger signs that your stockbroker is not doing a great job for you. *Here's what to watch out for, and what to do if your account is mismanaged…*

RED FLAGS

• **Your portfolio is entirely invested in stocks.** The safest allocation for most investors includes a mix of stocks, bonds and cash. Unless you feel comfortable taking major risks—and unless you and your broker have agreed on such a strategy—you should not be 100% in stocks.

Example: Sally placed $2 million with a full-service brokerage firm and explained that the money was for her retirement. The broker invested nearly everything in high-risk technology stocks. Over three years, her account lost $1.5 million. An arbitration panel awarded Sally only $600,000.

• **Your portfolio seems unusually volatile.** Beware when swings in your stock portfolio's value exceed those of the overall market, as measured by the Standard & Poor's 500 stock index.

Example: Jorge, a man in his 70s, told his broker that he wanted investments suitable for a retiree.

The broker picked highly speculative stocks that were five times as volatile as the S&P 500. In 18 months, Jorge's nest egg went from $400,000 to $6,000. Luckily, arbitration awarded Jorge $550,000 in damages.

• **Account expenses seem unusually high.** The annual total you pay in commissions and margin interest (if you buy stocks with borrowed money) shouldn't exceed 3% of the total value of your portfolio. If it does, you need to earn unrealistically high returns, year after year, just to break even.

Example: Kathleen invested $380,000 with a broker at a major national brokerage firm. Over five years, her account lost $275,000. Trading commissions and interest on margin loans amounted to more than 16% of the value of her portfolio—meaning that she would have needed to earn at least that much just to break even. When Kathleen threatened the firm with arbitration, it reimbursed her for 100% of her losses.

WHAT TO DO IF YOUR ACCOUNT IS MISMANAGED

If you are unhappy with your stockbroker, complaining to your brokerage firm is not necessarily the best course of action. Why? When you established your account, you almost certainly signed an agreement requiring any complaint to go to arbitration, rather than to court. If you complain to the firm, you might inadvertently make statements that will hurt you in arbitration.

Even if you have lost money based on a stockbroker's recommendations, you might not have a case against him/her. However, if any of the above warning signs are present, you might be able to bring a successful arbitration claim against your broker. Aim to recover all of your "well-managed account" losses. This term refers to how your portfolio should have performed if it had had reasonable fees and an appropriate asset allocation based on your age and risk tolerance.

• **If your claim is for less than $25,000,** there is a simple procedure to file for arbitration without an attorney. Contact the Financial Industry Regulatory Authority (301-590-6500, *www.finra.org*).

• **If your claim is for more than $25,000,** consult an attorney experienced in securities arbitration law. The Public Investors Arbitration Bar Association comprises more than 750 lawyers who represent complainants in securities arbitration proceedings. Go to *https://piaba.org* and click on "PIABA Bar Journal" or call 888-621-7484.

Ask up front how the attorney expects to be compensated. Some work on a fee basis, but many work on a contingency basis. They take a percentage of what you win in the arbitration.

How to Protect Your Stock's Value

You can protect the value of your stock by using options.

Example: If a stock is priced at $100/share, buy *put options* that give you the right to sell the stock at $90/share within 12 or 24 months. Then sell *call options*, which let someone else have the right to buy your stock at $120/share over the same period. This structure is called a *collar*. The cost of the put and the proceeds from the call should be equal to limit your downside and ensure that you get at least $90 a share. If the stock price falls below $90, you still can sell it for $90. If it rises above $120, you can sell it or buy back the call option.

Caution: Options trading is complex—consult a knowledgeable financial adviser.

Christopher Cordaro, CFA, CFP, RegentAtlantic Capital LLC, Morristown, New Jersey. *www.regentatlantic.com*

How to Protect Yourself from Bad Broker Advice

If you lost money as a direct result of a broker's advice, you may be able to recover some of it through arbitration. But you must be able to prove you bought the stock based directly and solely on the broker's flawed recommendation. Write a letter of complaint to the firm. If the matter is not resolved to your satisfaction within two months, file an arbitration claim quickly. Investors recover about half of their money more than half the time in securities arbitration.

To file a claim: The Financial Industry Regulatory Authority provides rules and filing costs for claims. Go to *www.finra.org* and click on the "Arbitration & Mediation" tab.

David E. Robbins, Esq., Kaufmann, Gildin, Robbins & Oppenheim, LLP, and author of the *Securities Arbitration Procedure Manual* (LexisNexis, Matthew Bender).

Hidden Bank Overdraft Fees

Banks charge fees for what they call courtesy overdraft or bounce protection. But the fees can be larger than the amount overdrawn—such as a $29 fee for going over by $20. Bank customers must opt into overdraft protection, but banks provide overdraft protection without always making the costs clear.

Best: When you establish a checking account, set up standard overdraft protection linked to another account at the same bank, such as a savings or credit card account. If the checking account is overdrawn, the linked account is automatically used—and the usual fee is $10 or more.

Jean Ann Fox, director of financial services, Consumer Federation of America, Washington, DC.

It's Not Too Late! You Can Still Build A Solid Nest Egg

Economist, attorney, actor and comedian Ben Stein, who lives in Beverly Hills, California, with his wife, six cats and three dogs. He was a speechwriter for presidents Richard Nixon and Gerald Ford. He is author of *Yes, You Can Become a Successful Income Investor! Reaching for Yield in Today's Market* (Hay House).

Many American workers have not saved enough for retirement. Less than half have even calculated how much they will need for retirement.

Rectifying this situation has become a personal mission for economist Ben Stein. The notoriously frugal Stein based his Emmy Award–winning TV game show, *Win Ben Stein's Money*, on his passion for saving. Recently, he served as spokesman for National Retirement Planning Week, sponsored by a coalition of financial education organizations, and testified before Congress about America's retirement savings problem.

Stein answered some questions about America's growing retirement crisis and how he is investing his money...

• **Can Americans count on the Social Security privatization plan to boost their savings?** No. It's actually a distraction from real retirement planning. Squeezing extra returns from your government benefits—the average payout for retirees currently is just $1,262 per month—is not going to enable you to retire comfortably. That will happen only if you make saving an everyday priority.

• **How much do you put away?** I have been worrying about my retirement since I was 13. I'm in my 60s now, and although I expect a modest pension from the Screen Actors Guild, I'm also trying to save very aggressively on my own—about 20% of my annual income.

• **Few people can afford to save that much. How can the average person squirrel away more money?** People in China, which has only 14% the gross domestic product per capita that we have, save 40% of their incomes. Americans save roughly 1%, so we can do a lot better.

A clear-cut goal makes it easier to deprive yourself of indulgences. You can calculate how much you will need in retirement at the AARP Web site, *www.aarp.org/money/*. Click on "Retirement Calculator." Be sure to use 100% of your current living expenses as your goal.

You can live on less—but a man of 65 today is likely to live to 80...a woman of 65 is likely to live to 83½. Prices could increase by 75% or more by then, so you must generate income in excess of what you need today.

• **Where do you invest additional money after you have maxed out retirement plan contributions?** Any additional money goes into variable annuities. That advice came from my father, who served as chairman of the Council of

Economic Advisors under presidents Nixon and Ford. He did not earn a lot of money in his lifetime, but he had a comfortable retirement because owning annuities meant that he never had to worry about outliving his money.

• Haven't a lot of people been burned by variable annuities? Annuities have taken a lot of heat in recent years because of overaggressive selling by the insurance industry and lots of hidden fees.

But if you do your homework, you'll realize that transferring the financial risk of living a long life to the insurance company and away from yourself is worth a look.

For a primer on annuities, visit *www.sec.gov/investor/pubs/varannty.htm*...or research low-cost offerings from TIAA-CREF (877-825-0411, *www.tiaa-cref.org*) and The Vanguard Group (877-662-7447, *www.vanguard.com*).

• How do you invest your retirement money? I have always been very diversified, so I have never suffered a catastrophic loss.

I spread my money around the way a large institutional investor does. I use different brokerage firms. I manage some of my accounts myself...I hire money managers for others. I own wide-ranging global asset classes—from emerging-market bonds to real estate investment trusts (REITs).

• What mistakes have you made? The mistakes I have made as an investor have come from ignoring my own advice.

I bought Berkshire Hathaway class A shares when it was cheap—$900 a share—but I didn't buy with conviction and should have scooped up a lot more. It's now worth $156,330* a share. I also got caught up a bit in the quest for Internet stock riches, even though my indicators told me that the market was overvalued.

• You detailed those indicators in your book, *Yes, You Can Time the Market* (Wiley). How do you use this strategy for retirement investing? My definition of market timing bears no resemblance to that of most financial gurus.

No one can consistently predict what will happen in the stock market within the next year or the next five, but you can identify when stocks are cheaper by historical standards.

*Stock price is subject to daily fluctuation.

If you buy stocks in those periods, your likelihood of making money over 20 years or longer is far better than if you dollar cost average into stock investments year after year, as many advisers recommend.

• Tell us more about your research. I sifted through 100 years of stock market data and found four simple measurements, or "metrics," that indicate with uncanny consistency when the S&P 500 was over- or undervalued. They include the current inflation-adjusted average price of stocks in the index...the index's average price-to-earnings ratio based on the trailing 12 months...average dividend yield...and average price-to-book value.

You can find current figures, along with historical returns, on my book's Web site, *www.yesyoucantimethemarket.com*.

Next, I compared each of these metrics to their own 15-year moving averages. The optimal time to buy is at market lows—when the dividend yield is above its moving average and the rest of the metrics are well below theirs. You avoid stocks when the situation reverses itself.

Following this strategy, you would have bought stocks in 15 out of 15 of the best years to invest since 1926 and would have avoided the worst 15 years.

• What do you do during overpriced stock market cycles? Stay invested in the stocks I own, but I use new money to buy bonds (or bond funds), REITs (or REIT funds) and shares in a money market fund.

Can You Still Make Money in Real Estate?

Dean Graziosi, real estate investor for more than 20 years. Based in Phoenix, he is author of two books on real estate, including *Be a Real Estate Millionaire* (Vanguard). *www.deangraziosi.com*

Millions of Americans have lost their jobs in the past few years, and finding new employment in this economy is very difficult. Some of the newly unemployed are searching for ways to make money on their own until the economy improves further and employers are hiring on a regular basis.

Creative real estate investor Dean Graziosi says that despite the bursting of the real estate bubble, there still is money to be made. You don't even need to invest a lot of money—all you need is a smart strategy and the patience to wait for great deals.

• **Home prices have fallen by more than 20% from their 2006 peak. Where are they headed from here?** I believe real estate prices finally are bottoming out in most regions—but I don't expect a quick rebound. Lenders are making it very difficult to obtain mortgages, and many Americans lack confidence in the economy. Real estate will not rebound substantially from its current levels until both of these things change. Real estate prices are unlikely to overtake their 2006 peak until perhaps 2015.

• **Given this bleak outlook for home prices, why do you believe people should invest in real estate?** Because home buyers are scarce these days, and some home owners are so desperate to sell that they are willing to accept very low offers. The only way to make money in this market is to buy property when it can be had for considerably less than its market value.

This typically means offering 30% to 50% less than the asking price. Most sellers will turn you down, but a small percentage—perhaps one in 25—will accept your lowball offer.

• **How can people who have lost their jobs take advantage of their free time to make money in real estate?** Mortgage lenders are being very cautious these days, so people who are out of work are likely to have trouble obtaining mortgages on the properties they want to buy. But there is a low-risk real estate investment strategy that does not require big financial risks, mortgage loans or long time horizons.

First, put together a list of local real estate investors. To find them, check area real estate investment clubs. You can find real estate clubs through the Web site of the National Real Estate Investors Association (*www.nationalreia.com*) or REIClub.com.

Next, make lowball offers on dozens of local properties. Most of your offers will be turned down, but in this market, some desperate sellers are likely to accept your offer. When someone does, execute a contract that gives you the exclusive right to buy the property at the agreed-upon price within a certain period of time, usually seven to 30 days. Make sure this contract includes an "assignment clause" that allows you to transfer the contract to another real estate investor. If you find a great deal on a house, other investors likely will be more than willing to pay you to take over the deal themselves. I know real estate investors who have made $2,000 to $20,000 per house by selling contracts—it all depends on how good the deal is that you have found.

Speak with a real estate attorney before attempting this. Your bid must be made properly in order for you to back out of the deal if you cannot find a buyer for the contract...and contracts you sign must be written properly in order to be transferable. An attorney typically charges an hourly rate of $200 to $500. Most contracts can be written up in an hour or less.

• **How can real estate investors find sellers willing to accept low offers?** Start by finding a helpful real estate agent. Explain to him/her that you intend to make many lowball offers, and confirm that he is willing to help you do this—some consider the strategy too time-consuming even in this economy.

Your agent can use the Multiple Listing Service (MLS) to search for homes that are likely to have motivated sellers. *These include...*

- Homes that have been on the market for at least 90 days. The longer a home sits, the more desperate its owner.
- Homes in preforeclosure. Owners might lose their homes to their lenders if they do not sell quickly.
- Foreclosed homes being sold by lenders (also known as "Real Estate Owned," or REO, properties). Banks and other mortgage lenders sometimes sell such homes at steep discounts.

If a home has been on the market or owned by a lender for more than six months—or a preforeclosure is very near its foreclosure date—offer 40% to 50% below the asking price rather than the upper end of the range (30%).

• **Which locations are best?** Stick with neighborhoods in your region where prices have fallen the least. It's tempting to buy in neighborhoods where prices have fallen furthest and the bargains seem greatest, but when a real estate bear market ends, prices rebound fastest and most dependably in the most desirable neighborhoods.

Within these relatively strong neighborhoods, favor homes in the price bracket that has best held its value. In some neighborhoods, high-end properties have held up best—in others, it is the moderately priced homes. Your real estate agent can use the MLS to identify homes that meet these criteria.

• **How can home owners afford to sell way below market value?** Many sellers cannot afford to accept lowball offers, but some can. Home owners who have lived in their homes for a decade or longer are most likely to have enough equity to do so.

• **Is selling the contract to another investor always the best strategy?** If you don't need to turn a quick profit and you can qualify for a mortgage on the property (or buy it outright), consider buying the home and renting it out until the real estate market recovers. Demand for rental homes is quite strong in most regions because people who are unable to obtain mortgages or unwilling to buy property in this declining market are renting instead.

Mortgages are available for borrowers with great credit scores. If your credit score is above 700, you should be able to obtain a mortgage without a problem. If it is between 650 and 700, it might take some shopping around, but you probably can find a lender.

To gauge your local rental market, check the "homes for rent" section of the local newspaper to see how much properties are renting for in the neighborhoods that you are considering. If the rents are more than high enough to cover your anticipated tax, insurance and mortgage payments as well as maintenance costs, odds are good that your property will at least break even until the real estate market rebounds and you can sell for a decent profit.

You also can run a home-for-rent ad in a local paper or on Craigslist.org before you buy a property. The ad should imply that you already have a home for rent in the neighborhood where you intend to buy. It should describe a typical home for that region and list a rent high enough to cover your expenses. If you get a lot of calls in response to the ad, it's an excellent sign that you would be able to rent out an investment property in that area. (Tell would-be renters who call that you might have something opening up in the area soon, and take their names and numbers.)

You Can Buy Real Estate With Your IRA

Patrick W. Rice, licensed real estate broker and investment manager for more than 25 years. His former firm, IRA Resource Associates, in Camas, Washington, purchases properties for its clients' IRAs. He is coauthor of *IRA Wealth: Revolutionary IRA Strategies for Real Estate Investment* (Square One).

There's something your stockbroker won't tell you—you can purchase the retirement home of your dreams with your IRA.

Traditional and Roth IRAs can be used to purchase all kinds of property, from single-family homes to apartment buildings.

By owning real estate, you diversify away from stocks and bonds and keep ahead of inflation. Returns for real estate average 11.9% a year, versus the 10.8% 30-year average for stocks.*

Although banks and brokerage firms typically don't offer this alternative—it is costly to administer and does not generate trading commissions—it's easy to add a real estate strategy to your retirement plan.

Reasonable allocation now: 25% or more of your retirement assets.

Beware: If you buy a home for retirement, you can't live in it until you take its entire value as a distribution from your IRA after age 59½. Until then, rent it out to a permissible third party. Profits are reinvested in your IRA.

CASE STUDIES

• **Residential property.** Harry dreamed of retiring to Galveston, Texas, near his brother. He bought a house there using money in his IRA.

Purchase price: $120,000.

*According to Ibbotson Associates, which used real estate investment trusts as a proxy for real estate.

Expenses: $4,500/year for taxes, insurance, utilities, etc.

Net operating income: $7,500/year (annual rent of $12,000 less annual expenses of $4,500).

Annual income: 6.25% (net operating income divided by the purchase price). Assuming that the home appreciates in value by 6% a year, Harry ends up with a 12.25% annual return.

Harry achieved his goal by renting out the house until retirement and then taking the house as a distribution from his IRA. His tenants moved out. He moved in and became the new owner instead of his IRA.

• **Commercial property.** Steve's IRA purchased a building that housed a Pizza Hut restaurant in Malta, Montana. The tenant was three years into a 10-year lease with options to extend the lease for five years.

Purchase price: $325,000.

Expenses: Nominal. Utilities, taxes and insurance were paid by the tenant.

Net operating income: $30,000/year.

Annual income: 9.23%.

While Steve's income is at the low end of the average for commercial property (the range is 8% to 14% a year), Steve liked the security of the long-term lease. The costs were also contained because the tenant was responsible for most expenses. Steve got the building for less than the $350,000 asking price because he agreed to pay cash and was able to close quickly. He still owns this building.

SET UP A SELF-DIRECTED IRA

Transfer your existing IRA or roll over money from a qualified plan—a 401(k) or a pension—to a special account called a *self-directed IRA*. It should be overseen by a custodian, such as a bank, which receives an annual fee of 0.5% to 1.5% of assets. Fees decline as assets increase.

My favorite custodians: Lincoln Trust Company, 855-719-5796, *www.lincolntrustco.com* PENSCO Trust Co., 866-818-4472, *www.pensco.com*.

You will also need a property manager to maintain and rent out the property to tenants. You are not legally permitted to manage it yourself because the IRS considers you a "disqualified party."

A WAY TO FINANCE YOUR PURCHASES

If you don't have enough cash in the IRA to buy a property outright, invest your money with others in a limited liability company (LLC). The LLC invests in the property. There are no restrictions on eligible investors. For instance, the LLC can buy the property with your IRA and/or your spouse's IRA as well as with non-retirement accounts belonging to you and your spouse.

WATCH OUT FOR TAX TRAPS

If you want to rent the property to family members, consult a tax attorney. If you violate IRS rules, you will pay tax on the entire investment. *IRS rules are tricky...*

• **You cannot lease the property to parties that have been disqualified by the IRS,** such as yourself, parents, children, spouse, grandchildren or their spouses. The law *does* allow you to lease the property to siblings, cousins, uncles and aunts. You can also name a sibling, etc., to manage the property. You pay that person a salary.

• **You cannot use IRA-owned property** as collateral for a home-equity loan or line of credit.

• **You cannot use non-IRA funds to pay** for expenses, such as insurance, taxes and repairs.

Exception: Legal fees. Make sure the property generates enough income to cover these costs. If necessary, you could transfer money from other IRAs to your self-directed IRA in order to cover expenses.

To keep legal fees down, only use an attorney to draw up and review documents, not to negotiate deals. It is best to pay legal fees with non-IRA money so that you can deduct the cost from your taxes.

• **If you move into the property after age 59½,** you must take it as a distribution from your IRA and pay tax based on the current value of the property. Plan for the tax—it could be sizable. If the property is in a Roth IRA, you pay no taxes.

CHOOSE YOUR INVESTMENTS

Base real estate decisions on the amount of time you're willing to commit, your risk tolerance and the size of your IRA.

• **Residential property.**

Who it is good for: Conservative investors who want to secure their dream home now or purchase a home for an investment.

How it works: Since you will have to hire a property manager to take care of the property anyway, there is no reason to limit your search to just your own neighborhood. Consider homes around the US.

• **Commercial property.**

Who it is good for: Investors who are willing to take more risk for higher capital appreciation.

How it works: You will need a commercial broker to help you select potential investments —stores, office buildings, hotels and land.

For referrals to real estate agents, contact the National Council of Exchangors, a nonprofit organization, 800-324-1031, *www.nce1031.com.*

HIRE COMMERCIAL PROPERTY MANAGEMENT

Hire a firm to manage your commercial property. Look for firms that handle well-maintained properties in your area.

Cost: 4% to 10% of the annual rent collected.

There are good buys on commercial properties all over the US now. I recently purchased properties in California, Kentucky, Missouri, New York and Washington.

Stop Uncle Sam From Stealing Your Retirement Dollars

Ed Slott, CPA, editor, *Ed Slott's IRA Advisor,* 100 Merrick Rd., Rockville Centre, New York 11570, *www.irahelp.com.* He is a nationally recognized IRA distributions expert.

From the moment you make your very first deposit in a traditional IRA or 401(k), you're building up a savings account—*for the IRS.*

Uncle Sam eventually gets a big chunk of your money. All withdrawals are taxable and at ordinary income tax rates of as high as 39.6%, not at the lower capital gains rate. In addition, your heirs will owe estate tax on traditional and Roth IRAs upon your death because of the estate tax. The estate tax for 2013 is a $5.25 million individual exclusion with a 40% top tax rate. *Five ways to protect your money...*

USE ROTH IRAs

This is Uncle Sam's greatest gift to retirement savings. Yet several years after the Roth's debut, relatively few people have taken advantage of it. Roth IRAs give no up-front tax deduction, but your money grows tax free. Roth IRA beneficiaries do not owe income tax on the distributions. A beneficiary can "stretch" the benefit, leaving the money to continue growing tax free over his/her life. *Here's what to do...*

• **If you're planning to open a new IRA, make it a Roth.** Your adjusted gross income (AGI) for a full contribution in 2013, the limits are less than $112,000 (single) and less than $178,000 (married filling jointly).

• **Convert a traditional IRA to a Roth.** You will have to pay tax on income earned on the traditional IRA. Ask the financial institution that handles your IRA what your tax liability will be. If bear market losses have reduced the value of your IRA, you will owe less tax.

You can now make the rollover directly to a Roth IRA. Ask your tax adviser for advice.

HELP FUTURE GENERATIONS DODGE TAXES

When 401(k) or IRA assets pass to heirs, they in turn can stretch the tax shelter over their lives. *Examples...*

Example 1: A husband leaves an IRA to his wife. She names their children as her beneficiaries. After her death, her children can enjoy tax-free compounding on the amount remaining. In this manner, tax deferral could go on for many years.

Example 2: Your daughter is age 40 when she inherits your traditional IRA. According to IRS tables, a 40-year-old has a life expectancy of another 43.6 years. Despite taking *required minimum distributions* (RMDs), the account can continue to earn investment returns during this period.

WATCH OUT FOR WITHDRAWAL PENALTIES

Uncle Sam's 10% early withdrawal penalty applies to both Roth and traditional IRA withdrawals made before age 59½.

There is a 50% penalty if you fail to take RMDs on traditional IRAs. If your RMD is $20,000 and you miss the deadline, your penalty is $10,000. *What to do...*

- **Traditional IRAs.** Start taking RMDs by April 1 of the year after you turn 70½. The percentage you must withdraw each year is determined by the IRS from life expectancy tables. For more information, call 800-829-1040, or go to *www.irs.gov* or *www.irahelp.com*.
- **Roth IRAs.** There are no required distributions for Roth IRA owners.

Loophole: You can withdraw money without penalty from any IRA before age 59½ using one of three IRS formulas. But watch out—if you start spending your nest egg early, you might not have enough savings for retirement.

LET LIFE INSURANCE PAY YOUR TAXES

Employer-sponsored retirement plans—such as 401(k)s—and traditional and Roth IRAs count toward your estate, so purchase insurance to pay the estate tax.

Estates over $5.25 million must pay the 40% federal estate tax.

What to do: The estate tax applies to the value of assets—cars, homes, retirement plans, other investments, etc. Purchase enough life insurance to cover the potential tax. At your death, insurance proceeds are free from income tax.

Important: Create a life insurance trust to own the policy so that the value is kept out of your estate. You can name beneficiaries—your spouse or children—as trustees. Make annual gifts to beneficiaries, which they should use to pay the insurance premiums. You won't owe gift tax if the payments are no more than $14,000 per recipient per year ($28,000 if given by a couple). For information, consult an experienced trust attorney.

PROVIDE FOR BENEFICIARIES NOW

Whether you have a traditional or Roth IRA, you must name your beneficiary on a retirement plan beneficiary form, which takes legal precedence over your will.

If you don't take the right steps, a lengthy, expensive probate court process will determine who inherits your IRA.

Update beneficiary forms when there is a marriage or divorce, new child or grandchild or other change that would affect your choice of a beneficiary.

Keep beneficiary forms filed with other important papers as well as with your attorney and tax adviser. Then they can be located readily by family members and the executor of your will upon your death.

Tax Traps to Avoid In Retirement Plan Distributions

Ed Slott, CPA, editor, *Ed Slott's IRA Advisor*, 100 Merrick Rd., Rockville Centre, New York 11570, *www.irahelp.com*. He is a nationally recognized IRA distributions expert.

Tax-deferred retirement plans, such as IRAs and 401(k)s, enable you to build up a sizable nest egg. However, you need to be careful when taking distributions and naming beneficiaries. *Tax traps to avoid...*

WITHDRAWALS

Trap: Withdrawals before age 59½ usually trigger a 10% penalty.

Loophole: There are several exceptions to this penalty, permitting you or your heirs to take some cash from your plan before age 59½.

Examples: Disability, death.

Also, if you retire or change jobs, you can withdraw money from an employer-sponsored plan, penalty free, if the separation occurs during or after the year you turn age 55.

In addition, you can take substantially equal periodic payments (SEPPs), penalty free, for at least five years or until the age of 59½, whichever comes later.

Caution: The rules for SEPPs are complex, so you need to work with a savvy tax pro.

Trap: If you don't start to take required minimum distributions (RMDs) by April 1 of the year after you reach age 70½, you could face a 50% penalty.

Once you reach that age, you must withdraw the minimum amount each year and pay tax on it. As long as you're alive and there is money left in your account, you will be required to continue to take these minimum distributions.

You can choose to take larger distributions from your retirement account, if you wish. However, you must withdraw at least the minimum amount each year.

Example: Suppose you are 76 years old and have $220,000 in your IRA. According to the IRS's Uniform Lifetime Table—found in Publication 590, *Individual Retirement Arrangements (IRAs)*, 800-829-3676 or *www.irs.gov*—you have a distribution period of 22 more years. Thus, you must withdraw at least 1/22 of your IRA this year, or $10,000.

If, instead, you withdraw only $2,000, you have an $8,000 shortfall. As a result, you'll owe a $4,000 penalty, which is 50% of the $8,000 shortfall.

Again, calculating the minimum withdrawal can be complicated. Consult your tax adviser (don't rely on bank information).

Loophole: There are no lifetime RMDs for Roth IRAs. And you don't need to take required distributions at age 70½ if you're still working. That's true as long as you don't own more than 5% of your company. If you begin working after having started RMDs, you can discontinue RMDs from that company's plan, assuming the plan allows it. You still have to take RMDs from other plans and IRAs.

The exception applies only to withdrawals from employer-sponsored plans. If you roll your account balance to an IRA, the minimum distribution rules apply, even if you're still working.

Loophole: You can roll IRA money into an employer-sponsored plan if the plan will accept it.

Strategy: If you're working after age 70½ and you don't need to take distributions, roll your IRA into your employer's plan, if possible. You will forgo having to take distributions and avoid the 50% penalty.

SAFE BUT SORRY

In order to avoid the 50% penalty, you might take out more money than you really need.

Example: Before you reach age 79, your required distribution will be less than 5% per year. Thus, if you withdraw 5% of your balance each year, you'll avoid a penalty.

Trap: Taking 5% per year from your retirement plan is fine if you need the money. However, if you currently don't need income and you withdraw more than the minimum, you'll pay more income tax than you need to pay and sooner than you need to pay it. More important, excess withdrawals reduce the amount of tax-deferred wealth-building that you (and possibly your beneficiaries) can enjoy.

If you do not need the money for living expenses, withdraw only the bare minimum.

NAMING BENEFICIARIES

Trap: If you don't name a beneficiary, whoever inherits your account will have to withdraw more money sooner and pay more income tax. The same is true if you name your estate as the beneficiary.

Strategy: Name one or more individuals as beneficiaries on the form provided by the custodian or on a custom form you provide.

If you have doubts about your beneficiary's ability to handle a large inheritance, name a trust as the beneficiary, then name your heirs as trust beneficiaries.

Loophole: If handled properly, setting up such a trust can permit your heirs to stretch out required withdrawals. Work with an experienced trust attorney.

COMPANY STOCK

If you work for a publicly traded company, chances are that your retirement plan account contains some company stock.

Trap: Mishandling the withdrawal of that stock could cost you a prime tax break.

Example: Your 401(k) is $200,000, including $50,000 of company stock. When you retire, you roll over the entire $200,000 to an IRA. All subsequent IRA withdrawals will be subject to ordinary income tax, at rates up to 39.6%.

Strategy: Before you execute the rollover, ask about your basis in the company stock. That's the amount it was worth when the shares were contributed to your retirement account.

Loophole: You can pull out those shares and pay tax only on your basis, and not on their current value.

Example: Say your company shares are now worth $50,000 but your basis in those shares is only $10,000. You could withdraw the $50,000 worth of shares but owe tax on only $10,000 worth of income.

The other $40,000 won't be taxed until you sell the shares, which might be right away or many years in the future. In the meantime, you can receive dividends from all the shares and you can borrow against them, if you wish.

Result: Whenever you decide to sell the shares, the $40,000 will be taxed as a long-term capital gain, at a top tax rate as high as 23.8%, depending on your income level instead of at ordinary income tax rates of up to 39.6% on regular IRA withdrawals. After more than one year, any additional gains will also qualify for the bargain tax rate.

The remaining assets in your 401(k) can be rolled into an IRA, tax free. You won't pay income tax until you begin making withdrawals.

Shrewd Tax Planning For Mutual Fund Investors

Dennis A. Ito, former partner in charge, personal financial planning, Western Area, and Rande Spiegelman, CPA, CFP, VP, financial planning, The Charles Schwab Corp. *www.aboutschwab.com*

Tax planning can help you keep more of what your mutual funds return. And recent changes in the tax rules for capital gains make it even *more* important to identify which funds are best for different accounts.

YOUR GOALS

Mutual fund investments are taxed at two levels...

- **You, the investor, face a capital gain—or loss—**when you sell your shares in a mutual fund.

- **The mutual fund *itself* realizes taxable investment income** in the form of the capital gains, dividends and interest it earns during the year. This income is distributed to its shareholders through a dividend paid before year-end.

Trap: Fund shareholders *owe the tax* on these gains—a fact that they often overlook in their planning. If a fund reports high investment gains and the gains are subject to high tax rates, your after-tax return from the fund will be *lower* than it appears.

Your two tax goals as a fund investor should be to...

- **Manage your own shareholdings** to minimize capital gains tax due on them.

- **Select funds for your portfolio** that are tax efficient, meaning portfolio turnover is low.

Payoff: With smart planning, just one percentage point added to your *after-tax* investment returns will compound over time to significantly increase future wealth.

MINIMIZE CAPITAL GAINS

Gains are taxed depending on how long you hold the investment...

- **Short-term gains,** on assets held one year or less, are taxed at ordinary rates of up to 39.6%.

- **Long-term gains,** on assets held more than one year, are taxed at a top rate of 23.8%—0% if you are in the 10% or 15% tax bracket in 2013.

You may own shares in a fund that you've purchased at different times and prices—giving you different amounts of gain and holding periods. If you sell *some* shares, you need a way to determine the amount and nature of your gain.

The IRS allows you to select from among four different methods of determining gain from the sale of mutual fund shares (see IRS Publication 564, *Mutual Fund Distributions*).

- **First-in, first-out (FIFO)** accounting treats your shares as being sold in the order in which you acquired them. The IRS presumes the use of FIFO unless you elect one of the other three methods.

- **Average cost method** computes your gain on a sale using the average cost of all the shares you own. Most mutual funds will compute this number for you, saving you work. However, this method often fails to produce the best possible tax result.

- **Average cost double category method** is rarely used. It allocates shares to long- and short-term holding periods according to the overall ratio of such holdings.

- **Specific share method** lets you select particular shares from among your holdings for sale.

Best option in most cases: The *specific share* method. It lets you choose among all your shares and select for sale the particular ones that produce the best tax result.

- You can sell your highest-cost shares to minimize taxable gain.
- If you have a capital loss elsewhere, you can sell your lowest-cost shares to maximize gain and use the loss to offset the gain from tax.
- You may even be able to generate a deductible loss when you've made a big profit on your shares overall.

The snag with the specific cost method is that you must have cost records for every share you own. And...when you sell shares, you must notify the fund in *writing* that you are using the method to identify the shares you are selling and their cost and receive written confirmation of your instructions.

Self-defense: From the day you set up your account with a fund, keep all the account records that the fund provides you, including trade confirmations and year-end statements.

Choose the best accounting method for you from the beginning. Once you use one of the four methods for a particular fund, you can't change it without IRS approval.

Dividend shares trap: Pay special attention to record keeping for shares acquired with reinvested dividends. These shares are taxed when you receive them and increase the cost basis of your total holdings. But many people forget to increase their tax basis to account for reinvested distributions and pay tax on the shares again when they sell them.

CUTTING TAXES

You control the taxable capital gains you report, but not the amount of taxable dividend income a mutual fund will distribute to you. So it's important to consider this income and the effect it has on a fund's total return.

Fund selection strategy: First look for funds that will meet your real investment needs. Then, among those, invest in the funds that have the lowest tax cost.

Beware: The most actively traded funds generally produce the largest taxable distributions—including short-term gains taxed at rates as high as 39.6%.

Contrast: Index funds that don't trade at all produce the smallest taxable distributions—near zero.

Some funds seek to trade "tax efficiently" by offsetting gains with losses and holding investments long enough to qualify as "long term."

Before buying a fund, study its prospectus for its trading philosophy and the record of gains it has produced.

Caution: Its pattern of performance may change, unless its prospectus states otherwise.

Helpful: Consider holding funds that produce taxable distributions in tax-favored retirement accounts, such as Roth IRAs and 401(k) plans, while holding tax-efficient funds in taxable accounts.

Trap: If you buy a fund and the market falls from a high level, the fund may distribute taxable gains to you even as you take a loss on your investment.

How that happens: As the value of your shares falls, the fund will be cashing in its appreciated gains to pay redemptions—and its gains will be taxed to you as a shareholder.

Some major fund groups are now making provisions against this event—so ask before investing.

Very Valuable Tax Deductions

Mary Wilson, CPA, JD, principal, Rothstein Kass, an international accounting and consulting firm in Roseland, New Jersey. *www.rkco.com*

Many taxpayers don't take common deductions—for mortgage interest, charitable donations and medical expenses. The reason? They don't "itemize" by claiming these or any other expenses on Schedule A of Form 1040.

It's easy to see why. For many people, the standard deduction for 2013—$12,200 for couples and $6,100 for singles—is higher than the total of their itemized deductions, so they're better off taking the standard deduction.

There are several smart ways to boost your tax savings even if you don't itemize and instead take the standard deduction. A number of so-called *above-the-line* write-offs are available. *Common examples...*

INDIVIDUAL RETIREMENT ACCOUNTS (IRAs)

For 2013, you can contribute up to $5,500 to an IRA ($6,500 for those age 50 and older). *Roth IRA contributions are never tax-deductible, but there are situations in which you can deduct contributions to a traditional IRA...*

• **If you are not covered by an employer-sponsored retirement plan.**

• **If your income is under certain thresholds,** even if you are covered by an employer-sponsored retirement plan. Single filers must have incomes of less than $59,000 in 2013 to be eligible for a full IRA write-off. Lesser deductions are available for those with incomes less than $69,000. For joint filers, the limits are $95,000 and less than $115,000, in 2013.

• **If your joint income is less than $169,000 and only one spouse works.** The nonworking spouse can take this deduction even if the working spouse is covered by an employer-sponsored retirement plan.

HEALTH SAVINGS ACCOUNTS (HSAs)

HSAs, created under the 2003 Medicare drug law, became effective in 2004.

How HSAs work: They are IRA-like accounts that can be used to pay health-care expenses.

Contributions: To deduct your contributions to an HSA, you must be covered by a high-deductible health plan and not covered by Medicare. In 2013, the annual deductible on health insurance must be at least $1,250 for single coverage ($2,500 for family coverage).

You can contribute up to the amount of your policy's deductible, to a maximum set by the IRS.

Example: If you are age 55 or older by the end of 2013, you can contribute $1,000 more than the policy deductible. The maximum HSA contribution for 2013 is $3,250...or $6,450 for those with family coverage. If you have an HSA, you can still contribute to an IRA, a 401(k) and a flexible spending account at work.

Withdrawals: Withdrawals can be made tax free from the HSA to pay medical bills. Unused HSA money can be carried over to subsequent years to grow tax deferred through investments in mutual funds, stocks, bonds, etc.—potentially for decades. Money withdrawn before age 65 that is not used for health-related purposes is subject to income tax and a 10% penalty. After age 65, you pay only income tax.

STUDENT-LOAN INTEREST

You can deduct up to $2,500 worth of interest paid on student loans this year, regardless of how many students there are in the family and whether the loan financed higher education for you, your spouse and/or a dependent, provided your income is below a set amount.

LEGAL FEES IN DISCRIMINATION SUITS

If you recover an award in a discrimination action (the full amount of which is taxable income), legal fees are deductible even if you do not itemize.

ALIMONY

Alimony is 100% deductible for the payer and is considered taxable income for the recipient. If you're the payer, you'll have to provide your former spouse's Social Security number on your return so that the IRS can check on the resulting tax collection.

MOVING EXPENSES

If you move because of a new job or for other business reasons, certain expenses are deductible —costs to transport household goods and personal effects as well as your travel to the new residence. This includes lodging but not meals. To qualify, your new workplace must be more than 50 miles farther from your old home than your former workplace was from your old home.

EARLY WITHDRAWAL PENALTIES

If you cash in a bank CD, any resulting penalty can be deducted.

SPECIAL WRITE-OFFS FOR THE SELF-EMPLOYED

• **Self-employment retirement plans.** If you have self-employment income, even from a sideline business, several types of retirement plans are available, among them SEP, SIMPLE, individual 401(k) and Keogh plans. Contributions to these plans are deductible regardless of whether you itemize. For rules on deducting these contributions, see IRS Publication 560, *Retirement Plans for Small Business,* available by calling 800-TAX-FORM or visiting *www.irs.gov.*

• **Self-employment tax.** The bad news is that self-employed individuals must pay both the employer's and the employee's share of Medicare and Social Security taxes. The good news is that you can deduct half of those payments even if you don't itemize.

• **Self-employment health insurance.** You can deduct 100% of health insurance premiums that you pay for yourself, your spouse and your dependents. The amount you deduct can't exceed your self-employment income.

What the IRS Won't Tell You About Audits

Frederick W. Daily, tax attorney, 741 Tyner Way, Incline Village, Nevada 85451. He is author of *Stand Up to the IRS* and *Tax Savvy for Small Business* (both from Nolo Press).

Most taxpayers who face an IRS auditor fear how much the IRS knows about them. Auditors use this fear to intimidate taxpayers into making concessions and revealing more.

With the right tactics, you can keep the IRS auditor from learning any more...and help move the audit to its best possible conclusion.

WHAT THE IRS KNOWS

When you appear for an IRS audit, the auditor will have a file on your case that typically contains only three sources of information about you...

• **Tax return being audited.**

• **Your tax-filing history for the past six years.** This tells whether you filed tax returns ...were audited...or had a tax bill adjusted for those years. It does *not* include copies of prior years' tax returns.

• **List of third-party payments made to you** that were reported to the IRS on W-2 and 1099 forms or other information returns.

In 90% of cases, that's all the information the auditor will have about you before the audit begins.

If information that could cause you audit problems is not contained among these three items, the overwhelming odds are that the auditor doesn't have it.

Then the only way the auditor can get it is from you or by issuing a summons on the record keeper.

The auditor will not have: Copies of bank statements, motor vehicle records, property deeds or police records. Nor will he/she have copies of 1099s or other information returns sent to the IRS under a Social Security or taxpayer ID number other than yours.

Key: Don't volunteer any information to the IRS auditor that you aren't legally obligated to give —even if he asks for it.

THE RIGHT REPRESENTATION

If there is information you want to protect from the IRS, consider being represented at your audit by a tax professional—instead of attending the audit personally. They are experienced at dealing with auditors.

A professional representative will not have the answers to some of the auditor's questions —including any information that you might reveal unintentionally.

Your representative will ask the auditor to put the request in writing. Then, in responding to a written request, your representative can discuss things with you and draft as narrow an answer as possible.

The whole process will slow the audit, which the auditor doesn't want. So attempts by the auditor to "go fishing" will be frustrated.

The IRS cannot conduct a "lifestyle or economic reality audit," asking questions that are unrelated to the preparation of the return being examined, unless it already has a reasonable indication that income has been understated.

A professional representative will also prevent your emotions or personal factors from complicating an audit. No matter how difficult the audit may be, your representative should be able to deal with the auditor in a calm and professional manner.

The fee you pay may be a bargain for both the taxes it saves and the anxiety you avoid by not dealing with the auditor personally.

And, last but not least, fees paid to a tax professional for defending an audit are deductible.

Minimizing Chances Of a Tax Audit

To be candid, there is no way of being sure that your federal income tax return won't be audited. Even overpaying won't protect you from IRS scrutiny. Some returns are pulled out by random selection. Others are chosen by IRS computers, which analyze returns to score the likelihood of collecting further. Computers select a return for audit if medical expenses, contributions, property taxes, etc., represent an unusually high percentage of the taxpayer's income (according to nationwide experience). Returns also invite scrutiny when figures do not agree with other information received by the IRS, such as when a corporation reports on Form 1099 that it paid $2,000 in dividends to a taxpayer, but that taxpayer reports only $1,000. And returns may also be selected for audit because of tips provided by tax informants.

But your chances of being audited can be greatly reduced by following these suggestions...

• **Answer *all* questions on the tax return form.**

• **Complete all schedules that are required.** Use the words *"None"* or *"Not applicable"* where appropriate.

• **Include full documentation of items that are certain to be questioned,** such as large casualty losses or large moving expenses. If the IRS asks for unsupplied substantiation, expect this request to lead to additional questions in other areas of the return at the same time.

• **Send tax returns and other documents to the right office** at the right time so that correspondence and personal contact aren't necessary. Once begun, such correspondence or contact is often difficult to end—one thing leads to another.

• **Don't deduct a type of item that had been disallowed** on a previous tax return. The IRS may remember this and look for a repeat.

• **Don't use a tax preparer of dubious character.** If the IRS, through its investigators, finds a preparer who is grossly incompetent or *worse*, the names of all his/her clients will be obtained. All of them, however innocent, will have their tax returns checked by experts.

• **Be certain that the return has the right signatures and identifying numbers.** If it is a corporate return, the title of the signer should be one of the officers *authorized by law* to sign.

Many audits are triggered by...

• **Information returns from banks,** investments or employers that show payments (dividends, interest, salaries or fees) that differ from those that were reported.

• **Unusually large deductions.** The computer flags deductions that are much larger than the average amount taken by most taxpayers in the same income group.

Suggestions: Provide some details on extra-large deductions. Big casualty loss? Describe the hurricane or flood, maybe even enclose a newspaper clipping. Give dates and details of a long illness or a serious accident that produced large medical deductions.

• **Unbelievable numbers.**

Examples: Claiming that you held real estate or IBM stock for 25 years and sold it at a loss... Large deductions and losses that leave no money to live on...Business expenses that are out of line with the amount of gross income or the nature of the business ...Mortgage interest and property tax deductions that are unusual for your area.

• **Large round numbers raise questions** as to whether you picked an exaggerated number out of the air without supporting documentation.

• **Office at home.** This set-up usually receives closer scrutiny.

Important: If the IRS strikes gold in auditing a return, it will often go after other members of the family, or partners, employees and other stockholders in the same S corporation.

Shrewd Ways to Use Your Home as a Tax Shelter

Diane Kennedy, CPA, tax strategist for more than 20 years, Diane Kennedy's Tax Services, certified public accountants, Phoenix. She is coauthor of several books, including *Real Estate Loopholes: Secrets of Successful Real Estate Investing* (Warner Business).

From a tax perspective, there's never been a better time to own a home. *Here are four loopholes to take advantage of...*

SHORT-TERM OWNERSHIP

The home-sale exclusion is one of the most generous tax breaks in the Internal Revenue Code. Married couples can avoid tax on up to

$500,000 in capital gains ($250,000 for a single person). This break can be used over and over.

To get it, you must have owned the home and used it as your principal residence for at least two of the five years before the sale. Most people, however, don't realize how easy it is to use the exclusion even if you don't meet this two-year test.

Loophole: If you had to move out of a house before the two years were up because of an "unforeseen circumstance," you still can get a partial tax break. Unforeseen circumstances are defined liberally. They include natural disasters, a change in employment or becoming self-employed, divorce or legal separation, and multiple births from the same pregnancy.

How it works: Say you are promoted—or even demoted—at work. This is considered a change in employment, so you can sell your house and take a partial tax break even if you don't satisfy the two-year test. The same is true if you start, change or discontinue a business.

Example: You want to move from an appreciated property in which you have lived for less than two years. Before selling, you start a simple home–based business. Assuming that you sell the house after living in it for one year, you would get half of the maximum tax break because one year is half of two. You and your spouse could exclude up to $250,000 (half of $500,000) of any gain on the sale. A single filer could exclude up to $125,000 (half of $250,000).

HOME-OFFICE DEDUCTION

Some people don't deduct depreciation for a home office because they think it will cause them to owe tax on the gain allocated to the office when they sell the home. This is not the case.

Loophole: As long as the home office is part of your house—and not a separate structure—you will get the full principal-residence capital gains exclusion.

How it works: If you have taken a depreciation deduction for the office portion of your residence, you need to "recapture" the depreciation when you sell the home.

Example: If you have taken $10,000 of depreciation and are in the 25% bracket, you would owe $2,500 in tax—25% of $10,000—when you sell the home. You can keep whatever is left of the $500,000 or $250,000 exclusion on gains.

Paying less tax now (by depreciating) is worth more than the cost of recapturing depreciation later. For rules on depreciation, see IRS Publication 946, *How to Depreciate Property*, available at *www.irs.gov* or by calling 800-829-3676.

ASSET PROTECTION

In these litigious times, it's easy to imagine someone tripping on your driveway and suing you, putting your home and other assets at risk.

Strategy: To protect your home from creditors, transfer it to a single-member limited liability company (LLC). This isn't necessary if you live in states with "unlimited homestead protection"—where equity is protected—such as Texas and Florida.

Loophole: Home owners who make such transfers will still be entitled to the mortgage interest deduction and capital gains exclusion. There can be only one owner, perhaps you and your spouse holding the title as joint tenants. You don't need to file an additional business tax return for the LLC.

DIVIDE AND CONQUER

You may be able to sell part of your property at a profit and still get the benefit of the capital gains exclusion.

Example: Your home sits on 40 acres. A developer buys 39 acres, from which you make a $300,000 profit. A year later, you sell the house and the remaining acre for an additional $150,000 profit.

Loophole: According to the Treasury Department, you can take the full $500,000 or $250,000 capital gains exclusion on the combined gain if you complete the "split sale" within two years.

In the above example, the total $450,000 gain ($300,000 plus $150,000) would be tax free, provided the house was sold within two years of the prior sale of the land and all other conditions were met.

Mortgage Payments Can Now Be Deducted on a Home You Don't Own

Saffet Uslu, TC Memo 1997-551.

A Tax Court decision shows how to save a mortgage interest deduction when one family member helps another obtain a home and mortgage payments are not made by the person whose name is on the mortgage.

Facts: A married couple found that they could not obtain a mortgage on the home they wanted to buy. The husband's brother then bought the home and let the couple live in it. The couple made all the mortgage payments on the house, even though both the mortgage and title to the home were in the brother's name.

The couple also paid all other ownership-related expenses, such as property taxes, utilities and so on, and acted in all ways as the owners of the home.

But when they tried to deduct the mortgage interest they paid, the IRS disallowed the deduction because they weren't legally obligated to pay the mortgage.

Tax Court: The couple were legally obligated to pay the mortgage because if they failed to do so, the brother would have a cause of action to evict them, and they would lose the home.

Because they had assumed all the rights and obligations of home ownership, and the brother hadn't taken the mortgage deduction, they could take the deduction.

14 Easy Ways to Boost The Value of Your Home

Jim Fite, president of Dallas-based Century 21 Judge Fite Company, one of the largest Century 21 affiliates in the world with 800 associates, *www.century21judgefite.com.*

Never underestimate the power of a good first impression. A home that looks attractive from the road can sell quickly, making it less likely that you'll have to reduce the asking price.

LANDSCAPE

1. Edge lawns and flowerbeds. A sharp edge gives a well-maintained look. Conversely, grass or weeds that are sprouting from cracks in paths implies neglect.

2. Add color. Plant flowers to make the front of a house come alive, particularly if the home itself is white or a dark color.

3. Patch cracks in walkways and sidewalks, even if the sidewalk is the town's responsibility. If tree roots have shattered a section, consider rerouting the sidewalk around the tree. Also, sweep all walks.

4. Trim overgrown trees and shrubs. Remove dead or dying plants.

HOUSE FACADE

5. Polish the doorknob. If the main entryway's doorknob or knocker shows signs of age, it's worth spending $150 or so to replace it.

6. Remove potted plants, statues and decorations from the front stoop. They make it look cluttered and smaller.

7. Use similar drapes in front windows. Most homeowners select drapes and blinds for the way they look inside the home—but different colors and shapes in front windows make a home look unbalanced from the outside.

8. Replace broken and missing shingles. Just a few bad shingles give the impression of roof problems—a big turnoff for potential buyers.

OTHER DETAILS

9. Remove weathered basketball hoops. Only keep the hoops up if they look new and have nets.

10. Match your mailbox with your home. A cutesy mailbox is appropriate for a cutesy home. A $500,000 home shouldn't have a $10 mailbox.

11. Take down a dilapidated backyard fence, especially if it can be seen from someone standing in the street or driveway.

12. Remove all decorative elements that could be considered clutter. Walkway lights and garden fountains are fine. Garden gnomes, out-of-season Christmas lights and other ornamentation should be packed away.

13. Keep garage doors closed. Even tidy garage interiors don't look as neat as closed garage doors. Garbage cans, rakes, bikes, etc., should be stored inside.

14. Maintain the "for sale" sign. A post that is leaning or in need of painting implies your home has been on the market for a long time. That suggests problems.

To Sell Your Home More Quickly...

Make your home more salable by paying attention to small details...

• **Take out the trash before prospective buyers visit.** If odors remain, bake bread or boil cinnamon to create a pleasant aroma.

• **Use higher-wattage bulbs** to make the house look brighter.

• **Make closets seem larger** by storing some of your clothes elsewhere temporarily.

• **If you have a cat,** be sure the litter box is clean and hidden.

Barbara Corcoran, chairman and founder, The Corcoran Group, real estate brokerage firm, New York City, *http://barbaracorcoran.com.*

You Don't Need a Lot Of Money to Make Big Money in Real Estate

Carleton Sheets, real estate entrepreneur and author of *Real Estate: The World's Greatest Wealth Builder* (Bonus). He created the training program "How to Buy Your First Home or Investment Property with No Down Payment." 800-201-9219, *www.carletonsheets.com.*

Buying and renting out single-family homes is one real estate strategy that can always be depended on. You don't have to be wealthy to be a successful landlord. You can use the equity in your existing home to get started, and you may qualify for generous tax breaks.

Owning one or two rental properties takes less time—and can be less risky—than managing a stock portfolio, and there's always an up-and-coming real estate market waiting to be discovered.

Reality check: Owning rental property is a classic get-rich-*slow* strategy. Rental income covers the mortgage payments and operating expenses while providing a small positive cash flow.

However, you can increase the rent to keep up with or outpace inflation over the long term. You can also expect a profit when you sell—historically, home values have appreciated by about 5% a year, which is above and beyond the rental income.

How you can make money in single-family properties...

THE RIGHT KIND OF HOUSE

• **Look within a 20-mile radius of where you live.** You'll be better able to figure out the value of real estate in a familiar area. Unless you live in a hot market, you should be able to find affordable properties in your town.

If you can't afford to buy property in your town, expand your radius to 50 miles. Look for middle-income neighborhoods—homes in these neighborhoods stand the best chance of appreciating.

• **Buy sought-after properties.** Single-family homes with three bedrooms and two bathrooms appeal to a range of tenants. Avoid houses with only one or two bedrooms—they may be less expensive, but they are harder to rent or sell.

Also avoid condominiums and co-ops—you lack control. The building association may have the right to approve tenants. For example, applicants may be turned down if they have pets.

• **Look for popular features.** Choose a house that has at least one of the features that renters want—fenced-in yard...garage...fireplace...central air-conditioning...finished basement...or proximity to good schools, public transportation and supermarkets/shopping districts.

THE RIGHT DEAL

To ensure that the price is right, look up sales of comparable properties. *My favorite resources for valuing property...*

• **Recorder's office** at your county courthouse has records of a home's past and current owners and sale prices.

• **Tax assessor's office** has information on a property's assessed value, square footage, improvements, etc.

You may also find this information online—*www.statelocalgov.net* has links to municipal sites for all states.

• **DataQuick.com** (888-604-3282) provides reports on comparable sales, local crime rates, neighborhood demographics and real estate market trends.

Cost: $0.50 and up per report.

Make sure you will profit from the investment. A rental property should generate monthly income of at least 1% of the purchase price.

Example: I was interested in a house in an area where rents were about $900 per month. Therefore, I knew I could pay up to $90,000 for the house ($900 is 1% of $90,000). Even after I subtracted my projected expenses, including mortgage payments, maintenance, property taxes and insurance, I was left with cash flow of $100 a month.

TURNAROUND OPPORTUNITIES

Consider deeply discounted properties as you become more experienced. *They are likely to need work and may entail complex legal issues...*

• **Real estate owned (REO) properties.** Banks and institutional lenders are anxious to sell these foreclosed properties. Ask to see the REO lists at local banks. Try my site, *www.bankforeclosurelist.com*, to view more than 40,000 REO properties around the country.

• **Government-auctioned property.** Contact the US Department of Housing and Urban Development, 202-708-1112, *www.hud.gov*...or the Department of the Treasury, 202-622-2000, *www.treasury.gov/auctions*, for information on auctions of federally owned properties.

FINANCING OPTIONS

Try to get financing from the seller. You'll be able to make a lower down payment than if you finance with a bank. In today's rental market, I find that as much as 15% of sellers are willing and able to finance purchases.

The seller acts like a bank, allowing you to use the property as collateral. You issue the seller a note with an agreed-upon interest rate (similar to the prevailing bank rate), then make mortgage payments directly to him/her.

If you default on your payments, the seller can foreclose on the property. As with any real estate deal, you should use an attorney or title company to assist with the closing.

Many sellers want extra assurances that you will make your mortgage payments. *Here's what you can offer...*

• **Earmark part of the rent you collect toward your principal.**

Example: When a student from my real estate seminar wanted to buy a residential property in Florida, the seller was willing to finance the $180,000 purchase but wanted 10% up front. The student only had $10,000. To close the deal, he gave the seller preference on the property's cash flow—the first $500 in rent each month—until the additional $8,000 was collected.

• **Put up more collateral than the property is worth.** This is known as a "blanket mortgage."

Example: Another student found a rental house that was selling for $480,000. The student already owned other property, and he had no cash for a down payment. So he offered additional collateral —a property he owned in Vermont that was worth $60,000 and his personal residence in which he had $40,000 worth of equity. In lieu of a down payment, he put up $580,000 in collateral for the $480,000 house.

Important: Use a blanket mortgage only if you are absolutely confident that you can make your mortgage payments.

MANAGING THE PROPERTY

• **Hire a management company if you don't want to maintain the property yourself.**

Typical cost: Half of one month's rent for finding and screening tenants...10% of the gross monthly rent for managing the property. Factor this in when you assess the net income of a prospective purchase. Ask for referrals from landlords in the area.

• **Run a credit and criminal check on prospective tenants.** Ask for references from employers and past landlords. Companies such as Intelius (888-445-2727, *www.intelius.com*) can run background checks for a fee.

• **Reward renters for prompt payments.** I charge rent that is 5% to 10% higher than the going rate, then offer that amount as a rental discount if the tenant pays on time.

• **Charge more than the monthly rent for the security deposit.** Otherwise, tenants may skip the last month's rent and tell you to use the deposit instead.

• **Keep two months' rental income in reserve** to protect against vacancies.

• **Make sure you have adequate property and liability coverage.** Consult an agent who has insured rental properties. *Helpful resources...*

• Landlord.com (408-374-9400) provides free forms, such as lease agreements, and online calculators.

• National Association of Independent Landlords (800-352-3395, *www.nail-usa.com*) has links to state laws.

A Great Business You Can Start in Your Home

Stephen Wagner, author of *Mind Your Own Business: The Best Businesses You Can Start Today for Under $500* (Adams Media).

You can start a credit-repair service out of your home with a minimal investment. Customers usually seek this service after being rejected for a home or car loan. You would resolve their credit disputes, set up payment schedules with credit card companies, etc.

Key: Screen potential clients. You want those you can actually help. To be eligible for your services, problem accounts must have been paid off for at least one year, preferably three or four. Guarantee clients an overall improvement in their credit.

The only cost to you is for office expenses, placement of ads in area newspapers, research of credit record keeping and reporting laws.

Earning potential: $100,000 a year.

What You Must Do Now as Your Home's Value Sinks

Mark Nash, real estate agent with Coldwell Banker Residential Brokerage in Chicago. He is author of *1001 Tips for Buying and Selling a Home* (South-Western Educational) and a columnist for the online real estate news and information site Realty Times (*http://realtytimes.com*). His annual survey, "What's In, What's Out with Homebuyers" is used by more than 500 news organizations in the US and Canada.

The residential real estate market now is one of the trickiest in decades. Prices are back to what they were in 2000—or less, depending on where you live—and continue to drop. Until the housing picture stabilizes, there's plenty that you can do to help yourself, whether you have paid off your mortgage and want to downsize...you're trying to refinance...your family is growing and you want a bigger place...you have to move because of a new job...or you're a first-time home buyer.

FIRST STEPS

Start by doing a computer search at *www.zillow.com* or *www.realtor.com* to find prices that comparable homes in your area have sold for and an estimate of how much your home is worth. But don't rely on these sites if you actually intend to buy or sell.

Reason: Most of their estimates are too high. The information comes from public records that may be several months old. In this real estate market, values change week to week. For greater accuracy, you need a comparative market analysis (CMA) from a real estate agent, which contains up-to-date data and factors in other criteria that can greatly affect home values. These factors include the exact condition inside and out and the location of a home in relation to street traffic, power lines, etc.

FOR LONGTIME HOME OWNERS

If you have owned your home for 25 years or more...

The good news: Even though your home has lost value in the last few years, it is probably still worth a lot more than you have put into it. So, if you need a home-equity loan, you are likely to qualify. There's also good news if you want to sell your home and buy another. Other homes that you might consider buying are likely to be just as discounted as yours, if not more. If you are in an urban area and plan to downsize to a hard-hit Sunbelt state, such as Arizona, California or Florida, you can buy your new home for nearly 50% less than what it would have cost you five years ago.

The bad news: You'll find that potential buyers are extremely selective, taking their time and demanding the lowest possible prices.

What to do if you want to sell...

• **Price your home realistically.** Set the price at what you can really get, not what you think it should be worth. Also, don't add an extra 20% to leave wiggle room for negotiating as you might have done in better times. Entering the market with the higher price means that many potential buyers will ignore your home.

• **Consider buying your new home before you sell the old one** if you have enough cash for a down payment. Then rent out the old one to cover its property taxes, insurance, etc., until the market recovers. This approach can get you an extra $50,000 or more when you do sell the home down the line in a better economic climate.

FOR MID-CYCLE HOME OWNERS

If you have owned your home for as long as 10 to 25 years...

The good news: Unless you have remortgaged your home and pulled out cash, you have built up enough equity so that you can withstand this market downturn. You may even be able to trade up to a nicer home.

The bad news: If you decide to stay where you are, spending money on remodeling won't increase the value of your home very much. Even kitchen and bathroom upgrades (considered the most profitable improvements) may return only 50% to 75% of what you paid when you sell your home, and that's only if you sell within a couple of years after the project is completed—otherwise it looks dated.

What to do...

• **Choose projects that preserve your home's value rather than just beautify it.** These include upgrades to the roof, the plumbing and the electrical system.

• **Make sure that your upgrades make your home competitive** with those of the neighbors. If most houses on your street have three bedrooms and yours has two, you'll get the most return for your money by adding a third bedroom, not finishing the basement.

FOR EARLY-CYCLE HOME OWNERS

If you have owned your home for less than 10 years...

The good news: You may be able to refinance to take advantage of the lowest mortgage interest rates in the past 50 years.

Rule of thumb for deciding whether it pays to refinance: It is worth refinancing if your current fixed-rate mortgage is high enough that the savings from the lowered mortgage rate will recoup the price of closing costs in 24 months or less... or if you have an adjustable mortgage rate that is set to adjust before you plan to sell the house.

The bad news: If you bought in the past few years and your home value has fallen by 25% or more, you could be "upside down" on your mortgage. That means you have lost the equity in your home because the mortgage balance is greater than the current value of the home. It's very unlikely that you can refinance, and selling is a poor option because you would still have to pay money to get out from under the mortgage.

Next steps...

• **Ask your lender to modify the mortgage agreement.** Ask for a reduction in interest rate or monthly payments. Under the Obama administration's $75 billion home owner affordability plan, qualifying for better terms will become easier.

More information: Visit *www.makinghome affordable.gov.*

• **Be prepared to stay put for several years.** It took about four years to fully recover from the previous housing slump in the late 1980s and early 1990s. For now, consider accelerating your mortgage payments so that you increase your equity and reduce your long-term interest expenses.

FOR FIRST-TIME BUYERS

If you have not owned a home before or don't own one currently...

The good news: This may be remembered as one of the greatest buyer's markets in our lifetime. You have a tremendous selection of new and existing homes with many sellers desperate to unload them. While lending requirements are tighter, you can still get a mortgage with a terrific interest rate if you can put down 20% of the property's cost up front and have a credit rating of 760 or higher (out of 850).

The bad news: As far as prices have fallen, they could fall further—perhaps much further in some areas. Buy now and you may get a bargain—or soon find yourself owning a home that's worth less than you paid.

Next step...

• **Buy soon and lock in a low interest rate** if you plan to stay in a home at least five years. Consult a tax attorney on how much the tax advantages of home ownership may help you. But avoid purchasing a home simply because you feel the market may be close to the bottom. Ask yourself if you would still be happy in your new home if you saw 20% of your equity vanish in the next year.

How to Find Your Lost Pension Money

Jim Miller, an advocate for older Americans, writes "Savvy Senior," a weekly information column syndicated in more than 400 newspapers nationwide. Based in Norman, Oklahoma, he also offers a free senior news service at *www.SavvySenior.org.*

It's not unusual for a worker to lose track of a pension benefit. Perhaps you left an employer long ago and forgot that you left behind a pension. Or maybe you worked for a company that changed owners or went belly up many years ago, and you figured the pension went with it...but you might have been wrong.

Today, millions of dollars in benefits are sitting in pension plans across the US or with the Pension Benefit Guaranty Corporation (PBGC), a federal government agency, waiting to be claimed by their rightful owners. The average unclaimed benefit with PBGC is $6,550.

To help you look for a pension, here are some steps to take and some free resources that can help you search if your previous employer has gone out of business, relocated, changed owners or merged with another firm...

CONTACT THE EMPLOYER

If you think you have a pension and the company you worked for still is in business, your first step is to call the human resources department and ask how to contact the pension plan administrator. Ask the administrator whether you have a pension, how much it is worth and how to claim it. Depending on how complete the administrator's records are, you may need to show proof that you once worked for the company and that you are pension eligible.

If you haven't saved your old tax returns from these years, you can get a copy of your earnings record from the Social Security Administration, which will show how much you were paid each calendar year by each employer. Call 800-772-1213, and ask for Form SSA-7050, *Request for Social Security Earnings Information*, or you can download it at *www.SSA.gov/online/ssa-7050.pdf.* You will pay a small fee for the report, depending on the number of years of data you request.

Some other old forms that can help you prove pension eligibility are summary plan descriptions that you should have received from your employer when you worked there...and any individual benefit statements that you received during your employment.

SEARCH PBGC

If your former employer went out of business or if the company still is in business but terminated its pension plan, check with the PBGC, which guarantees pension payouts to private-sector workers if their pension plans fail, up to annual limits. Most people receive the full benefit they earned before the plan was terminated. The PBGC offers an online pension-search directory tool at *http://Search.PBGC.gov/mp/mp.aspx*, or call 800-400-7242.

GET HELP

If you need help tracking down your former company because it may have moved, changed owners or merged with another firm, contact the Pension Rights Center, a nonprofit consumer organization that offers seven free Pension Counseling and Information Projects around the US that serve 30 states. For more information, visit *www.PensionRights.org* or call 888-420-6550.

If you, your company or your pension plan happens to be outside the 30-state area served by the projects, or if you're trying to locate a federal or military pension, use Pension Help America at *www.PensionHelp.org*. This resource can connect you with government agencies and private organizations that provide free information and assistance to help your search.

Also, the PBGC has a free publication called *Finding a Lost Pension*. Go to *www.PBGC.gov/res* (scroll down to "Additional Resources") to see it online, or call 800-400-7242 and ask for a copy to be mailed to you.

---

have issued split-rated bonds with maturities of four to eight years and yields of around 4.5%.

Marilyn Cohen, CEO of Envision Capital Management, which manages bond portfolios, Los Angeles. She is author of *Surviving the Bond Bear Market* (Wiley). *www.EnvisionCap.com*

What to Do If Your Adviser Switches Firms

If your financial adviser goes to a new firm, find out why. If you might want to move your account, you may have to reach out and contact your former adviser—firms often forbid advisers who leave from actively soliciting former clients.

Contact the person at your current firm who informed you, and ask some key questions—such as whether there has been a lot of turnover or if issues facing the firm could have caused your adviser to leave. If you get empty assurances that everything will be fine, that could be a red flag about the credibility or future of the firm. You want specific information—for instance, that your adviser left to start his/her own firm.

What to do: Decide whether the firm or the adviser matters more to you. Consider whether a new adviser at the same firm will meet your needs or whether you want to follow your previous one.

The Wall Street Journal

Benjamin Graham's Formula for Value Investing

Benjamin Graham's formula...You take current earnings, apply a base P/E ratio, add a growth factor if there is growth, and adjust according to current bond yield. The result is an intrinsic value that the stock can be expected to achieve in the real world if growth targets are met.

Formula: Intrinsic value = $\mathbf{E} \times (2\mathbf{g} + 8.5) \times 4.4/\mathbf{Y}$

E is the current annual earnings per share.

g is the annual earnings growth rate—5 percent would be figured as a "5." (Graham would have suggested using a conservative number for growth.)

8.5 is the base P/E ratio for a stock with no growth.

Y is the current interest rate, represented as the average rate on high-grade corporate bonds. Note that lower bond rates make the intrinsic value higher, as future earnings streams are worth more in a lower interest rate environment.

Value Investing for Dummies, Peter J. Sander and Janet Haley (For Dummies).

Earn 4% to 6% Yields On "Split-Rated" Bonds

Usually the three major credit-rating agencies agree on whether a company's bonds are investment-grade or higher-risk junk bonds. But split-rated bonds straddle the line. At least one agency has assigned them "junk" status, so they typically offer a higher interest rate.

Well-run companies such as home-products manufacturer Masco and travel service Expedia

Secrets of a Red-Hot Fund Manager

Jerome L. Dodson, founder and president of Parnassus Investments, San Francisco, which manages $5.5 billion in assets. He is lead fund manager of three funds. *www.parnassus.com*

Several mutual fund superstars dominate the investment landscape. They repeatedly get attention for their strategic shifts, market forecasts and award-winning ways.

But some superb managers fly below the radar, gaining little attention despite their outstanding performances and proven investment strategies. We spoke to one of these very impressive but little-known managers to find ways to pep up and protect your portfolio.

Jerome L. Dodson, manager of three mutual funds at Parnassus Investments, the San Francisco firm he founded in 1984, explains how a focus on misunderstood and underappreciated companies can pay off big.

Proof: His Parnassus Fund has performed within the top 5% of large-cap growth funds over the past five years. His Parnassus Small-Cap and Parnassus Workplace funds are in the top 1% of their categories over the past five years.

LOOKING BEYOND TODAY'S TRENDS

My investment strategy has always been shaped by my social conscience, and that has helped, rather than hindered, performance. When I started back in the 1980s, I refused to invest in lucrative but harmful industries such as defense, tobacco, alcohol and gambling. I even named my company after Mount Parnassus, a place of enlightenment in Greek mythology. This approach forced me to dig deeper and look beyond the obvious. The public often waits until a company has booming revenues before jumping in, but a company's stock frequently starts to rise when business is at its worst and won't turn around for 12 to 18 months.

Examples of trends I spotted early: In 2010, as smartphones were getting hotter and hotter, I realized that the proliferation of these devices was placing huge demands on cellular networks. Telecom-service providers, still recovering from the recession, were putting off expensive equipment upgrades, but they would be forced to make them in 2011 and 2012, which would mean a bonanza for telecom-equipment companies. I began investing in these stocks at the beginning of 2010, and many have since risen by triple-digit percentages.

Now I'm investing in home-building–related stocks, many of which trade for as much as 80% below their five-year highs. I expect employment to strengthen and people to start buying homes again, making now an ideal time to invest in these stocks.

LOVING UNLOVED STOCKS

Every company that my funds invest in is a solid, profitable business that has been ignored or unloved by investors, often with a stock price that is significantly below its five-year high. In the second half of 2010, investors abandoned the energy sector after the catastrophic Gulf of Mexico oil spill.

The stocks of natural gas companies, which had suffered during the recession, sank even lower.

In the future, natural gas, which is relatively cheap and plentiful, will increasingly serve as a substitute for oil.

That's because US crude production will continue to decline and, I expect, oil will only get more expensive, as it has during the recent uprisings in the Middle East. That should push up natural gas prices.

SEEKING HAPPY WORKERS

Years ago, I noticed that stocks of publicly traded companies that made *Fortune's* list of the "100 Best Companies to Work For" tended to perform exceptionally well.

While favorable work environments and ethical business practices are just two criteria in evaluating a stock, they proved so valuable that I created a separate large-cap growth fund at Parnassus focused on companies that treated their workers and the larger community right.

It just makes sense that equitable pay and benefits, family-friendly policies and ethnic diversity lead to positive-minded employees, better retention and greater productivity.

ANALYZING THE MISUNDERSTOOD

Most small investors buy stocks because of sound bites they hear from their friends or brokers or a guru on TV.

But I like to investigate how companies really make their money to find out if they have bigger growth prospects or secondary ways of generating revenue that aren't obvious to the public.

A World in Turmoil... What the Financial Aftershocks Mean for Your Investments

Mohamed El-Erian, CEO of Pimco, which manages $1.2 trillion for institutions and individuals in Newport Beach, California. Formerly, El-Erian served as president and CEO of Harvard Management Co., which oversees the university's huge endowment portfolio. He is author of *When Markets Collide: Investment Strategies for the Age of Global Economic Change* (McGraw-Hill).

An earthquake, a tsunami and a nuclear crisis have devastated Japan...uprisings have shaken the Middle East, causing oil prices to skyrocket...a debt crisis has roiled Europe...and the rising threat of runaway inflation has prompted many developing countries to tap the brakes on rapid economic growth. That's not exactly the kind of environment to give global investors an optimistic outlook, but the markets have held up surprisingly well.

Below, a top global investment strategist explains how investors should shape or reshape their portfolios in the face of repeated shocks to the global economy.

Is there a real danger that the world will fall back into recession because of all the turmoil?

There is a tug of war going on now that is promoting investor uncertainty and market volatility. We have negative factors, including oil priced at more than $90 per barrel.*

But I am cautiously optimistic at this point that the world can withstand all these recent shocks. It is a major positive that economies such as those of the US and Germany continue to heal and grow stronger. Investors would be shortsighted to run back to the safety of cash or US Treasuries now.

That said, additional shocks, such as a further sharp rise in oil prices due to heightened Middle East turmoil, could put severe stress on the global economy. Indeed, if oil prices topped $120 per barrel, I would have a darker outlook.

Given your current outlook, should investors cut back on foreign stocks and favor US investments until things settle down?

*This price fluctuates on a daily basis.

US markets have held up well. Part of that is due to the strong profit performance of the very large multinational companies that dominate the Dow Jones Industrial Average and the Standard & Poor's 500 stock index. Many of these companies cut costs sharply during the recession, reduced debt on their balance sheets and now are holding lots of cash. They also are tapping into the speedy growth of emerging economies. Indeed, many of these companies derive about half of their profits internationally, so if you invest in the Dow and the S&P 500, you are a global investor, not just a domestic one.

Being a global investor continues to be a good strategy because we're in a multispeed world now, where many emerging markets, for example China and Brazil, will continue to grow faster year after year than developed nations such as the US or European countries. For instance, I am very optimistic that China can manage its current high inflation without halting growth.

But differentiation among foreign markets is key. In contrast to Brazil and China, investors in European countries such as Greece, Ireland and Portugal might be even worse off than they were during the 2010 panic over insolvency. These countries have merely postponed their problems for a few years, piling up a lot more debt onto existing debt that they could not pay on their own.

Will the earthquake drastically set back Japan's efforts to improve its economy, or could the country's massive rebuilding needs actually help spur growth there and in other countries?

Many investors think that the 2011 Japanese disaster will play out like the 1995 earthquake in the city of Kobe, when there was a very sharp recovery after the terrible damage. But I'm more worried. I believe that the recovery will take longer this time. Japan's debt load is much larger, and the nuclear plant disaster complicates the situation.

The dominant images of this disaster have been the destroyed Fukushima nuclear reactor complex and the specter of radioactive dust descending on the 13 million residents of Tokyo—not to mention the radioactivity detected in tap water, vegetables and milk.

This has sparked a serious debate over nuclear energy's future as a source of safe, stable power, which in turn will have a larger consequence for oil prices.

Oil prices already were rising prior to the Japanese disaster, and they could climb even higher, not only because Japan will add to the global demand for oil to replace power from its stricken reactors but also because of the coming retreat from nuclear energy around the world. Already, since the Japanese earthquake, Germany has shut down its seven oldest nuclear power reactors for several months and China, which has 27 new reactors under construction, has said that it will delay approvals for pending nuclear projects.

Will energy and oil stocks present an opportunity for investors?

Yes. Energy has been a top-performing sector of the S&P 500.

I think high and volatile oil prices are going to be with us for a while. This is not due just to the spreading unrest in the Middle East. Because oil is such a critical import for many countries, whenever the price rises, it causes some industries around the world to initially buy or reserve even more oil because they are afraid of even higher prices to come. Right now, in the boardrooms of every airline, there are major discussions going on about how much fuel to stockpile as a hedge against higher prices. That means more revenue and more profits for oil exporters and the oil industry.

In the past few years, you have told investors to expect slower economic growth in developed countries and lower investment returns in the US, but the US stock market has been robust. Will it continue to rise?

The US stock market has done well since 2009 in large part because of bargain prices and steps taken by US policymakers. These measures have included keeping interest rates at practically zero and flooding the economy with money by purchasing more than $1 trillion worth of US Treasury bonds. All this has given investors great confidence that the government will do whatever it needs to do to get the economy moving again.

Your Pimco Total Return Fund sold its entire stake of US Treasury bonds in 2011 and started buying up emerging-market bonds. Should small investors be doing the same?

Bond investors would be wise to look for value throughout the global fixed-income markets, including government bonds of oil- and commodity-exporting nations like Brazil and bonds of large multinational US companies.

2

The Doctor's Handbook Of Healing Remedies and Medical Breakthroughs

Cut Your Risk of Cancer By Two-Thirds by Just Eating Wisely

Can changing your diet eliminate your risk of developing cancer? That proposition—the centerpiece of a book called *The Breast Cancer Prevention Diet* (Little, Brown)—caused a firestorm of controversy when it was first published.

Critics of the book, written by television correspondent Bob Arnot, MD, argue that nothing can eliminate the danger of cancer altogether. They're right. No diet, supplement or drug can *guarantee* you won't get cancer. But you *can* do a great deal to protect yourself.

Diet is now believed to be a factor in approximately 60% of all malignancies—with smoking, heredity and viral infections accounting for the rest of them.

Theoretically, an effective anticancer diet should be capable of cutting your cancer risk by approximately two-thirds.

NO QUICK FIX

The most compelling demonstrations of cancer risk reduction come from *population studies*. These experiments compare the incidence of certain diseases among different groups of people. Among other things, these studies show that cancer rates are much lower in developing nations than in the US.

Citizens of developing nations tend to eat *very* differently than the average American. The average American eats lots of fatty and/or highly processed foods. In developing countries, people eat mostly fruits, vegetables and grains.

WHAT TO AVOID

It's now well established that eating less dietary fat can cut your cancer risk. Dietary fat clearly raises the risk for breast, colon and prostate cancers.

In addition, you must avoid foods known to raise cancer risk—and boost consumption of foods that lower the risk...

J. Robert Hatherill, PhD, assistant professor of biology, department of natural sciences, Del Mar College, Corpus Christi, Texas. He is author of *Eat to Beat Cancer* (Renaissance).

• **Minimize consumption of beef, pork, poultry and fish.** These foods can be concentrated sources of *dioxin*, *polychlorinated biphenyls* (PCBs) and other potent carcinogens.

These compounds sap the body's cancer-fighting ability...and trigger genetic mutations that can lead to cancer.

• **Wash produce thoroughly.** If peeling is not an option, use VegiWash or another produce wash. Whenever possible, buy organic.

• **Drink more water.** Drinking eight eight-ounce glasses of water a day helps flush carcinogens out of the body.

• **Consume more dietary fiber**—in the form of fresh fruits, vegetables and whole grains. Fiber speeds the passage of feces through the intestines, reducing the amount of time any carcinogens present in the body remain in contact with body tissues.

• **Avoid processed foods.** Potato chips, baked goods and other processed foods tend to contain lots of trans fatty acids, refined sugar and/or sodium. Animal studies have linked each of these substances to cancer.

A SHIELD AGAINST CANCER

From the standpoint of cancer avoidance, virtually all fruits, vegetables and grains are beneficial. But certain plant foods are special—because they contain cancer-preventing compounds.

Eight plant foods are particularly rich sources of these *phytochemicals*. They should be eaten every day.

• **Onions and garlic.** The same sulfur compounds that give these herbs their characteristic aromas protect cells against oxidative damage. That's the first step in the cancer process.

Onions and garlic also block the formation of *nitrosamines*. These potent carcinogens are formed in the stomach following the consumption of cured meats and other nitrate-containing foods.

• **Crucifers.** Broccoli, cauliflower, cabbage and Brussels sprouts are rich sources of potent anticancer compounds known as *glucosinolates*.

Crucifer consumption has been linked with a reduced risk for lung and colon cancer.

• **Nuts and seeds.** In addition to antioxidants, nuts and seeds contain *protease inhibitors*. These compounds help block the growth of blood vessels that tumors need to obtain nutrients from the bloodstream.

• **Whole grains.** Oats, wheat and other grains contain fiber that helps isolate cancer-causing compounds and remove them from the body.

Flaxseed, rye and millet are rich in *lignans*. These compounds act as weak estrogens, helping stymie the growth of breast cancer and other malignancies that are often estrogen-dependent.

• **Legumes.** Beans, peas and lentils are rich in fiber and *saponins*, compounds that block tumor growth by inhibiting DNA synthesis. Soybeans are the most potent anticancer legume.

• **Fruits.** In addition to vitamin C—a potent antioxidant—citrus fruits contain cancer-fighting compounds known as *monoterpenes* and *glutathiones*.

Ellagic acid—in blackberries, strawberries and raspberries—binds to carcinogens and thereby deactivates them.

• **Tomatoes.** Tomatoes get their red color from *lycopene*, a phytochemical that blocks the formation of carcinogens. Lycopene appears to be especially effective at preventing prostate cancer.

Important: Lycopene is more easily absorbed from cooked tomatoes than from raw tomatoes.

• **Umbellifers.** Carrots, parsley, celery and the spices cumin, anise, caraway and coriander are rich sources of phytochemicals.

The *carotenoids* in carrots are strong antioxidants. Compounds found in celery boost the action of the carcinogen-deactivating enzyme *glutathione S-transferase*.

Amazing Cancer Stoppers

Patrick Quillin, PhD, RD, clinical nutritionist in San Diego, California, and former vice president of nutrition, Cancer Treatment Centers of America, *www.nutritioncancer.com*. He is author of numerous books, including *Beating Cancer with Nutrition* (Nutrition Times).

Every year, more than 1.4 million Americans are diagnosed with cancer. Nearly half of all Americans eventually will get the disease—and about 25% of them will die from it. But there is a powerful way to reduce your risk of getting cancer.

Specific nutrients and foods can help prevent or correct cellular, hormonal and other imbalances that may lead to cancer. The supplements mentioned here are available at health-food stores and some supermarkets.

FISH OIL

The most common nutritional deficiency in Americans is low *eicosapentaenoic acid* (EPA). It is one of the omega-3 fatty acids found in the oil of fatty fish, such as salmon and tuna. A healthy diet has a 1:1 ratio of omega-3 to omega-6 fatty acids (found in vegetable oils). The typical American diet has a 1:16 ratio.

EPA helps prevent cancer by improving cell membrane dynamics—the ability of each cell to receive hormones and signals from other cells while absorbing essential nutrients and expelling waste products. EPA also boosts immune function and lowers levels of hormones, such as *estradiol,* that contribute to breast and other cancers.

What I recommend to my patients: One tablespoon of fish oil daily. For capsules, follow dosage recommendations on labels. Carlson Laboratories, Dr. Sears, Nordic Naturals and Pharmax brands are reliable. Take it in the middle of a meal to avoid "fishy" belching or reflux.

CLA

Another fat that helps prevent cancer is *conjugated linoleic acid* (CLA), found in the meat and milk of grass-eating animals, such as cattle, sheep and goats. CLA helps build healthy cell membranes, allowing cells to absorb nutrients, process hormones and expel waste. It's hard to find CLA-rich foods in markets because most livestock in America are fed grain, not grass.

What I recommend to my patients: Three grams of CLA a day. You can get that from an eight-ounce serving of grass-fed beef. Look for such brands as Lasater Grasslands Beef, available at specialty food stores. On days when you don't eat grass-fed red meat, you can take a CLA supplement—three one-gram soft-gel capsules a day.

VITAMIN D

People living in Boston have, on average, double the risk of breast, colon and prostate cancers, compared with residents of San Diego. Why? Many scientists think it's because Bostonians, like other northerners, don't get enough vitamin D, which is produced when skin is exposed to sun. Vitamin D is one of the most powerful anticancer nutrients. It facilitates the absorption of calcium, a mineral that not only builds strong bones but is also critical for "telegraphing" messages between cells. Poor cell-to-cell communication can contribute to cancer. Studies show that levels of vitamin D in fortified foods rarely equal the claims made on the labels. There is a debate as to whether synthetic vitamin D—the kind found in supplements—provides the same cancer protection as the naturally produced variety.

What I recommend to my patients: During the summer, get 15 minutes a day of midday sunshine with no sunscreen (without burning) on your face and bare arms. The body stockpiles vitamin D in the liver, so you're set for the rest of the year.

VITAMIN C

In a report published in *American Journal of Clinical Nutrition,* 33 of 46 studies showed that vitamin C protects against cancer. Cancer feeds on blood sugar (glucose)—and lowering chronically high blood sugar is crucial to preventing cancer. When you get enough vitamin C, you cut in half the amount of blood sugar that enters cells.

What I recommend to my patients: 500 to 1,000 milligrams (mg) of vitamin C a day, in three divided doses, taken with meals. Cancer patients may need higher doses, which usually are given intravenously.

Other ways to normalize blood sugar levels include regular exercise, weight loss and a diet that emphasizes lean meats, beans, nuts and produce. Five daily servings of fruits and vegetables nets you 300 mg of vitamin C.

SELENIUM

In the four-year Nutritional Prevention of Cancer Trial, scientists gave 1,312 participants either 200 micrograms (mcg) of the trace mineral selenium or a placebo. The results showed that selenium lowered the risk of prostate cancer by 63%, colon cancer by 58% and lung cancer by 46%.

Selenium strengthens the immune system, helps repair DNA damage and protects cells against toxins.

What I recommend to my patients: 200 mcg of selenium a day. Look for *selenomethionine*—selenium bound in yeast—which is absorbed the best. A particularly good food source is Brazil nuts (four nuts provide 200 mcg).

Caution: More is not better in this case. Selenium supplements in doses of 2,000 mcg or higher can be toxic.

GREEN TEA

Literally hundreds of studies have proven that green tea and its various extracts can prevent and, in some experiments, reverse cancer. These extracts work by different mechanisms, among them *apoptosis* ("programmed cell death"). In other words, green tea orders cancer cells to commit suicide.

What I recommend to my patients: Drink three eight-ounce cups of green tea a day. If you don't like the taste, take supplements of green tea extract, available in capsules, following the dosage recommendation on the label.

KILLER CONSTIPATION

Chronic constipation creates toxemia in the colon. Cancer-causing chemicals from the environment are ingested but not expelled quickly. Normally friendly food-digesting bacteria then produce toxins that end up in the bloodstream.

What I recommend to my patients: To ensure a daily bowel movement, get plenty of high-fiber foods...drink 64 ounces of filtered or bottled water a day...and exercise regularly. Prune juice and figs often relieve constipation. Or try a gentle herbal laxative, such as *psyllium* (Metamucil), following the dosage recommendation on the label.

Surprising Study About Breast Cancer

Taking an Advil or Motrin tablet might help save your life. Ibuprofen—the active ingredient in these over-the-counter pain medicines—may protect against breast cancer.

Recent study: Women who took two or more ibuprofen tablets every week for more than 10 years decreased breast cancer risk by 49%, compared with a 28% reduction for women who took aspirin.

Caution: Long-term use of ibuprofen or aspirin may cause stomach trouble—consult your doctor.

Randall E. Harris, MD, PhD, professor of preventive medicine and public health, the Ohio State University College of Medicine and Public Health, Columbus, and lead researcher, National Cancer Center's Women's Health Initiative Observational Study of 90,000 women, reported in *Proceedings*.

Mayo Clinic: New Scans Help Find Small Tumors

Mayo Clinic news release.

A new technique that uses a specially designed gamma camera was found to improve the detection of small breast tumors, according to a study.

TECHNIQUE ALLOWS EARLIER DETECTION

A team from the Mayo Clinic in Rochester, Minnesota, used the technique, called *molecular breast imaging*, on 40 women who had suspicious mammogram findings.

The imaging detected 33 of the 36 malignant lesions that were confirmed in 26 of the women during surgery.

Overall, molecular breast imaging had an 86% detection rate of small breast tumors.

"By optimizing the camera to detect smaller breast lesions, this technique should aid in the detection of early-stage breast cancer, something that was not possible with conventional gamma cameras," says Dr. Michael O'Connor, a Mayo Clinic radiologist.

BETTER THAN MAMMOGRAPHY

Mammography uses differences in the anatomic appearance of tumors and normal tissue to detect breast cancer. These differences can be subtle and can often be obscured by dense breast tissue.

In contrast, molecular breast imaging detects cancer by identifying differences in the metabolic behavior of tumors and normal tissue.

"Approximately 25% to 40% of women have dense breast tissue, which decreases the chance that a cancer will be visible on their mammograms," says Dr. Douglas Collins, another radiologist from the Mayo Clinic.

"With molecular breast imaging, the visibility of the tumor is not influenced by the density of the surrounding tissue, so this technique is well-suited to find cancers in women whose mammograms may not be very accurate," Collins explains.

Avoid Skin Cancer... Debunk the Myths

Barney J. Kenet, MD, dermatologist specializing in skin cancer. He is an assistant attending physician at New York-Presbyterian Hospital–Weill Medical College of Cornell University, and is coauthor of *Saving Your Skin—Prevention, Early Detection, and Treatment of Melanoma and Other Skin Cancers* (Da Capo).

Everyone knows that excessive sun exposure is dangerous, yet up to 50% of people over age 65 are diagnosed with melanoma or some other type of skin cancer.

Why? Even health-savvy individuals remain confused about the best ways to adequately protect their skin.

Here are three of the most dangerous myths...

Myth #1: A beach umbrella keeps you safe from the sun.

Reality: When you're at the beach, a large percentage of ultraviolet (UV) light bounces off the sand onto your skin, even if you're under an umbrella. Water and snow have the same reflective effect.

When boating or sitting beneath a beach umbrella, apply sunscreen to all exposed areas, including your face and neck—even if you're wearing a brimmed hat. When skiing, apply sunscreen to your face and neck.

Myth #2: Sunscreen with a sun-protection factor (SPF) of 45 is three times more effective than SPF 15.

Reality: Most doctors recommend using a sunscreen with an SPF of at least 15. A higher SPF will not give you much additional protection. A sunscreen with an SPF of 45 is only about 5% more protective than an SPF 15 sunscreen. The higher-rated sunscreen doesn't last any longer, either.

All sunscreens need to be reapplied every two hours—and whenever you're exposed to water. This includes "waterproof" sunscreens, which provide some protection while swimming but still must be reapplied.

Make sure your sunscreen is labeled "broad spectrum"—meaning it blocks both ultraviolet A (UVA) and ultraviolet B (UVB) rays. Look for titanium dioxide or Parsol 1789 in the list of ingredients on the label.

Myth #3: Sunscreen provides complete sun protection.

Reality: While sunscreen is essential, there are other steps you should also take. The most important is to minimize sun exposure between 10 am and 4 pm, when the sun's rays are most intense. Hit the beach in the early morning or late afternoon instead.

To protect commonly neglected areas, wear...

- **UV-protective lip balm** with an SPF of 15 or higher.
- **A hat with a three-inch brim.** Baseball caps don't protect the ears or the back of the neck—common skin cancer sites, especially for golf and tennis players.
- **UV-protective sunglasses.** UV exposure can cause cataracts.
- **Sun-protective clothing.** UV rays can pass through many fabrics, including cotton. If you hold a garment up to a light and can see the shape of the bulb shining through, it's not providing adequate sun protection.

Many companies now offer lightweight, tightly woven garments designed for comfort and maximum protection.

Example: Solumbra 100+ SPF sun protective clothing, 800-882-7860, *www.sunprecautions.com.*

If you will be outdoors and don't have any special clothing, be sure to wear sunscreen *under* your shirt.

The Amazing Powers Of Aspirin

Charles H. Hennekens, MD, DrPH, Sir Richard Doll research professor of Biomedical Science, Florida Atlantic University College of Biomedical Science, Boca Raton. He is an expert on low-dose aspirin for the treatment and prevention of cardiovascular disease and was the founding principal investigator for the Harvard-based Physicians' Health Study and Women's Health Study.

Aspirin is one of the best treatments for fever, headache and other aches and pains. It is also the safest and least expensive drug for preventing heart attacks—and it can greatly increase survival in those who have just had a heart attack.

Recent research suggests that aspirin may have other important uses as well. It prevents colon cancer and may prevent breast cancer. It may even slow the progression of Alzheimer's disease.

Important: Don't exceed the recommended dosage on the label *without consulting your doctor.* Regular use can cause intestinal upset or bleeding, although these side effects are rare at the low doses required for prevention of chronic diseases.

Here, a look at the latest findings...

HEART ATTACK PREVENTION

Most heart attacks occur when a clot in a coronary artery prevents blood from reaching the heart. Aspirin blocks the effects of *thromboxane A2*, a substance that initiates clotting. The Physicians' Health Study (PHS), a landmark study that followed 22,071 men age 40 and older, showed that aspirin reduced the risk of a first heart attack by 44%.

New finding: It is now believed that inflammation in the arteries may be just as important as blood clots in causing heart attacks. In the PHS, patients with the highest levels of *C-reactive protein*, a marker of inflammation, had a 52% drop in heart attack risk when taking aspirin.

The aspirin dose currently recommended to reduce clotting is too low to have a significant effect on inflammation. However, studies are under way to determine if higher doses of aspirin would be beneficial.

Who should consider aspirin: Anyone who has a history of heart problems or a greater-than-10% risk of having a heart attack within the next decade based on a standardized scoring method developed by the Framingham Heart Study. (Ask your doctor to calculate your risk, or go to *www.nhlbi.nih.gov* and click on "Public" then "10-Year Heart Attack Risk Calculator".) Those at risk include many men over age 40 and women who are over age 50—especially those who smoke or have high cholesterol or high blood pressure. There would be 100,000 fewer first heart attacks each year if patients in these groups took aspirin regularly.

Dose: Up to 325 milligrams (mg)—one adult aspirin—daily. A dose as low as 81 mg (one baby aspirin) daily can be effective.

New warning #1: If you have a history of heart problems, don't stop taking aspirin without talking to your cardiologist. Patients routinely are advised to stop taking aspirin before surgery or other invasive procedures, such as colonoscopy, tooth extraction and biopsy, to reduce the risk of bleeding.

Recent study: More than 4% of 1,236 heart patients who stopped taking aspirin had coronary "events," such as a heart attack, within one week.

New warning #2: Take aspirin at least two hours before other nonsteroidal anti-inflammatory drugs (NSAIDs). Data from the PHS found that men who regularly took aspirin and other NSAIDs, such as *ibuprofen* (Motrin) and *naproxen* (Aleve), had no reduction in heart attack risk. That's because NSAIDs can inhibit the heart-protecting effects of aspirin.

DURING A HEART ATTACK

In a study of more than 17,000 heart attack patients, those given aspirin during a heart attack had a 23% lower death rate during the first 35 days as well as significant decreases in subsequent heart attacks and strokes.

Taking aspirin inhibits the activity of blood platelets, responsible for clotting, within 10 to 15 minutes.

The clot-dissolving drug *streptokinase*, routinely given after heart attacks, decreases the death rate by 25% but causes hemorrhagic stroke (bleeding in the brain) in about three of every 1,000 patients. It also has to be given within six hours of a heart attack to be effective. Aspirin has a much longer "therapeutic window"—24 hours after the onset of heart attack symptoms.

Dose: 325 mg at the first sign of symptoms, such as chest pain or pressure, shortness of breath, light-headedness or pain that spreads to the shoulder, neck or arms. Be sure to tell emergency personnel that you have taken aspirin.

Important: If the tablet is coated, crush it before taking to hasten absorption. If the person having a heart attack is unconscious, put a noncoated 325-mg aspirin under his/her tongue.

MIGRAINE

Migraine sufferers have a 20% to 30% decrease in attacks when they take aspirin every other day. Platelets contain *histamine*, a chemical that triggers spasms in brain blood vessels, causing pain.

Aspirin makes platelets less "sticky" and inhibits the release of histamine.

New finding: Aspirin is as effective as *sumatriptan* (Imitrex), a prescription migraine drug. A study of migraine patients showed that those who took high doses of aspirin at the onset of symptoms had a better response and fewer side effects than those taking intravenous Imitrex.

Dose: 81- to 325-mg aspirin daily or every other day for prevention...at least 1,000 mg for an acute attack.

ARTHRITIS

Aspirin inhibits the synthesis of *prostaglandins*, chemicals that cause inflammation and pain. It's the best NSAID for any condition that involves inflammation, such as arthritis. If arthritis pain is managed with other medication, low-dose aspirin therapy should also be considered to reduce the risk of cardiovascular disease. Patients with rheumatoid arthritis have a higher risk of cardiovascular disease.

Dose: Two 325-mg tablets six times daily...or two 500-mg tablets four times a day for treatment and prevention.

COLON CANCER

Aspirin reduces the risk of colorectal cancer. Researchers looked at more than 1,100 people diagnosed with colon cancer. Those given aspirin had a lower incidence of recurring polyps, and their risk of advanced lesions declined by more than 40%.

Aspirin is thought to block two enzymes, *cyclooxygenase 1* and *cyclooxygenase 2*, inhibiting the growth of cancer cells and their ability to establish a blood supply.

Dose: 81-mg aspirin daily if you have a family history of colorectal cancer or other risk factors, such as polyps.

MORE RESEARCH NEEDED

- **Breast cancer.** Women who take aspirin seven or more times a week are 26% less likely to get the most common form of breast cancer. Between 60% and 70% of breast cancer cases are estrogen receptor–positive, meaning that the presence of estrogen causes tumors to grow. It's thought that aspirin blocks an enzyme used in estrogen production.

Even though women taking aspirin for other conditions may gain protection against breast cancer, the research is too preliminary to recommend aspirin solely for this purpose.

- **Alzheimer's disease.** Alzheimer's patients who take aspirin regularly perform better on language, memory and other cognitive tests. Aspirin reduces brain inflammation and improves circulation—but it's still not clear if it slows the progression of the disease.
- **Gum disease.** Studies suggest that aspirin may reduce the risk of periodontal disease. This is probably due to its anti-inflammatory and antiplatelet effects.

Prevent Diabetes

With type 1 diabetes (juvenile diabetes), white blood cells attack and destroy insulin-producing pancreatic cells. Vitamin D receptors, which attach to white blood cells, reduce the chance that this will happen. In addition, vitamin D appears to improve the ability of cells to accept insulin for better glucose uptake, helping to prevent type 2 diabetes (adult onset diabetes).

Best: Get 10 to 15 minutes of sunlight daily without sunscreen. Get 400 to 600 international units (IU) of vitamin D daily (through diet and supplements).

Foods high in vitamin D: Salmon, eggs, sardines, herring and milk.

Mark A. Stengler, NMD, licensed naturopathic medical doctor in private practice, Stengler Center for Integrative Medicine, Encinitas, California...adjunct associate clinical professor at the National College of Natural Medicine, Portland, Oregon...author of *The Natural Physician's Healing Therapies* (Bottom Line Books).

Secrets to Living Longer: Miraculous Antiaging Supplements

Ronald Klatz, MD, president, American Academy of Anti-Aging Medicine, Chicago, *www.worldhealth.net*, and co-founder, National Academy of Sports Medicine, Calabasas, California. He is author of numerous books, including *The New Anti-Aging Revolution* (Basic Health).

Aging damages the cells in our bodies—in our eyes, ears, brain, heart, lungs, skin, etc. The cells are assaulted by free radicals (by-products of the cells' normal metabolism) as well as by sunlight and pollutants. The accumulation of toxins hinders cell growth and repair. If we can prevent or reverse this cell damage, we can slow aging and live longer.

An important way to fight cell damage is with antiaging supplements. Below are seven of the most effective. You can choose to take one, several or all of them.

Important: Don't take supplements without the approval of a qualified physician. To find one experienced in antiaging medicine, contact the American Academy of Anti-Aging Medicine at 888-997-0112 or go to the organization's Web site, *www.worldhealth.net*, and click on "Anti-Aging Resources," then go to "Find a Doctor."

ALPHA-GPC

Derived from soy, this nutrient provides high levels of *choline*, which protects brain cells. It also increases levels of the neurotransmitter *acetylcholine*, which triggers an increased release of human growth hormone (HGH)—a hormone that is naturally present in the human body when we're young but that decreases steadily as we age.

Studies show that increased HGH can reduce body fat, boost energy levels and restore youthful immune function.

In animal studies, alpha-GPC corrected age-related brain decline. In human studies, it helped stroke victims retain cognitive functioning and improved the mental functioning and mood of people with dementia.

Dose: 600 to 1,200 milligrams (mg) per day.*

*Dosages vary by body weight. Consult your doctor for more details.

ASHWAGANDHA ROOT

This herb is used extensively in Ayurveda, the traditional medicine of India. It stimulates immunity and, as an antioxidant, reduces cell-damaging free radicals, particularly within brain cells. Its anti-inflammatory properties have been shown to be helpful for such inflammatory conditions as arthritis.

In one study, it increased oxygen-carrying hemoglobin, which rejuvenates cells. In addition, 70% of the men in the study said that their sexual performance improved—some men have even reported fewer gray hairs.

Dose: 3 to 6 grams (g) of the dried root in capsule form per day.

BETA-GLUCAN

This nutrient is derived from baker's yeast, young rye plants and medicinal mushrooms. It activates *macrophages*, key immune cells that fight bacteria, viruses and other disease-causing organisms. Beta-glucan enhances the effectiveness of conventional antibiotic therapy. It acts as a free-radical scavenger, removing cells damaged by exposure to radiation, chemotherapy and pollutants. It also lowers total and LDL ("bad") cholesterol while increasing HDL ("good") cholesterol. In addition, it reduces the risk of infection by stimulating white blood cell activity.

Dose: 300 to 1,000 mg per day.

LEMON BALM

Lemon balm is an important antioxidant. It contains a high concentration of *phenols*, chemicals that fight cell-damaging toxins. This herb can improve sleep...decrease the pain of inflammatory conditions such as arthritis...boost mental functioning...and combat viruses and bacteria.

Dose: 1,000 to 1,500 mg per day.

Caution: Avoid lemon balm if you have glaucoma. Some animal studies have shown that it may raise pressure in the eye, which can worsen the condition.

OMEGA-3 FATTY ACIDS

Omega-3 fatty acids, also called essential fatty acids (EFAs), aren't manufactured by the human body and must be supplied by diet or supplements. They are found primarily in fish but are also present in smaller amounts in green, leafy vegetables...soybeans...nuts...and flaxseed and canola oils.

Omega-3s decrease blood levels of *triglycerides* (bad fats) and *homocysteine* (an artery-damaging amino acid) as well as lower blood pressure. They also help thin the blood, preventing blood clots. These effects lower the risk of heart disease and stroke, the number-one and number-three killers of Americans (cancer is number two).

Omega-3s also act as anti-inflammatories, helpful in the treatment of such autoimmune diseases as rheumatoid arthritis, chronic inflammatory bowel disease and psoriasis. They are a building block of the outer layer of brain cells and may help treat depression.

Dose: 3 to 10 g a day of fish oil capsules. Follow the instructions on the label.

Caution: If you have heart disease or diabetes, consult your doctor before taking these high doses, which may raise cholesterol and blood sugar levels.

To get omega-3 fatty acids in your diet, eat oily fish three to four times per week. These include mackerel, salmon, sea bass, trout, herring, sardines, sablefish (black cod), anchovies and tuna. Use omega-3–rich canola oil in cooking and salad dressings.

EVENING PRIMROSE OIL

Evening primrose oil is derived from the seeds of the evening primrose plant. The active ingredient is *gamma-linolenic acid* (GLA), an omega-6 fatty acid.

As the body ages, it loses its ability to convert the dietary fats into GLA. Supplementing with evening primrose oil is important in combating the general effects of aging. It may also help in treating rheumatoid arthritis, diabetes, nerve damage (neuropathy), multiple sclerosis and Alzheimer's-related memory problems.

Dose: 3,000 to 6,000 mg daily, which contains about 270 to 540 mg of GLA.

Caution: Evening primrose oil may worsen temporal-lobe epilepsy. It should be avoided by epileptics and schizophrenics who are prescribed phenothiazine epileptogenic drugs.

RESVERATROL

This is a naturally occurring antioxidant found in many plants—including the skins of grapes. Red wine is the main dietary source. Resveratrol decreases the "stickiness" of blood platelets, reducing the risk of blood clots. It may also help prevent the development and progression of various cancers.

Dose: 200 to 650 micrograms (mcg) daily. One eight-ounce glass of red wine contains roughly 640 mcg. Grapes, grape juice and raisins are *not* good sources of resveratrol.

Change Your Biological Age

William J. Evans, PhD, former adviser to NASA and head of its nutrition, physical fitness and rapid rehabilitation team. He is adjunct professor of geriatrics, Duke University Medical Center, Durham, North Carolina. He is coauthor of *AstroFit: The Astronaut Program for Anti-Aging* (The Free Press).

Gray hair, wrinkled skin, flabbiness, loss of vitality and reduced resistance to injury and disease...

To most Americans, these are harbingers of old age, unwelcome but inevitable milestones along a path that leads inexorably to the grave. In fact, recent research suggests something quite different—that the body's gradual decline stems not from the passing of years but from the combined effects of inactivity and poor nutrition. So, no matter what your present health status or your chronological age, regular exercise and better eating habits can help lower your biological age.

Benefits: Reduced body fat...increased muscle mass...strength increases of 200% to 300%...increases in aerobic capacity of 20% or more...and reduced risk of heart disease, diabetes, osteoporosis and other age-related ailments.

Your goal should not be to become immortal, but to remain healthy and vigorous for as long as possible...and to compress the inevitable period of decline preceding death from several years into a few weeks or months.

To gauge your biological age: Forget how many birthdays you've marked...instead consider how you stack up in terms of the 10 key "biomarkers" identified by our lab...

- **Muscle mass.** As Americans move from adolescence to old age, we lose almost seven pounds of lean body mass each decade—a rate that accelerates after age 45.

Reduced muscle mass leads not only to reduced strength, but also to an increased risk of heart disease and diabetes, reduced aerobic capacity and a slower metabolism (which promotes fat gain). All of this happens because of bad habits like driving instead of walking or riding a bike, taking elevators rather than stairs...and because we're all too willing to let younger friends and relatives do chores we should do ourselves.

Good news: Those who remain physically active lose little muscle tissue as they age. All it takes is 20 to 30 minutes of aerobic exercise two or three times weekly.

• **Strength.** Between the ages of 20 and 70, the average American loses about 30% of his/her muscle cells—including a large proportion of "fast-twitch" cells needed for sprinting and other high-exertion exercises.

Unchecked, this loss of muscle leads eventually to sarcopenia, the severe, debilitating weakness that makes independent living impossible.

Good news: While we cannot prevent the loss of muscle cells, a weight-lifting regimen will compensate by boosting the size and strength of the cells that remain.

Essential: Two or three sets of 10 lifts with a weight that should leave your muscles completely fatigued. If not, add more weight.

• **Metabolic rate.** Because more energy is needed to maintain muscle than fat, the less muscle tissue in your body, the slower your metabolism—and the fewer calories you must consume to maintain ideal body weight.

Beginning at age 20, the average person's metabolic rate drops about 2% per decade. Thus, the average 70-year-old needs 500 fewer calories a day than the average 25-year-old.

To fight fat, eat fewer calories and get enough exercise to maintain your muscle mass.

• **Body-fat percentage.** In most cases, advancing age brings not only muscle loss but fat gain. Even if our weight (as measured by a scale) changes little, the ratio of fat to lean tissue in our bodies can rise markedly over the years.

The body of the average 25-year-old woman is 25% fat, for example, while the average 65-year-old woman is about 43% fat.

For men, the numbers rise from 18% fat at age 25 to 38% at 65.

Danger: Excessive fat leads to chronic disease and premature death.

Especially dangerous: Fat around the waist. It's far more unhealthy than fat on the buttocks or thighs.

To lose fat and gain muscle: Combine some restriction in calories with regular exercise.

• **Aerobic capacity.** To gauge fitness, doctors often measure the body's ability to process oxygen during exercise. The greater this aerobic capacity, the faster oxygen is pumped throughout the body—and the fitter the individual.

Like other biomarkers, aerobic capacity often declines with age. Typically, by age 65 it is 30% to 40% below its level in young adulthood.

Good news: Regular aerobic exercise—the kind that causes some huffing and puffing—will raise your aerobic capacity no matter what your present age.

• **Blood-sugar tolerance.** For most Americans, aging brings about a gradual decline in the body's ability to metabolize blood sugar (glucose). So common is this problem that by age 70, 20% of men and 30% of women are at an increased risk of diabetes, a potential killer.

At special risk for problems: People who are overweight, sedentary and those who eat a fatty diet.

Good news: A low-fat, high-fiber diet that restricts total calories consumed, combined with regular exercise, will cut your diabetes risk. Be sure to include both strength-building and aerobic exercise in your routine.

• **Cholesterol ratio.** As most of us know, high cholesterol boosts your risk of heart disease. But total cholesterol isn't the only thing that counts.

Very important: The ratio of total cholesterol to HDL (good) cholesterol. For older people, the ideal ratio is 4.5 or lower. A person whose total cholesterol is 200 and whose HDL is 50, for example, has a ratio of 200/50, or 4.0.

To lower your ratio: Stop smoking, lose weight, decrease your intake of fatty, cholesterol-rich foods (especially animal products) and exercise regularly, a good way to boost HDL levels.

• **Blood pressure.** In many parts of the world, advancing age brings little if any change in blood pressure.

In the US, however, where older people tend to be both overweight and sedentary, blood pressure does rise with age, often spiraling far above the maximum "safe" level.

To keep your pressure in check: Stay slim, don't smoke, get regular exercise and limit your consumption of fat, salt and alcohol. If these steps fail, pressure-lowering drugs may be necessary.

- **Bone density.** As we age, our skeletons slowly become weaker and more brittle.

While some mineral loss is inevitable, the severe and potentially deadly condition known as osteoporosis is not.

Prevention: Although consuming at least 1,000 milligrams (mg) of calcium a day will retard the loss of bone, that alone rarely does the trick.

Also needed: Weight-bearing exercise, such as walking, running or aerobics.

Not helpful for bones: Swimming and other forms of exercise that do not subject the long bones of the body to the stress of weight-bearing activity.

- **Temperature regulation.** Our ability to control our internal body temperature declines as we get older, due to a reduction in our ability both to shiver, which raises body temperature, and to sweat, which lowers it. This means cold and hot weather pose a danger to elderly people. To some extent, this can't be avoided.

Regular aerobic exercise causes you to sweat more readily whenever you exert yourself, not just during exercise. It also increases your total blood volume—which will make you less likely to overheat or dehydrate in hot weather.

Important: Force yourself to drink during exercise and in hot weather, even if you're not thirsty. In winter, be sure to dress warmly in layers.

How to Feel And Look Younger

David Ryback, PhD, antiaging/stress reduction consultant in Atlanta. He is author of *Look 10 Years Younger, Live 10 Years Longer*, which is available in editions for men and for women (Galahad Books).

Following are five strategies that will really help you to feel and look younger than you actually are...

- **Practice stretching each morning.** Regular stretching helps you feel more flexible and, as a result, you will feel and look younger. By stretching, you relax your muscles, and movements become more graceful and youthful.

- **Stand up straight.** By maintaining good posture, you'll look 10 pounds thinner. Practice in front of the mirror, and you'll notice that your stomach looks flatter, your torso appears longer and thinner—and you don't have that old, tired, hunched look.

- **Exercise at least 15 minutes a day.** Physical activity alleviates depression and improves your mood. It also sends more blood to the skin, giving your complexion a healthy, rosy and youthful glow.

- **Eat more fruits and vegetables.** A vegetarian or even a semi-vegetarian diet that includes lots of fruits, vegetables and grains will help you maintain a stable energy level. By eating sensibly, you can increase your energy level and feel younger.

- **Reduce stress.** If left unchecked, stress puts unnecessary wear and tear on your body's internal organs, which causes you to look tired and years older.

Eyesight Danger

Sunlight's blue wavelengths can contribute to macular degeneration, the main cause of blindness in people older than 55.

Most susceptible: People with fair skin and light eyes.

Self-defense: Wear yellow or amber sunglasses (they also block UV rays).

For healthy eyes: Don't smoke, and avoid secondhand smoke...eat dark green, leafy vegetables and foods with omega-3 fatty acids, such as flaxseeds and fish.

Lylas G. Mogk, MD, founding director, Visual Rehabilitation and Research Center, Grosse Pointe, Michigan, and coauthor of *Macular Degeneration: The Complete Guide to Saving and Maximizing Your Sight* (Ballantine).

Live Longer, Feel Better

Mark A. Stengler, NMD, licensed naturopathic medical doctor in private practice, Stengler Center for Integrative Medicine, Encinitas, California...adjunct associate clinical professor at the National College of Natural Medicine, Portland, Oregon...author of *The Natural Physician's Healing Therapies* (Bottom Line Books).

We age when the body's cells die at faster rates than new ones are generated. Many of us age prematurely because the traditional American diet hastens cellular destruction and boosts the already too-high rate of obesity, diabetes, cancer and other chronic diseases.

The body produces enormous quantities of highly reactive oxygen molecules, called free radicals, when we eat high-fat foods...are exposed to environmental pollutants, such as pesticides and ultraviolet radiation...or consume too many calories. Free radicals attack healthy cells and accelerate the aging process.

I advise my patients to take a high-potency multivitamin/mineral supplement. This offers general protection against free radicals and helps eliminate toxins.

Caution: Don't choose a formula that contains iron unless you have been diagnosed with iron-deficiency anemia. High levels of iron can be toxic.

In addition, I suggest the following...

TAKE SPIRULINA

Spirulina is a blue-green algae that grows wild in warm waters around the world. It has become a staple in Africa because it contains all the essential amino acids in a highly absorbable form and is a rich source of protein. It also contains *carotenoids*, fat-soluble pigments that act as antioxidants...*gamma-linoleic acid* (GLA), an essential fatty acid...*chlorophyll*, a pigment that has potent antioxidant and anticancer properties...and *phytocyanins*, which stimulate red blood cell production.

Several studies have shown that spirulina improves immune system activity. In one study, tobacco chewers who had mouth cancer were given one gram of spirulina daily for a year. Nearly half of those who took the supplement showed improvement, while only three of 43 in the nonsupplement group had any reversal of symptoms. Spirulina has also been shown to have antiviral effects and a mild cholesterol-reducing benefit.

What I recommend to my patients: Take 2,000 to 3,000 milligrams (mg) per day.

EAT BERRIES

Strawberries, raspberries and blueberries—as well as grapes and cherries—all contain phytonutrients known as *flavonoids*, which have potent antioxidant activity that can fight heart disease. The fruits' ellagic acid promotes excretion of carcinogenic chemicals.

Trap: Soft fruits, such as berries and grapes, absorb pesticides more readily than firm produce, such as apples and oranges. Be sure to eat organic.

What I recommend to my patients: Eat one-half cup of berries, cherries or grapes or drink four ounces of purple grape juice or red wine daily.

DRINK GREEN TEA

Green tea comes from the leaves of *Camellia sinensis*, the same plant used to make black tea—but because it's processed differently, it has more of the potent antioxidants called polyphenols than black tea. The most potent is *epigallocatechin gallate* (EGCG).

Green tea helps protect the liver and fight cancer. One study looked at 472 Japanese women with breast cancer. Increased green tea consumption was associated with a decreased risk of lymph node metastasis. Researchers also found that when women with breast cancer drank five cups of green tea a day, they were more likely to be in remission six months later.

Green tea has also been shown to reduce cholesterol levels, fight tooth decay and aid in weight loss.

What I recommend to my patients: Drink two or more cups of green tea daily. If you don't like tea, you can take 1,500 mg daily of a green tea extract formula that contains 35% to 55% EGCG.

LIMIT DAIRY

Milk, cheese and other dairy foods contain *casein*, one of the most common food allergens. It can deplete immune cells.

Milk also contains *xanthine oxidase*, an enzyme that may increase the buildup of plaque in the arteries.

You don't need dairy to get enough calcium. Substitute with calcium-enriched foods, such as juice and soy, rice and almond milk. Broccoli, collard greens, sardines and canned salmon with bones are also rich in calcium.

What I recommend to my patients: No more than five servings of dairy a week.

SELECT EZEKIEL BREAD

Ezekiel bread, a type of bread found in health-food stores, uses younger sprouted grains, which have a higher nutritional content than typical mature grains. If you can't find Ezekiel bread, choose other breads with whole grains (wheat, amaranth, spelt, etc.).

All whole grains are rich in fiber, which prevents constipation and reduces toxins in the digestive tract. They also contain phytonutrients, which block free-radical damage and improve immune function.

What I recommend to my patients: Eat at least one slice of Ezekiel bread a day.

TAKE FISH OIL AND EVENING PRIMROSE OIL

Both of these oils contain essential fatty acids—fish oil is a source of *eicosapentaenoic acid* (EPA) and *docosahexaenoic acid* (DHA)... evening primrose oil is a source of GLA.

Fatty acids are involved in proper functioning of the brain and immune system. They also reduce the risk of heart disease and cancer...and relieve pain.

What I recommend to my patients: Take 3,000 to 5,000 mg of fish oil and 1,000 mg of evening primrose oil daily. If you are on blood-thinning medications such as *warfarin* (Coumadin), check with your doctor first. Strict vegetarians can substitute flaxseed oil or hemp oil for fish oil (one to two tablespoons daily).

EAT GARLIC

Garlic contains *allicin*, a sulfur compound that builds immunity and prevents infections. It reduces the risk of colon, esophageal and stomach cancers. One study of 41,000 American women found that one or more servings of garlic a week decreased colon cancer risk by 35%. It also lowers cholesterol and has mild blood pressure–lowering effects.

What I recommend to my patients: One-half to one whole raw clove daily (cooking reduces its benefits)—or try an odor-free supplement containing 4,000 to 5,000 micrograms (mcg) of allicin.

DINE EARLY

Americans typically have their dinner a few hours before bedtime—but studies have shown that digestive juices lose potency later in the day. This means that you absorb fewer nutrients and have more trouble metabolizing toxins.

What I recommend to my patients: Eat no later than 7 pm.

Managing Menopause Without Drugs... Commonly Overlooked Strategies That Really Work

Toni M. Cutson, MD, assistant director, Extended Care and Rehabilitation Center at the Durham Veterans Affairs Medical Center. She is the medical director of the Palliative Care Consult Team at the DVAMC and of the VISN 6 (network) Palliative Care Consult Team. Dr. Cutson serves as the medical director for the hospice of the DVAMC affiliate teaching institution, Duke University Medical Center.

Hot flashes, mood swings, vaginal dryness, sleep disturbances and osteoporosis are some of the symptoms that affect about 75% of menopausal women.

To help control these common problems, doctors in the past often prescribed hormone-replacement therapy (HRT). However, HRT has been linked to an increased risk for breast cancer, stroke and blood clots. Therefore, many women have decided to treat their symptoms with a wide variety of nondrug alternatives—eating a low-fat, high-fiber diet...exercising on a regular basis...and quitting smoking.

These are a good start. But there are additional ways to relieve the symptoms. *A woman can benefit from these eight commonly overlooked strategies...*

- **Eat at least eight servings of fruits and vegetables each day.** These high-fiber, low-fat foods are typically rich in folic acid and other B vitamins, which reduce the risk for heart disease by helping to prevent arterial blood clots.

One serving equals one piece of fruit, one-half cup of cooked vegetables or one cup of raw vegetables. It is actually surprisingly easy to get into the habit of eating many small, healthful snacks each day, and the benefits that it affords you are enormous.

Also, make sure to consume calcium-rich products, such as dairy products (milk and yogurt) and fortified orange juice to combat osteoporosis.

• **Eat whole soy foods.** They contain *isoflavones*, estrogen-like compounds that reduce hot flashes, bone loss and LDL ("bad") cholesterol. Sources include soy nuts, soy milk and tofu, and can usually be found in your local supermarket.

Caution: Avoid nutritional supplements and powders that claim to have the same active ingredients as soy foods. These products may contain unknown chemicals that could be harmful.

Worse, they may contain *excessive* levels of isoflavones, which increase breast cancer risk. Limit your soy intake to about 60 grams of isoflavones a day.

• **Take a daily multivitamin.** Choose a name brand, such as One-a-Day or Centrum, to get the recommended requirements for most vitamins and minerals. Do *not* take individual vitamin megadoses, however. They can be harmful.

Too much vitamin A, for example, can damage the eyes and skin. Megadoses of vitamin D can cause excess calcium in the bloodstream.

To prevent liver damage, avoid pills that provide more than 18 milligrams (mg) of iron. Because menopausal women no longer lose iron through menstruation, iron supplements make sense only if you've been diagnosed with an iron deficiency.

• **Take a calcium supplement.** A daily 1,500-mg dose helps prevent osteoporosis.

Calcium carbonate found in Tums is cheap and readily absorbed. Each Tums tablet provides 200 mg of calcium. For higher doses, try Tums E-X with 300 mg or Tums 500 with 500 mg.

• **Try proven herbal remedies.** Some menopausal women are now taking chasteberry in order to prevent hot flashes. But little scientific research exists to support its effectiveness.

Similarly, avoid dong quai and licorice root. Dong quai can cause excessive blood thinning. Licorice root may precipitate headaches or high blood pressure.

Better: Black cohosh.* This herb suppresses *luteinizing hormone* (LH), which triggers hot flashes. Some women claim it also improves their sex drive and eases night sweats and sleep disturbances.

Black cohosh is sold as *Remifemin* at health-food stores.

• **Limit alcohol consumption.** Have no more than three glasses of wine—or three ounces of hard liquor—a week. Drinking wine in moderation may be beneficial to the heart, but too much alcohol exacerbates hot flashes.

• **Relax.** Many menopausal women blame hormone fluctuations for mood and memory problems. But psychological stress is often the real cause. While they're going through menopause, they may also be caring for elderly parents, sending children off to college or dealing with job stress.

To combat stress: Seek help if you find yourself in difficult situations...turn down extra projects at work...ask siblings to help care for an elderly parent...or find a day program that caters to the social needs of seniors.

Get plenty of restorative sleep and give yourself 30 minutes of quiet time each day.

• **Rethink your sex life.** The physical and psychological aspects of menopause often put a damper on a woman's sex life. But abstinence is not the answer.

Frequent sexual activity decreases vaginal dryness, improves sleep, reduces stress and helps alleviate moodiness.

Bonus: Regular sex also increases your libido.

*Please check with your medical professional before taking this or any other herb.

Jump-Start Your Sex Life...Naturally

Chris D. Meletis, ND, author of several books, including *Better Sex Naturally* (HarperResource), *Complete Guide to Safe Herbs* (DK Publishing) and *Instant Guide to Drug–Herb Interactions* (DK Publishing). *www.drmeletis.com*

Well before *sildenafil* (Viagra), *vardenafil* (Levitra) and *tadalafil* (Cialis) people relied on aphrodisiacs to increase sexual desire...boost stamina...improve performance... and increase pleasure.

Many of these compounds owe their reputation to folklore, but several herbs and dietary supplements have proven sex-enhancing effects.

Good news: Products that improve sex naturally may be less likely to cause serious side effects than prescription drugs. Many strengthen the cardiovascular system and help regulate hormone production. That's as important for good sex as having an erection or being sufficiently lubricated.

Sex-enhancing herbs and supplements aren't taken just an hour or so before sex. They're taken daily until there's a noticeable improvement in sexual performance.

At that point, some people take a pause to see if the herbs and supplements are no longer necessary. Others continue taking the preparations indefinitely.

Important: Use herbs and supplements only under medical supervision to be sure to get the product and dosage that's right for you.

Caution: Fresh or dried herbs differ greatly in potency from batch to batch. Use capsules or tinctures, ideally ones that have been standardized to contain the proper amounts of active ingredients.

For better sex, try one of the following natural enhancers. Select the one that best suits your needs. Give each preparation a few months to work. If you see no effect, try another.

GINKGO BILOBA*

Ginkgo contains a variety of compounds that relax blood vessels and increase circulation to the brain and pelvic area.

For women, increased blood flow improves vaginal lubrication and sexual responsiveness.

For men, adequate blood flow is essential to achieve and sustain erections.

Typical dosage: Capsules—40 to 60 milligrams (mg) of 24% standardized powdered extract three to four times daily. Tincture—30 drops three to four times daily.

Side effects: Ginkgo may cause dizziness, headache or heart palpitations.

Caution: Ginkgo is a blood thinner and can increase the blood-thinning effects of aspirin and *warfarin* (Coumadin). Check with your physician before using ginkgo if you're taking either medication.

*Please check with your medical professional before taking this or any other herb.

MUIRA PUAMA*

Also known as "potency wood," this herb contains sterols and other compounds that boost levels of testosterone, a hormone that plays a critical role in sexual desire in women and men.

Muira puama also contains volatile oils that are thought to restore sex drive by stimulating the brain's pleasure center.

Typical dosage: 250 mg three times daily in capsule form.

Side effect: Muira puama may lower blood pressure by as much as 10%. Check with your doctor before using this herb if you have low blood pressure (hypotension).

GINSENG

This herb is an "adaptogen," meaning it helps the body compensate for extended periods of stress. Stress can cause sexual desire and performance to plummet.

Compounds in ginseng root lower levels of adrenaline and other stress hormones.

These compounds also improve blood flow to the penis, help tissues use oxygen more efficiently and boost the production of testosterone in men and progesterone in women.

Typical dosage: Capsules—10 to 50 mg one to three times daily. Tincture—take 30 to 60 drops daily.

Side effect: Ginseng may cause diarrhea... high blood pressure...sleeplessness.

ASHWAGANDHA

A member of the pepper family, this herb contains *withanolides*, substances that increase the activity of testosterone and progesterone.

Ashwagandha also relieves stress and anxiety.

Typical dosage: Capsules—1,000 mg once or twice daily. Tincture—60 to 90 drops two or three times daily.

Side effects: Because ashwagandha has anti-anxiety properties, it should not be used by anyone taking medications to treat anxiety and/or depression. The herb could intensify the drugs' actions as well as their side effects. Ashwagandha may also trigger miscarriages.

*Please check with your medical professional before taking this or any other herb.

ARGININE

Taken in supplement form, this amino acid has been shown to relax smooth muscle contractions. This boosts arterial dilation, bringing more blood to the pelvic area.

The body uses arginine to produce nitric oxide, a chemical needed to achieve erections. (Sildenafil works, in part, by making nitric oxide more readily available in the body.)

Typical dosage: 1,000 to 2,000 mg twice daily in capsule form. Take capsules between meals, since many foods contain lysine, an amino acid that counteracts arginine's effects.

Side effect: Don't take this herb if you get cold sores caused by the herpes simplex virus. Arginine stimulates viral replication.

Secrets of Much More Satisfying Sexuality— How to Have Great Sex Every Time

Edward W. Eichel, MA, psychotherapist in private practice in New York City. He is the originator of the coital alignment technique (CAT), which is described in greater detail—and, yes, illustrated—in his book *The Perfect Fit* (Signet).

Of all the concerns voiced by women undergoing sex therapy, none is more common—or emotionally distressing—than an inability to achieve orgasm during sexual intercourse.

Only about 30% of women achieve orgasm regularly during intercourse (coitus).

Some women endure years of sex without a single coital orgasm. Typically, a woman relies upon a partner who "jumps through hoops" to bring her there, but never achieves the ideal.

Result: Sexuality is robbed of its playfulness and spontaneity and becomes more a chore than a pleasure.

TO THE RESCUE

A variant of the standard missionary position —known as the *coital alignment technique* (CAT)—not only helps the woman achieve orgasm during coitus, but boosts the odds that she and her partner will climax simultaneously.

Men who have long considered themselves sexually inadequate, as well as women who have worried they were frigid, can begin to experience sex with all its physical pleasure and emotional intimacy.

Bonus: Because good sex is usually synonymous with good communication, this improvement in a couple's sex life often carries over into other aspects of their relationship, bringing new levels of intimacy, contentment and commitment —important in this age of AIDS and other sexually transmitted diseases.

Unlike some other alternative lovemaking techniques, CAT is relatively straightforward. Couples have differed in the time necessary to master the technique, but with persistence, most have succeeded. Once mastered, it is remarkably effective—and quite reliable.

Recent study: Sexual response was measured in couples involved in committed relationships —before and after receiving CAT training.

Prior to the CAT training, only 23% of the women reported achieving orgasm during intercourse on a regular basis. After CAT, that figure jumped to 77%.

Before CAT, no women reported having regular simultaneous orgasms with their partners. Afterward, one-third of the women reported doing so.

Almost all participants reported at least some improvement in their sex lives following CAT training. In fact, the only participants who failed to benefit were those whose relationships were already jeopardized by nonsexual issues.

CAT BASICS

CAT encompasses five distinct elements, each designed to maximize contact between the penis and the clitoris, thus maximizing sexual response in both partners...

- **Positioning.** The woman lies on her back. The man lies atop her, facing her much as in the conventional missionary position, but with his pelvis overriding hers in a "riding high" orientation. His penis should be inserted into her vagina, with its shaft pressed firmly against her *mons veneris*—the soft fleshy mound covering the pubic bone above the vagina. She wraps her legs around his thighs, with her legs bent at an angle not exceeding 45 degrees and her ankles resting on his calves.

Important: He must let his full weight fall on her and must avoid using his hands or elbows to support his weight. While she may find this uncomfortable initially, it is essential to keep his pelvis from sliding back down off of hers.

• **Limited movement.** Conventional intercourse involves a great deal of pushing, pulling and bracing of the arms and legs.

CAT coitus focuses on the couples' pelvic movement. In fact, little additional movement is possible during CAT, given the partners' positioning. If additional movement is possible, the positioning is faulty.

• **Pressure-counterpressure.** During ordinary intercourse, the man sets the rhythm while the woman moves little, if at all. In contrast, CAT calls for a rhythmic movement that is virtually identical for both partners.

Procedure: She performs an upward stroke, forcing his pelvis backward. He allows his pelvis to move, yet maintains a continuous counterpressure against her pelvis (and her clitoris).

In the downward movement, the pattern of movement is then reversed, with the man pushing downward and the woman maintaining the counterpressure against his penis. As her pelvis moves backward and downward, the penis shaft rocks forward against her mons veneris, sliding to a shallow position in the vagina.

Note: Although the force of pressure and counterpressure is quite intense during CAT, the partners' actual movement is surprisingly slight.

• **Full genital contact.** Repeated thrusting of the penis into and out of the vaginal "barrel," typical of conventional missionary intercourse, affords little direct stimulation of the primary erogenous zones that facilitate a complete coital orgasm—the front base of the penis for the male and the clitoris and the urethral meatus (tissue around the urinary opening) of the female.

Typical result: His orgasm, even if perceived as pleasurable, is far less powerful than it might be...and she, having gotten little if any clitoral stimulation, fails to climax at all.

In CAT, the penis and clitoris are held tightly together by pressure and counterpressure...and the penile-clitoral "connection" is rocked up and down in an evenly paced, lever-like fashion. This vibratory motion all but guarantees orgasms for both partners.

Bonus: Orgasms produced by CAT differ significantly from those produced by conventional in-and-out sex. Whereas a conventional orgasm is limited to a pulsating sensation, a CAT orgasm will combine this with a "melting" sensation.

Among 86 participants of the recent study, 90% of all subjects said that CAT intensified their orgasms...and 60% said that it increased their desire for more frequent sex.

• **"Passive" orgasm.** In ordinary coitus, the man thrusts faster and more deeply as he becomes increasingly aroused, while the woman typically slows down or even stops moving altogether. At the moment of climax, the partners' movements often become disconnected and may fall completely out of sync.

Result: The orgasm is incomplete.

Better: CAT prescribes complete coordination of movement by the partners, up to and beyond the moment of climax. In other words, both partners make no effort to "grab" for orgasm. Instead they let it "overtake" them. The transition from voluntary motion preceding orgasm to the reflexive, involuntary movements typical of orgasm itself is thus fully coordinated. The possibility of incomplete orgasm is drastically limited.

Crucial: A conscious effort by both partners not to hold their breath or suppress natural sounds. Breathing freely and giving full rein to sighs, grunts, moans, spoken words and other vocalizations greatly facilitate orgasm—for the noisemaker and the listener alike.

Some couples report that the "reversed" CAT (woman on top) is an effective variation—especially if the man is much heavier than his partner.

Supercharge Your Immunity with Just a Few Herbs

James A. Duke, PhD, leading authority on medicinal plants and former chief of the US Department of Agriculture Plant Laboratory. He is a distinguished lecturer at the Tai Sophia Institute, a center for patient care and graduate education in complementary medicine, Laurel, Maryland. He is author of *Dr. Duke's Essential Herbs* (Rodale).

Medicinal herbs are rich in antioxidants that maintain health and slow the aging process. They can also prevent or alleviate age-related problems, such as arthritis, high blood pressure and failing vision.

World-renowned botanist James A. Duke, PhD, feels that certain herbs are essential to healthy aging. Dr. Duke has a half-acre medicinal herb garden on his six-acre homestead in Fulton, Maryland. There are seven potent herbs that he uses himself.

While these herbs have no significant side effects and are far safer than most synthetic drugs, it is always wise to consult your doctor before treating a medical problem yourself.

Some herbs can interact with prescription and nonprescription drugs, magnifying or weakening their effects. In addition, some people may be allergic to herbs. Be alert to symptoms, such as a rash, when taking any herb.

With your doctor's approval, you can take these herbs all at the same time, along with vitamins, if you wish. Follow the dosages suggested on the labels.

BILBERRY: VISION DISORDERS

Bilberry is rich in *anthocyanins*, chemicals that keep the capillary walls strong and flexible. It is also loaded with antioxidants that defend delicate tissue against free-radical damage.

In particular, bilberry protects the retina and its blood supply, preventing and improving vision disorders, such as macular degeneration. Bilberry can ward off other eye problems, too, including cataracts, glaucoma and poor night vision.

ECHINACEA: COLDS AND FLU

Contrary to some recent reports, I believe that this herbal medicine is a powerful ally against colds and flu. The purple coneflower from which it comes has been used medicinally by Native Americans for centuries. At least three of the chemicals it contains—*caffeic acid, echinacoside* and *cichoric acid*—have known antiviral properties. Echinacea also boosts the body's own infection-fighting powers.

Take echinacea at the first sign of an upper-respiratory infection or flu. I also take it when I know I'll be in crowds or around other sources of infection.

This is not an herb for everyday use—the immune system may eventually stop responding to it. I don't take it for more than eight weeks in a row.

GARLIC: BLOOD PRESSURE AND CHOLESTEROL

This pungent bulb was prescribed by Hippocrates, the fifth-century BC Greek physician, and cited as a cure-all in an ancient Sanskrit manuscript. Today, we attribute its medicinal powers to a high concentration of sulfur compounds.

Garlic lowers blood pressure and cholesterol. In addition, there is evidence that garlic can reduce the risk of cancer, particularly in the gastrointestinal tract.

Garlic contains at least 25 germ-killing compounds working to fight bacterial, viral and fungal infections.

Eat at least one raw clove or four cooked cloves daily...or take garlic capsules.

HAWTHORN: POTENT HEART DRUG

An extract made from this flowering shrub can be useful against irregular heart rhythm, angina and shortness of breath. Hawthorn contains seven compounds known to prevent dangerous clotting and three that lower blood pressure. One study at the University of Madras in India suggests that hawthorn may also reduce cholesterol.

MILK THISTLE: LIVER PROTECTION

The liver, the organ vital to detoxifying the blood, is under constant assault by pollution. Alcohol, also, is bad for the liver. Milk thistle, a relative of the artichoke, appears to protect the liver. It contains *silymarin*, which strengthens cell membranes and boosts the organ's ability to repair itself. Milk thistle has even been used to treat hepatitis A and C.

I take milk thistle capsules when I'm traveling and will be exposed to smog. If I lived in a major city with pollution problems, I would take it every day.

I also take it before a celebration, when I may be drinking a bit more alcohol than usual.

You can take silymarin capsules or eat milk thistle seeds, available in health-food stores, as you would sunflower seeds.

SAW PALMETTO: PROSTATE PROBLEMS

At least half of men over age 50 have difficulty urinating because benign prostate enlargement chokes off the flow. An extract of saw palmetto, a tropical shrub, has been used for years to treat this problem. A review in *The Journal of the American Medical Association* (JAMA) concluded that saw palmetto facilitates urination in men with prostate problems about as well as medication. Natural chemicals in the herb appear to block a testosterone-type hormone that promotes prostate growth. Men without prostate problems may choose to take it as a preventive measure.

Saw palmetto may also slow down male pattern baldness.

TURMERIC: HEART AND ARTHRITIS

This spice, made from the root of the tropical plant *Curcuma longa,* is a common ingredient in mustard and Indian food, and is what makes curry bright yellow. Turmeric is packed with antioxidants and contains powerful anti-inflammatory compounds called Cox-2 inhibitors.

Some research suggests turmeric can stop inflammation about half as effectively as steroids such as cortisone—but without the troubling side effects. This makes it a valuable ally against arthritis. In addition, turmeric protects the heart. It makes blood platelets less likely to clump and form dangerous clots. It also fights cholesterol buildup in the arteries.

Turmeric is available as an herbal preparation. You can also add turmeric to your diet when cooking. I like to use it to make a curried celery soup.

WHICH BRANDS TO BUY

Herbal products are sold by many manufacturers, but there is no federal regulation to ensure quality control.

To be safe, select major brands, such as Nature's Herb, Nature's Way and Solgar. These are available at most supermarkets, drugstores and health-food stores. Buy preparations that clearly indicate on the labels the exact amounts of active ingredients.

Natural Ways to Lower Your Cholesterol

Marjory Abrams, president of Boardroom Inc., 281 Tresser Blvd., Stamford, Connecticut 06901.

Tedd Mitchell, MD, president and CEO of the Cooper Wellness Program in Dallas (*www.cooperaerobics.com*), explains the most recent cholesterol guidelines, saying, "Many news reports have suggested that the new LDL ['bad' cholesterol] goal is 70 milligrams per deciliter (mg/dL) or less. In reality, this aggressively low target is only for people with a very high risk of heart attack—individuals with cardiovascular disease plus multiple risk factors [diabetes, continued smoking, high triglycerides and/or low HDL ('good') cholesterol].

"Goals for others range from 100 mg/dL or less (moderately high risk) to 160 or less (minimal risk). Consult your physician to determine your personal risk."

Cholesterol is an essential component of cell membranes. It is also required for the synthesis of estrogen, testosterone, adrenaline and other hormones. Even "bad" cholesterol is necessary for optimal health.

Dr. Mitchell says that many people can decrease LDL without taking statins by stepping up exercise and making dietary changes—reducing their intake of red meat and eggs...avoiding products that contain coconut oil and palm oil... increasing their intake of cholesterol-lowering margarine (Benecol, Smart Balance, etc.), oat bran and raw garlic. However, few people can cut LDL to 70 or less without taking Lipitor or another statin drug.

Integrative medicine expert Robban Sica, MD, medical director at the Center for Healing Arts, in Orange, Connecticut, suggests the following LDL-lowering supplements. *Dr. Sica starts most patients with one supplement and adds the others one by one in the order listed until the desired LDL level is met...*

- **Tocotrienols,** a form of vitamin E. Take 200 mg at dinner. Any other vitamin E supplement should be taken in the morning so that it doesn't interfere with tocotrienols.

- **Policosanol/guggulipid,** a sugarcane extract/herb combination. Take 500 mg with breakfast and dinner.

  Caution: Policosanol and tocotrienols have a blood-thinning effect. Don't use them if you regularly use aspirin or other nonsteroidal anti-inflammatories (NSAIDs) or if you take *warfarin* (Coumadin).

- **Inositol hexaniacinate,** a timed-release niacin that, unlike other niacin supplements, does not cause flushing and is not toxic to the liver. Take 600 mg three times daily with meals.

• **Red yeast rice.** Take 800 mg twice daily. (This supplement is not safe for people who take statins.)

Her favorite suppliers: Thorne Research (800-228-1966, *www.thorne.com*) and Designs for Health (800-367-4325, *www.designsforhealth.com*).

Of course, always talk to your doctor before taking a new supplement or changing regimens on prescriptions.

Natural Remedies for Headache Pain

Alexander Mauskop, MD, associate professor of clinical neurology, State University of New York in Brooklyn and director, New York Headache Center, New York City. He is coauthor of *The Headache Alternative: A Neurologist's Guide to Drug-Free Relief* (Bantam Dell).

Which medication works best for headache pain? *That depends on the type of headache...*

• **Migraines** are usually treated with *sumatriptan* (Imitrex), *zolmitriptan* (Zomig) or another "triptan" drug.

• **Tension headaches** are usually treated with anti-inflammatory drugs like *ibuprofen* (Motrin) or *naproxen* (Aleve).

• **Cluster headaches** are usually treated with sumatriptan or inhaled oxygen.

These treatments are reliable and safe for occasional use. But when patients start to use headache medication more than twice a week, stomach upset and other side effects become a serious concern.*

For this reason, headache sufferers should be sure to ask their doctors about trying nondrug approaches as well.

DIETARY MODIFICATION

Chronic headaches often have their origins in food sensitivities. *To identify the food or foods underlying your pain, try this elimination diet...*

*See a doctor at once if your headache is accompanied by confusion, convulsions or loss of consciousness ...pain in the eye or ear...slurred speech, numbness, blurred vision or trouble walking...fever or nausea.

• **For one week,** keep a list of all foods and beverages you consume. Be sure you also include seasonings.

• **For the next 30 days,** avoid all of the foods and beverages you consumed during the 24 hours preceding each headache you had during the week.

• **After 30 days,** reintroduce suspect foods one per meal. Before eating the food, take your resting pulse. Twenty minutes after eating, take your pulse again.

If your pulse after eating is 10 beats or more per minute faster than your pulse before eating, you may be sensitive to the food you've just reintroduced. Avoid the food for another 30 days.

If you remain sensitive to this food for several months, eliminate it permanently.

NUTRITIONAL SUPPLEMENTS

Headaches occur less frequently in individuals whose intake of certain key nutrients is adequate. *Ask your doctor about taking...*

• **Magnesium** (400 milligrams [mg] a day). This mineral has no effect on tension headaches but is moderately effective against migraines and cluster headaches.

Most effective: Slow-release or chelated magnesium tablets. They're better absorbed than conventional tablets.

• **Fish oil or flaxseed oil** (15 grams [g] per day). These oils are rich in omega-3 fatty acids, which have been associated with reduced migraine frequency and severity.

• **Lecithin** (200 mg a day). This protein—sold as a powder that can be mixed into beverages —reduces symptoms of cluster headaches.

• **Vitamin B-2** (riboflavin). Megadoses of this B vitamin—400 mg a day for two to three months —have been shown to reduce the frequency and severity of migraines.

Megadoses should be taken only under a doctor's supervision.

ACUPUNCTURE

Acupuncture works against tension and migraine headaches. Typically, the patient undergoes weekly or twice-weekly sessions for 10 weeks, followed by monthly "maintenance" sessions.

For the name of an acupuncturist in your area, contact the American Academy of Medical Acupuncture at 310-364-0193, *www.medicalacupuncture.org.*

Caution: Make sure the acupuncturist uses disposable needles.

In many cases, headaches can be prevented via acupressure, the self-help variant of acupuncture. *Try the following techniques at the first sign of pain...*

- **Press your thumbs against the hollows between the muscles in the neck**—just below the base of the skull and in line with your ears. Hold for two minutes. Breathe deeply throughout.
- **Use your thumbs to press the upper inside corners of the eye sockets.** Hold for one minute while breathing deeply.
- **Use your right thumb to press on the top of the fleshy mound between your left thumb and index finger.** Hold for one minute while breathing deeply. Switch hands and repeat.

ENVIRONMENTAL FACTORS

To avoid the eyestrain that triggers some headaches, be sure to have adequate lighting for the task at hand.

Trap: Fluorescent bulbs often produce a barely perceptible flicker that can cause headaches. If there's a chance fluorescent flicker is behind your headaches, switch to incandescent bulbs.

Important: Have a professional eye exam once a year. Straining to compensate for poor vision can cause headaches.

Mold, dust mites and fungi can also trigger headaches. To eliminate these airborne irritants, install exhaust fans in your bathrooms and kitchen...and a dehumidifier in your basement or any other damp area. Indoor humidity should stay between 35% and 40%.

Use soap that is scent-free and hypoallergenic, and use nonaerosol sprays.

Some headaches are triggered by chronic low-level exposure to carbon monoxide (CO). Never leave a car idling in an attached garage. Consider installing a CO detector in your home.

HERBAL REMEDIES

Feverfew can reduce the frequency and severity of migraines. If you would like to try this herb, chew two fresh or freeze-dried leaves a day...or take 125 mg of dried feverfew that contains at least 0.2% parthenolide.

There's no evidence that herbal remedies are effective for tension or cluster headaches.

MASSAGE THERAPY

Massage has been found to reduce pain caused by tension and migraine headaches—but not cluster headaches.

For referral to a massage therapist in your area, contact the American Massage Therapy Association at 877-905-0577, *www.amtamassage.org.*

BIOFEEDBACK

By using devices that measure muscle tension and blood flow, biofeedback teaches you to relax tense muscles...and boost blood flow to your scalp. Each technique can ease headache pain.

For adults, 10 or more 30- to 60-minute sessions may be necessary. Children typically need only five or six.

To find a biofeedback therapist in your area, send a self-addressed, stamped, business-sized envelope to the Biofeedback Certification Institute of America, 10200 W. 44th Ave., Suite 310, Wheat Ridge, Colorado 80033, or contact it at 866-908-8713, *www.bcia.org.*

EXERCISE

Aerobic activity is beneficial for people with chronic headaches. Adding a *mantra*—a word repeated over and over to focus the mind—enhances the effect.

Caution: Exercising during a headache tends to intensify the pain.

FOR PERSISTENT HEADACHES

If nondrug therapies fail to work within three months, consult a headache specialist.

For a list of specialists in your area, contact the National Headache Foundation (NHF) at 888-643-5552, *www.headaches.org*...or send a self-addressed, stamped, business-sized envelope to the NHF at 820 N. Orleans, Suite 411, Chicago 60610.

Best Pain Relievers for Arthritis, Backaches, Headaches, More

Jacob Teitelbaum, MD, director of the Fibromyalgia & Fatigue Centers, Inc., Annapolis, Maryland. For 25 years, he has researched ways to relieve pain. He is author of *Pain Free 1-2-3!* (McGraw-Hill) and *From Fatigued to Fantastic!* (Avery). *www.endfatigue.com*

Most of us turn to *acetaminophen* (Tylenol) and *ibuprofen* (Advil, Motrin) for pain relief—but there can be more effective approaches, including combining conventional and natural pain relievers.

Caution: Check with your doctor before taking any new medication or supplement.

ARTHRITIS

There are two types of arthritis—osteoarthritis, in which cartilage between bones wears away... and rheumatoid arthritis, an autoimmune disease that inflames joints. For relief, people with either type often take nonsteroidal anti-inflammatory drugs (NSAIDs), such as aspirin, ibuprofen and *naproxen* (Aleve, Naprosyn)—but 16,000 Americans die annually from side effects of these drugs. Another estimated 55,000 died from taking the recalled prescription drugs Vioxx, Bextra and other Cox-2 inhibitors (a class of NSAIDs). *Instead, try...*

For osteoarthritis...

- **Glucosamine sulfate.** Take 1,500 milligrams (mg) of this supplement—made from chitin, which is derived from shellfish—with 3 grams (g) a day of *methylsulfonylmethane* (MSM), a natural substance in the human body. These nutrients repair cartilage, reducing arthritis pain within six weeks. For maximum tissue repair, take these supplements for two to five months. For chronic arthritis, you may continue for up to a year.
- **Lidoderm.** Put a patch, available by prescription, on the joint. It contains the anesthetics Novocain and Lidocaine. Wear it for about 12 hours a day (one patch lasts that long) for two to six weeks. For a large area, some people may use as many as four patches (the package says three). Many patients experience a 30% to 50% decrease in pain within two weeks.
- **Willow bark and Boswellia*.** These herbs are as effective as Vioxx and Motrin. Take 240 milligrams (mg) of willow bark and 1,000 mg of Boswellia daily. It can take six weeks to work. For chronic arthritis, you may need to take these for up to a year to feel the full effect.

For rheumatoid arthritis...

- **Fish oil.** Studies show that fish oil (one to two tablespoons a day for at least three months) can reduce inflammation and pain. Eskimo-3, available at health-food stores, and Nordic Naturals (800-662-2544, *www.nordicnaturals.com*) don't have the high levels of mercury that may be present in other brands. Keep taking the fish oil after the pain is gone as a preventive measure.

BACK PAIN

Back pain can occur for no apparent reason and at any point on your spine. *For relief, try...*

- **Lidoderm.** For low back pain, apply a Lidoderm patch in the morning and remove it in the evening. Expect relief in two to six weeks.
- **Colchicine.** About 70% of back pain can be eliminated without surgery, with six intravenous injections of the gout medicine *colchicine.* It enters the space between the discs of the vertebrae and reduces inflammation. Colchicine's main risk is a rare but severe allergic reaction (similar to that caused by penicillin).

CARPAL TUNNEL SYNDROME

When a nerve passing under a ligament through two bones in the wrist becomes swollen and pinched, it causes pain, numbness and tingling in the hand or forearm. *For relief, try...*

- **Vitamin B6 and thyroid hormone.** Take 250 mg a day of B6. Also ask your doctor about a prescription for natural thyroid hormone. The combination of B6 and thyroid hormone decreases swelling and usually clears up the problem after six to 12 weeks. You can stay on this treatment for six months to prevent a recurrence. During treatment, wear a wrist splint at night and, if possible, during the day.

HEADACHES

Tension headaches begin and end gradually. They can last for minutes or sometimes hours. The pain comes from tightened muscles across the forehead and/or at the base of the skull.

*Please check with your medical professional before taking this or any other herb.

• **Ultram** (*tramadol hydrochloride*) is an often-overlooked but effective prescription pain reliever. Take up to 100 mg as many as four times a day.

Migraines—severe headaches that may be preceded by lights flashing before your eyes and accompanied by nausea, vomiting, sweating and dizziness—can last for hours, even days. *Natural remedies are more effective than prescription drugs at preventing migraines...*

• **Butterbur,** from the butterbur plant, can prevent—and even eliminate—migraines. Take 50 mg three times a day for one month, then one 50-mg dose twice a day to prevent attacks. Take 100 mg every three hours to eliminate an acute migraine. Use only high-quality brands, such as Enzymatic Therapy (800-783-2286, *www.enzymatictherapy.com*) and Integrative Therapeutics, Inc. (800-931-1709, *www.integrativeinc.com*).

• ***Sumatriptan* (Imitrex).** When a migraine is developing, 75% of patients experience tenderness and pain around the eyes. Sumatriptan knocks out 93% of migraines when taken before the pain around the eyes occurs. When it is taken later, it helps in only 13% of cases. Therefore, if you have a migraine, it is best to take sumatriptan within the first five to 20 minutes.

• **Magnesium.** In the doctor's office or the hospital emergency room, intravenous magnesium can eliminate a migraine in five minutes.

IRRITABLE BOWEL SYNDROME

Irritable bowel syndrome (IBS), also known as spastic colon, is a digestive disorder characterized by bloating, abdominal cramps and diarrhea and/or constipation. *Consider...*

• **Peppermint oil.** For symptomatic relief, take one or two enteric-coated peppermint oil capsules three times a day. Peppermint oil decreases spasms of the bowel muscles. Effective brands include Enzymatic Therapy and Mentharil, available at most health-food stores.

• ***Hyoscyamine* (Anaspaz, Levsin).** Take this prescription antispasmodic as needed. It relaxes the muscular contractions of the stomach and intestines. Dosages range from 0.125 to 0.375 mg, taken 30 to 60 minutes before a meal.

SHINGLES

This itchy, blistering rash—from *herpes zoster*, the virus associated with chicken pox—strikes in middle or old age and usually afflicts one side of the upper body. The virus affects the nerves, so it can leave victims in chronic pain, a condition called postherpetic neuralgia (PHN). *Discuss these options with your doctor...*

• **Ketamine.** This prescription anesthetic can decrease shingles pain within days in 65% of cases. Apply a gel of 5% ketamine to the painful area two to three times daily.

• **Lidoderm.** Place a patch over the area of maximum pain.

• **Neurontin.** This prescription medication can also reduce pain. To avoid side effects, start with 100 to 300 mg, one to four times a day.

• **Tricyclic antidepressant.** A prescription tricyclic such as *amitriptyline* can relieve nerve pain. To avoid side effects, use a low dose of 10 to 50 mg.

Breakthrough Treatments for Arthritis

Harris H. McIlwain, MD, specialist in pain-related diseases, practices with the Tampa Medical Group, Tampa, Florida. Board-certified in rheumatology and geriatric medicine, he is coauthor of *Pain-Free Arthritis: A 7-Step Program for Feeling Better Again* (Holt).

If you have arthritis, chances are you have a well-worn heating pad and a medicine cabinet full of painkillers. Unfortunately, these approaches offer only temporary relief for both osteoarthritis (an age-related disease that causes joint pain and stiffness) and rheumatoid arthritis (an autoimmune disease that causes joint inflammation).

Even though there's no cure for arthritis, several underutilized treatments can dramatically curb your symptoms...

EXERCISE

Arthritis patients often avoid exercise, fearing it will exacerbate muscle and joint pain. Yet research consistently shows that exercise alleviates arthritis symptoms and improves strength and flexibility. Exercise also helps prevent weight gain, which has been shown to worsen arthritis pain.

Scientific evidence: Researchers at Wake Forest University School of Medicine found that aerobic or resistance exercise reduces the incidence of disability for key daily activities (eating, dressing, bathing, etc.) in arthritis patients by about 50%.

What to do: Stretch at least 10 minutes daily. Perform an aerobic activity, such as biking or walking, gradually working up to 30 minutes, five days a week. Do strengthening exercises, such as resistance machines or weight lifting, gradually working up to 15 minutes, three times a week.*

To minimize pain and prevent injury, apply warm, moist heat to arthritic joints or sore muscles for 15 minutes before and after exercise.

BOOST YOUR C AND D

Vitamin C is believed to slow the loss of cartilage due to osteoarthritis, while a diet low in vitamin D may speed the progression of osteoarthritis.

Scientific evidence: In research conducted as part of the ongoing Framingham Heart Study, doctors discovered that patients who ate a diet high in vitamin D, or took D supplements, reduced their risk for worsening arthritis by 75%. A study of 25,000 people by the Arthritis Research Campaign in England found that a low intake of vitamin C may increase the risk of developing arthritis.

What to do: Take daily supplements that provide 500 to 1,000 milligrams (mg) of vitamin C and 400 international units (IU) of vitamin D.

DRINK TEA

Tea may help reduce arthritis inflammation and bone deterioration.

Scientific evidence: Researchers recently discovered that green tea contains a *polyphenol*, or chemical compound, that suppresses the expression of a key gene involved in arthritis inflammation. Black tea is made of the same leaves and may be as beneficial, even though it is processed differently.

What to do: Drink one to two cups of hot or cold tea daily.

EAT GRAPES

Grape skins contain *resveratrol*, the only natural compound known to act as a Cox-2 inhibitor. Like *celecoxib* (Celebrex**), resveratrol both suppresses the Cox-2 gene and deactivates the Cox-2 enzyme, which produces inflammation at the site of injury or pain.

Scientific evidence: A study published in the *Journal of Biological Chemistry* confirmed that resveratrol acts as an antioxidant and a Cox-2 inhibitor.

What to do: Eat one cup of white or red grapes daily.

Good news: Imbibing your grapes may be as healthful as munching them. All wines have some resveratrol. Red wine packs the biggest punch.

TRY SUPPLEMENTS

Dietary supplements can be a valuable adjunct to traditional drug treatments, allowing patients to reduce or, in some cases, eliminate expensive medications.* *The most effective are...*

- **Glucosamine.** Derived from the shells of shellfish, this supplement appears to help lubricate joints and reduce arthritis pain and stiffness.

Scientific evidence: In a *British Medical Journal* report, 1,500 mg of glucosamine daily was found to slow cartilage deterioration in patients with osteoarthritis.

What to do: Ask your doctor about taking 1,500 mg of glucosamine daily. Glucosamine is often packaged with chondroitin, but there is less evidence to support the effectiveness of chondroitin.

Warning: People who have shellfish allergies should *not* take glucosamine.

- **SAMe** (*S-adenosylmethionine*). Doctors in Europe commonly prescribe this natural supplement for depression and arthritis.

Scientific evidence: Studies show it relieves pain and inflammation about as well as *naproxen* (Aleve), but without the stomach upset and other side effects. It has the added benefit of boosting mood, possibly by increasing production of the brain chemical *dopamine*.

What to do: If your arthritis does not improve with glucosamine, ask your doctor about taking 400 to 1,200 mg of SAMe daily.

GET A MASSAGE

Manual manipulation by physical or massage therapists is among the most effective treatments known for relieving neck and back pain.

*A physician or physical therapist can help you to devise a safe movement program that combines stretching, aerobic and strengthening exercises.

**Celebrex may increase the chance of heart attack or stroke that can lead to death.

*Always consult your doctor before taking supplements. Some may interfere with the action or efficacy of certain drugs.

Scientific evidence: In a study reported in the *Archives of Internal Medicine*, back pain patients who underwent 10 weeks of therapeutic massage took fewer medications the following year than did patients who were not massaged.

What to do: Consider getting regular massages, as needed, for pain.

Whenever possible, choose a state licensed massage therapist. To find one, contact the American Massage Therapy Association, 877-905-0577, *www.amtamassage.org*.

CONSIDER THERAPEUTIC TAPING

Therapeutic taping—in which rigid tape is wrapped around a joint to realign, support and take pressure from it—may have significant pain relief benefits for some osteoarthritis patients.

Scientific evidence: In an Australian study, 73% of patients with osteoarthritis of the knee experienced substantially reduced symptoms after three weeks of therapeutic taping. The benefits were comparable with those achieved with standard drug treatments and lasted three weeks after taping was stopped. Though the study looked only at knees, taping may work as well for elbows, wrists and ankles.

What to do: Ask your doctor if therapeutic taping is right for you.

Important: Taping must be done properly to be effective. If you try taping, you should have your sore joint wrapped by a physician or physical therapist who is familiar with the procedure. He/she can show you or a family member the proper technique.

If taping proves too difficult or cumbersome, a fitted neoprene sleeve (an elastic sleeve used by athletes) may offer similar benefits.

PAIN RELIEF STRATEGIES

To minimize your arthritis pain and protect your joints...

- **When grocery shopping,** request plastic bags that can be looped over your arms, between the wrist and elbow.
- **Put foam "grips" around pens and pencils** (you'll find them in office-supply stores).
- **Use pump toothpastes** rather than the traditional squeeze tubes.
- **Choose clothing with Velcro closures** instead of zippers and buttons.
- **Women should wear the type of bra** that opens in the front.

All About the Amazing Power of Acupuncture

Gary Kaplan, DO, clinical associate professor of community and family medicine, Georgetown University School of Medicine, Washington, DC, and past president, Medical Acupuncture Research Foundation. He is founder and owner of The Kaplan Center, McLean, Virginia, which integrates conventional and family medicine with complementary approaches, such as acupuncture, osteopathic manipulative therapy, homeopathy, nutritional remedies and mind-body medicine. *www.kaplanclinic.com*

Acupuncture is no longer a "fringe" treatment. Since 1997, when it was formally recognized as a legitimate medical technique,* acupuncture's uses in Western medicine have been growing. *Here's what it can do for you...*

HOW IT WORKS

Acupuncture involves the insertion of hair-thin needles into one or more of the body's 2,000-plus acupuncture points. In traditional Chinese medicine, it's thought that the needles rebalance the flow of energy (*chi*) through 14 major pathways, or meridians. Acupuncture used to be considered questionable because meridians couldn't be readily identified.

Fact: Acupuncture points do exist. Each one is located near a vascular bundle that contains a nerve, artery, vein and lymphatic vessel in the space between muscles. The effects of stimulating specific points have been scientifically verified.

Example: One acupuncture point on the foot has traditionally been linked to eye disorders. Brain scans performed at the University of California, Irvine, showed that stimulating that point increased activity in the brain's occipital region, the area involved with vision.

Acupuncture therapy usually involves a series of six to 12 treatments over a period of weeks or months. The cost per treatment is $45 to $150, with the average around $90. It is sometimes covered by insurance.

It used to be thought that acupuncture provided only short-term relief. In some cases, however, acupuncture appears to permanently alter the way cells function—for example, increasing the ability of nerve cells to release painkilling neurotransmitters. This shows promise for the treatment of

*By the National Institutes of Health Consensus Development Conference.

chronic conditions such as osteoarthritis, tendinitis, headaches and irritable bowel syndrome.

The World Health Organization has identified more than 40 conditions that may be helped by acupuncture. *The best evidence is for the following conditions...*

BACK PAIN

Many physicians routinely recommend acupuncture for low-back pain, and insurance companies often pay for it. Acupuncture works at least as well as over-the-counter drugs—without causing stomach upset or other side effects.

Acupuncture appears to increase blood supply to injured areas and promote faster healing. It may also encourage the release of painkilling endorphins and stimulate nerve fibers to block pain sensations. Patients with acute back sprains or spasms who are treated with acupuncture in addition to conventional treatments (ice packs, massage, physical therapy, etc.) can cut their healing time in half, from an average of about four weeks to two.

TOOTH EXTRACTION

Patients who have teeth extracted or other oral surgeries experience less postsurgical pain and require lower doses of analgesics when given acupuncture afterward. They also have less swelling and inflammation. In addition to causing an increase in painkilling endorphins, acupuncture lowers levels of *prostaglandins*, inflammatory chemicals that cause nerve and tissue irritation.

SURGICAL PAIN

Studies have shown that patients given acupuncture during surgery require lower levels of anesthesia—and have fewer anesthesia-related complications such as nausea. Acupuncture can also be used postsurgically to help control pain.

NAUSEA AND VOMITING

More than three dozen randomized controlled studies have shown that acupuncture is effective for treating and preventing nausea and vomiting—important for cancer patients getting chemotherapy. A study of 104 women undergoing high-dose chemotherapy found that those given acupuncture had significantly less nausea and vomiting than those who didn't get the treatments. Acupuncture may also be helpful for reducing morning sickness during pregnancy.

PAINFUL MENSTRUATION

A number of studies have shown that women with dysmenorrhea (painful menstrual periods) can get long-lasting relief with acupuncture. In a typical case, a woman might receive several treatments prior to her period, then additional treatments afterward. A total of six to 12 treatments can potentially eliminate the problem for good.

The uterine contractions that result in menstrual cramps are caused by an upsurge in prostaglandins. Acupuncture can calm the nervous system and potentially cause a permanent reduction in prostaglandins.

ADDICTION

Acupuncture has been used to treat just about every form of addiction—tobacco, alcohol, heroin, etc. It may reduce physical and emotional withdrawal when combined with conventional approaches, such as psychotherapy and medication.

Example: Studies have shown that about 60% of addicts drop out of traditional treatment programs, but the dropout rate declines to approximately 40% when acupuncture is included.

ACUPUNCTURE SAFETY

To get proper treatment...

- **Get a diagnosis from a medical doctor** before getting acupuncture treatments. Otherwise you might be misdiagnosed.

  Example: My brother-in-law had a high fever and went to an acupuncturist, who treated him for flu and a urinary tract infection. What he really had was prostatitis with early sepsis, a potentially life-threatening infection that required antibiotic treatment.

- **See a qualified acupuncturist**—either a medical acupuncturist (MD or DO), a practitioner who is a member of the American Academy of Medical Acupuncture (AAMA, 310-364-0193, *www.medicalacupuncture.org*) or one who is board-certified by the American Board of Medical Acupuncture, an independent entity within the AAMA...or a licensed acupuncturist, a practitioner who has completed the state or national exams conducted by the National Certification Commission for Acupuncture and Oriental Medicine (NCCAOM, 904-598-1005, *www.nccaom.org*).
- **Ask how many treatments will be needed.** If it's more than 12 or the practitioner won't be specific, get a second opinion.
- **Avoid acupuncture if you are taking anticoagulant medications** such as *Coumadin* or

heparin, or if you have a bleeding disorder such as hemophilia.

Folk Remedies That Really Work

Earl Mindell, PhD, RPh, former professor of nutrition at Pacific Western University (now California Miramar University in San Diego), and an expert on nutrition, drugs, vitamins and herbal remedies. He is author of *Natural Remedies for 150 Ailments* (Basic Health) and *Earl Mindell's New Vitamin Bible* (Grand Central).

Physicians often dismiss folk cures as quaint, ineffective or potentially unsafe. But that could be a mistake.

Research has found that some traditional remedies work as well as—or even better than—drugs. What's more, most of these traditional treatments are safer than drugs because they rarely cause side effects or interact with other medical treatments.

Best folk cures...*

COLDS

There's a good reason that mothers have long recommended chicken soup as a cold remedy. Studies have confirmed that chicken soup increases the activity of antiviral immune cells and also reduces throat and sinus inflammation.

What to do: Eat a bowl of chicken soup twice daily at the first sign of a cold.

Helpful: Add a pinch of cayenne to chicken soup. *Capsaicin,* the chemical that makes cayenne and other peppers taste hot, reduces congestion as effectively as over-the-counter (OTC) medications.

HEADACHES

Most headaches are caused by muscle tension and/or emotional stress. Millions of Americans can't take aspirin or other painkillers because of drug interactions or uncomfortable side effects, such as stomach irritation.

What to do: Using your thumb and forefinger, squeeze the area between your upper lip and nose for five seconds. Repeat as needed. This technique blocks nerve signals and reduces headache pain in many sufferers.

*Check with your doctor before trying these remedies. Herbs can be dangerous for some people, including pregnant or breast-feeding women.

INSOMNIA

Sleeping pills can be addictive and are notorious for side effects, such as dizziness, depression and headache.

What to do: Drink a cup of valerian tea at bedtime. Valerian root, available in tea bags at health-food stores, contains *valepotriates* and other sleep-inducing compounds. A traditional remedy for anxiety as well as sleeplessness, valerian root is recommended by Commission E, the European equivalent of the FDA.

Chamomile, hops and lavender teas will also help you rest, but they are not as potent as valerian root.

NAUSEA

Ginger is the best remedy for all forms of nausea, including motion and morning sickness. The active ingredients, *gingerols,* are more effective than OTC antinausea drugs.

What to do: Each day you have nausea, drink two to three cups of ginger ale that contains natural ginger. This variety is available at health-food stores. The ginger-flavored ingredients in commercial brands of ginger ale won't have the same effect.

As an alternative, make ginger tea. To prepare, chop about one tablespoon of fresh gingerroot and steep it in hot water for about 10 minutes. Drink one to three cups daily.

SORE THROATS

Most people have heard that gargling with warm salt water reduces sore throat pain. However, few prepare and use the mixture properly.

What to do: Add three teaspoons of table salt to one cup of warm water and stir. Gargle with a full one-cup mixture at least two to three times daily. Viruses, which cause colds, can't survive in a high-salt environment.

TOOTHACHES

Conventional treatments for toothaches range from OTC products, such as Orajel, to powerful prescription painkillers. But one of the best treatments is a generations-old folk remedy.

What to do: Dip a toothpick in oil of clove, available at health-food stores and some pharmacies, and apply it to the sore area. The pain will disappear almost instantly. Reapply as needed. If pain persists for more than a few days, see a dentist.

Scents to Boost Energy, Mood, Memory and More

Alan Hirsch, MD, founder and neurologic director, The Smell & Taste Treatment and Research Foundation, 845 N. Michigan Ave., Chicago 60611, *www.scienceofsmell.com*.

Scents stimulate important mental and physical functions. They often trigger the release of neurotransmitters, chemicals that send signals to the brain. *What scents can do for you...*

CONTROL APPETITE

In a study of 105 people, we found that those who inhaled a chocolate-like aroma whenever they felt like eating lost nearly three pounds in two weeks. A study of 3,193 volunteers found that sniffing banana, green apple or peppermint scents resulted in an average weight loss of 30 pounds in six months.

Sniff the above scents often, and smell every food before you eat it. Your brain will perceive that you're eating more, thus suppressing your appetite.

INCREASE ENERGY

These odors stimulate the part of the brain that promotes wakefulness...

- **Jasmine** causes an increase in beta waves in the brain, a sign of alertness. Jasmine tea is a great pick-me-up.
- **Strawberries and buttered popcorn** cause exercisers to burn more calories.
- **Peppermint** works on sensory nerves and increases alertness. Try it as candy or gum.
- **Freshly brewed coffee** is very stimulating, probably because we associate the aroma with the energizing effects of caffeine.

BOOST ROMANCE

Both men and women are sexually stimulated by scents, but the odors that arouse them aren't the same.

For men: The smell of lavender or pumpkin pie increases blood flow to the penis by about 40%. The smell of doughnuts, black licorice, vanilla and women's perfume (any scent) are also sexually stimulating to men.

For women: The odors of cucumber and licorice are stimulating. Women are turned off by the smell of cherries, barbecued meat and men's cologne.

REDUCE ANXIETY

Fresh, natural scents, in general, induce calm. In a study we conducted, volunteers became extremely anxious when put in coffin-like tubes —but then calmed down when the tubes were infused with the smells of green apple and cucumber. These odors act on the limbic system, the emotional center of the brain.

If you anticipate a situation in which you will feel anxious, wash your hair that morning with a green apple–scented shampoo and/or put a dab of the shampoo in a cloth to take with you.

IMPROVE MEMORY

People who sniff floral scents increase their retention of new material by 17%.

Sniff a floral odor when learning new material, then smell it again when you want to recall it. This is known as *state-dependent learning*. The material you learn in one state—while smelling roses—will be more accessible when you replicate that state in the future.

Surprising Causes of Memory Problems...and What to Do About Them

Majid Fotuhi, MD, PhD, assistant professor of neurology, Johns Hopkins University School of Medicine, and director, Center for Memory and Brain Health, Sinai Hospital, both in Baltimore. He is author of *The Memory Cure: How to Protect Your Brain Against Memory Loss and Alzheimer's Disease* (McGraw-Hill).

Everyone forgets things sometimes. Though many people believe that memory loss is an early sign of Alzheimer's disease, more than 90% of those who complain about poor memory don't have Alzheimer's.

If it's not Alzheimer's, what is it? *Common causes of memory loss and best treatments...*

DEPRESSION

This is the leading cause of memory loss. Depressed people have low brain levels of *serotonin* and *norepinephrine*, neurochemicals that normally activate the hippocampus. The hippocampus is the memory part of the brain where information is stored and retrieved.

Besides memory loss, warning signs of depression include changes in appetite and/or sleep patterns...lack of enjoyment in things that used to give pleasure...mood swings or emotional unresponsiveness...and/or frequent self-criticism.

What to do: Antidepressants such as Paxil, Prozac, Zoloft and other *selective serotonin reuptake inhibitors* (SSRIs) relieve depression in the majority of patients. Memory, concentration and other cognitive functions usually start to improve quickly, often within six weeks.

STRESS

People who experience chronic stress due to job issues, family or money worries, etc., often experience memory problems.

Stress raises levels of *cortisol*, a hormone that improves concentration briefly during acute stressful situations. However, cortisol damages the hippocampus when brain levels remain high due to continuous stress.

Even stress caused by transitory life events such as a divorce can make it hard to concentrate and absorb information. You can't retrieve information that doesn't make it into memory storage in the first place.

What to do: Take stress seriously. Your memory problems will continue to worsen if you don't control it.

Get regular exercise...practice relaxation techniques, such as deep breathing and yoga...and spend more time doing pleasurable activities to reduce stress.

POOR SLEEP

Lack of sleep increases stress and anxiety, which raises cortisol levels. Depression can cause insomnia, as can stress. Once the underlying condition is relieved, sleep usually improves.

Disturbed sleep can also be caused by obstructive sleep apnea, periodic interruptions in breathing. Some sufferers experience hundreds of "micro-awakenings" each night that prevent them from entering deep-sleep stages. Apnea warning signs include morning headaches...gasping or snorting during sleep...waking up with a dry mouth or throat...depression...excessive fatigue...high blood pressure...and bedding that's extremely rumpled.

What to do: Your doctor may recommend a treatment called *nasal continuous positive airway pressure* (nCPAP). A mask worn while sleeping creates air pressure that keeps the upper airways open, preventing apnea and snoring. Many of my patients who use nCPAP report dramatic improvements in sleep and memory almost immediately.

Most people who have sleep apnea are overweight. Fatty tissue around the upper airway sags during sleep and obstructs the normal flow of air. Apnea as well as snoring often diminish significantly when people lose as little as 10 pounds.

VITAMIN B-12 DEFICIENCY

This accounts for approximately 10% of non-Alzheimer's memory loss cases. The body uses vitamin B-12 to produce *myelin*, the sheathing on nerve cells. Low levels of this nutrient cause myelin abnormalities that slow the transmission of nerve signals. This can impair memory and other cognitive functions, especially when accompanied by ministrokes or other types of vascular problems.

Even people who consume enough vitamin B-12—found in meat, dairy, eggs and fish—may have low blood levels because they don't produce enough *intrinsic factor*, a protein secreted by stomach cells that is required for vitamin B-12 absorption.

Low intrinsic factor is seen more commonly in young people. Low B-12 levels in elderly people are usually caused by slower absorption in the gastrointestinal tract.

What to do: Doctors routinely check the blood for B-12 in those with unexplained memory problems. You'll need supplementation if levels are low. Oral B-12 isn't effective if the body isn't producing enough intrinsic factor. Most patients require monthly injections of B-12.

People who follow a strict vegan diet (no animal foods whatsoever) should supplement with six micrograms (mcg) of vitamin B-12 daily. A vegan diet doesn't affect levels of intrinsic factor, so oral supplements are effective. In general, it is a good idea for most people to take a multivitamin daily.

THYROID DISEASE

Too little or too much thyroid hormone can cause mental slowing, declines in vision and hearing and persistent memory problems. *Hyperthyroidism* (too much hormone) is usually caused by a tumor or an immune-system disorder. Symptoms may include palpitations and weight loss. *Hypothyroidism* (too little hormone) can also be caused by immune-system problems and is often associated with dry skin, hair loss and weight gain.

What to do: Talk to your doctor. Both hyper- and hypothyroidism are easy to treat with surgery or thyroid hormone supplements. Most people will experience dramatic improvements in memory and other cognitive functions when thyroid hormone is maintained at proper levels.

MINI-STROKES

These strokes are caused by a blockage of blood vessels in the brain. Most affect tiny, rice-sized areas of the brain and can cause minor (and sometimes transitory) memory loss.

Mini-strokes often are so subtle that patients can have 10 of them without serious symptoms.

Example: A healthy adult might be able to name 10 different fruits in a minute. Someone who has had a mini-stroke might be able to name only five. He/she also might walk a little more slowly than he did before and have a slightly weaker handshake.

What to do: Your doctor will recommend a brain CT scan if he/she suspects that you have had a mini-stroke. You can't reverse the damage, but you can reduce the risk of future mini-strokes (and a major stroke) by doing the same things that you would do to prevent a heart attack—maintain healthy blood pressure, stop smoking, lose weight, etc.

New Ways to Prevent and Treat Alzheimer's Disease

Gary W. Small, MD, director, Memory Clinic and Center on Aging, University of California, Los Angeles. He is author of *The Memory Bible: An Innovative Strategy for Keeping Your Brain Young* (Hyperion). For additional information, go to *www.semel.ucla.edu/longevity.*

Recent research has revealed new strategies for preventing, treating and diagnosing Alzheimer's disease (AD). More than 4 million Americans suffer from AD, a progressive brain condition that ultimately leads to death. The older you get, the more likely it is that AD will strike. About 5% of people ages 65 to 74 have AD, and nearly 50% of those older than 85 may have the disease.

WARNING SIGNS OF ALZHEIMER'S

Consult a doctor if any of these symptoms cause you or others distress...

- **You often forget recently learned information**—names, appointments, phone numbers.
- **You forget how to perform simple tasks,** such as cooking or getting dressed.
- **You can't recall simple words and perhaps resort to descriptions,** such as "that thing you drink out of" instead of "glass."

Changes in brain function that go beyond memory can indicate AD. *These include...*

- **Confusion or agitation.**
- **Mood changes.** These may include anxiety or depression.
- **Personality changes,** such as unusual suspiciousness, anger or loss of motivation.

Steps you should take now...

EAT RIGHT

The brain, like the heart, depends on strong circulation to stay healthy. *To be safe...*

- **Choose "good" fats.** Some fats are healthful, particularly the omega-3 fatty acids in nuts and olive oil and especially in fish. Studies have found that people who eat just one serving of fish a week are 60% less likely to develop AD.

A study at Case Western Reserve University in Cleveland found that young and middle-aged adults who ate a low-fat diet had a reduced risk of AD decades later, particularly compared with those whose diets were higher in saturated fat—the kind found in animal products such as meats and whole-fat dairy items.

- **Watch cholesterol.** High cholesterol, which is associated with diets high in saturated fat, has been linked to AD. In a recent clinical trial, a cholesterol-lowering statin drug reduced the incidence of AD and heart disease.

If you have high cholesterol, treat it aggressively—with statin drugs if necessary.

- **Maximize antioxidants.** Numerous fruits and vegetables contain antioxidants, such as vitamins C and E, that can neutralize the free radicals that kill brain cells. Prime sources of antioxidants include citrus fruits, berries, broccoli, carrots and tomatoes.

New study: A Johns Hopkins survey of nearly 5,000 people age 65 and older suggests that antioxidant supplements offer potent protection.

The study found that those who took both vitamins C and E had about one-third the risk of AD compared with those who took neither.

Ideal daily dosage: Take 500 milligrams (mg) of vitamin C and 400 international units (IU) of vitamin E.*

• **Control calories.** Being overweight makes you more vulnerable to diabetes and high blood pressure, both of which raise the risk of AD. A recent study conducted by Utah State University also found an association between obesity and higher rates of AD, which is unconnected to other health problems.

• **Drink in moderation.** People who consume modest amounts of alcohol (one glass of wine, one bottle of beer or one shot of spirits daily for women...two for men) are less likely to develop AD than those who drink more or not at all.

REDUCE STRESS

Chronic stress appears to damage the parts of the brain that control memory, such as the hippocampus, and may increase the risk of AD. In one study of nearly 800 men reported in *Neurology*, those most prone to psychological distress were twice as likely to develop AD as those who were least stressed.

Ask yourself if the things that bother you really are so important. Are there sources of stress that you can modify? Also regularly practice relaxation exercises, such as meditation, deep breathing and peaceful imagery.

STAY ACTIVE

Regular aerobic exercise increases brain circulation. Physical activity also fosters connections between brain cells, which helps to maintain healthy mental function.

Exercise reduces stress, too. A Canadian study found that just 15 to 30 minutes of brisk walking three times a week cuts the risk of AD by about one-third.

DO MENTAL AEROBICS

Any activity that challenges your mind increases the strength and stamina of brain cells. A study in *The New England Journal of Medicine* found that adults who regularly enjoyed such leisure activities as chess, board games and crossword puzzles were 63% less likely to get AD than those who did not. Expand your mind with something new. Take an adult education course, learn a new language, read a challenging book, study a musical instrument.

PROTECT YOUR HEAD

A number of studies have confirmed that a single serious concussion—an injury that causes unconsciousness for 60 minutes or longer—doubles the risk of AD later in life. Whether lesser traumas are also dangerous is uncertain. Repeated impact ("heading" a soccer ball, for example) does appear to be associated with impaired memory.

Use seat belts in the car. Wear a helmet when riding a bicycle or motorcycle, skiing, skating, etc. You even may want to wear a helmet in the car. An Australian study found that wearing a bicycle-style helmet in the car lessened the severity of brain injuries by 50% and saved the life of one in five head-injury victims.

IF ALZHEIMER'S STRIKES

A doctor will review your symptoms. He/she may order tests such as magnetic resonance imaging (MRI) to rule out other conditions that can cause similar symptoms, such as a stroke or possibly a tumor.

New: Positron emission tomography (PET) scan is a brain-imaging test that can show damage caused by AD, even in early stages. The cost ranges from $700 to $1,500.

There is no cure for AD, but modern medications can slow its progression.

Common drugs: Cholinesterase inhibitors —*donepezil* (Aricept), *galantamine* (Razadyne) and *rivastigmine* (Exelon). These block the enzyme that breaks down the brain chemical acetylcholine and may delay the progression of symptoms for up to a year.

A drug for AD has been approved by the Food and Drug Administration. *Memantine* (Namenda) works on the brain chemical glutamate. An excess of glutamate apparently interferes with the transmission of brain signals.

New: A combination of a cholinesterase inhibitor and memantine seems to be more effective than either drug used alone. In a recent clinical trial reported in *The Journal of the American Medical Association*, patients with moderate to severe

*Due to the possible interactions between vitamin E and various drugs and supplements as well as other safety considerations, be sure to consult your doctor before starting a vitamin E regimen.

AD who were taking the cholinesterase inhibitor *donepezil* improved significantly when memantine was added, while those who added a placebo did not improve and in some ways worsened.

Vitamin E may also slow the progress of AD once it develops, but in much higher doses than what is recommended for prevention—around 2,000 IU daily. Only take high doses as part of a medically supervised treatment program because vitamin E can cause internal bleeding.

What You Can Do Now To Stay Healthy and Keep Out of a Nursing Home

The late Robert N. Butler, MD, founding president of the International Longevity Center at the Mailman School of Public Health, Columbia University, New York City. He won the Pulitzer Prize for *Why Survive? Being Old in America* (Johns Hopkins University Press). *www.mailman.columbia.edu/academic-departments/centers/international-longevity-center*

People of a certain age get lots of sales pitches for nursing home insurance. Insurance companies assume that nearly everyone will spend time in such a facility. It's a distressing thought. Fortunately, it is a fate you can avoid.

Key: Don't wait. The sooner you start a no-nursing home plan, the better your chances of having it succeed.

GOOD NEWS ABOUT DEMENTIA

Dementia is common among nursing home residents. Not too long ago, we assumed that cognitive decline was simply a part of getting old. However, new research shows this isn't the case. *There are three specific factors that help maintain cognitive health...*

- **Daily physical activity.** This often surprises people, but the research is clear—we can actually measure that people who are active physically are stronger cognitively. When the Roman poet and satirist Juvenal said, "A healthy mind in a healthy body," he knew what he was talking about.

We recommend that people walk 10,000 steps a day to be sure they are getting enough exercise. The average person walks just 4,000 steps, so you'll probably need to establish new habits (and buy a pedometer) to make 10,000 steps part of your everyday life.

- **Social interaction.** Being socially engaged doesn't mean that you have to maintain a full social calendar. What it does mean is that you remain involved with other people, whether through work or volunteering. For those who are retired, there are many volunteer opportunities, from your local community to the Peace Corps. And don't forget the importance of being active as a grandparent. That benefits all three generations.

- **Intellectual stimulation.** This directly impacts the brain. Many older people enjoy studying academic subjects from history to astronomy, but we have found that learning another language is particularly good for strong cognitive skills. The work that goes into mastering foreign words and an unfamiliar language structure keeps the brain's neurons firing and busy.

FITNESS FACTS

The next crucial part of a no-nursing home plan is to create and maintain very good health habits. *To start, you must practice all forms of fitness, such as...*

- **Aerobic exercise.** Aerobic exercise—the kind that gets your heart rate up and keeps it there—is a must. To maintain heart and lung stamina, perform aerobic exercise for at least 20 minutes three or more times a week.

Examples: Fast walking, jogging, swimming.

- **Strength training.** This form of fitness is often overlooked by many older people and it's incredibly important as you age.

Being strong allows you to more easily perform what are called ADLs, activities of daily living. Without strong quads—the muscles in front of the thigh—you lose the ability to get up out of a chair, go to the bathroom, sit down easily. Without strong arm muscles, you have trouble lifting bags or opening and closing windows. Strength training is crucial and you must keep it up throughout your life.

Examples: Squats, getting out of a chair without using your arms, chest presses.

- **Balance exercises.** Among older people, there are some 250,000 fractures a year and many of these fractures land the elderly in nursing homes. This is especially sad because many of the falls that cause broken bones can be prevented by improving balance. The sense of balance is like a muscle—you must exercise it regularly or it will weaken and lose its usefulness to you. The easiest way to practice balance is to stand on one leg and move the other, bent at the knee, through space. Do this several times a day. Or try standing on one leg while you brush your teeth.

Safety reminder: Be sure to have something sturdy nearby to grab hold of in case you need additional support.

• **Stretching exercises.** Finally, you must practice flexibility, which refers to the range of motion of your joints.

Range of motion becomes increasingly important as you age. If compromised, it, too, intrudes on your ability to function in your everyday life. Your shoulders need range of motion to enable you to reach for things...your hips and knees need range of motion to bend properly. Keep your joints flexible through regular stretching exercises. Try stretching your arms across your chest. Or stretch the backs of your legs by standing with the palms of your hands braced against a wall while you stretch one leg at a time behind you.

OTHER HEALTH POINTERS

• **Eat a nutritious diet.** In addition to plenty of fruits and vegetables, your diet should be low in fats and have no trans fatty acids at all. Processed baked foods virtually always contain unhealthy trans fatty acids, but you're more likely to see "partially hydrogenated fat" on the label. They are the same thing and you shouldn't eat them. Trans fats are created during the chemical process of hydrogenating oils and they increase "bad" LDL cholesterol, increasing your risk of stroke and heart disease.

• **Maintain a healthy weight.** This will help you avoid many diseases that often bring patients into a nursing home, such as type 2 diabetes and some cardiovascular diseases, especially high blood pressure that leads to stroke.

• **Quit smoking.** We wish we had no need to say quit smoking, but there are still people who haven't kicked the habit even though statistics show it cuts seven years off the normal life span.

Subtle Stroke Signs

The telltale symptoms of stroke include weakness or numbness on one side of the body, difficulty speaking and/or vision loss.

These symptoms often go unrecognized. In fact, only 25% of stroke victims know they're having a stroke.

If you notice suspicious symptoms, seek immediate medical attention. If you wait, you may be unable to benefit from new "clot-busting" drugs, which minimize brain damage.

Linda S. Williams, MD, associate professor of neurology, Indiana University School of Medicine, Indianapolis. Her study of 67 stroke patients was published in *Stroke.*

Stroke Stopper

An FDA-approved device removes blood clots in people experiencing a stroke. The *mechanical embolus removal in cerebral ischemia* (MERCI) retriever is threaded up from the groin into the affected artery and used like a corkscrew to pluck out the clot. It can be used up to eight hours after stroke onset. The intravenous drug tissue plasminogen activator (tPA) can dissolve clots, but it can't be used more than three hours after stroke onset...or in patients with bleeding disorders or who have had surgery recently.

Gary R. Duckwiler, MD, past president, American Society of Interventional and Therapeutic Neuroradiology (ASITN), Fairfax, Virginia, and professor of radiology, University of California, Los Angeles.

Good for the Heart ...And More

Beans have even more antioxidants than blueberries, commonly thought to have the most antioxidants. One-half cup of dried small red beans has more antioxidant capacity than one full cup of wild blueberries. Red kidney beans have almost as much antioxidant capacity as wild blueberries...followed by pinto beans, cultivated blueberries and cranberries.

Ronald L. Prior, PhD, research chemist and nutritionist, US Department of Agriculture's Arkansas Children's Nutrition Center, Little Rock, and leader of a study of 100 different types of fruits, vegetables, berries, nuts and spices, published in *Journal of Agricultural and Food Chemistry.*

Heart Doctor's Stop-Smoking Plan

Most people need a strategy to quit smoking. *Following is one heart doctor's suggestions...*

- **Write down the day you will quit**—between two and four weeks from the day you decide—and keep the date in sight.
- **Pick a nonworking day to quit**—to limit stress.
- **For seven days, record every cigarette smoked.** Number each, and write when you smoked it and why.
- **See which cigarettes you smoked from habit and boredom,** and drop them first. Work toward dropping the harder ones.
- **Start walking or bike riding regularly.** Fight smoking urges by brushing your hair or playing with a rubber band.
- **Take it one day at a time**—most withdrawal symptoms end within four weeks.

Mary McGowan, MD, former director, Concord Hospital's Cholesterol Treatment Center, Concord, New Hampshire, and author of *Heart Fitness for Life: The Essential Guide to Preventing and Reversing Heart Disease* (Oxford University Press).

Weight-Loss Secret

You can lose five pounds a year just by drinking two liters of water a day. Drinking water speeds your metabolism—in fact, you start to burn fat after you drink just two glasses.

Jens Jordan, MD, former professor of clinical pharmacology and medicine, Franz-Volhard Clinical Research Center, Berlin, Germany, and leader of a study published in *Journal of Clinical Endocrinology & Metabolism.*

Very Effective Weight-Loss Strategies

Stephen Gullo, PhD, president, Institute for Health and Weight Sciences, 16 E. 65th St., New York City 10021, and author of *Thin Tastes Better: Control Your Food Triggers Without Feeling Deprived* (Bantam Dell).

It's difficult to stay on your diet when you are in certain situations. *Here are some suggestions on how to master them...*

- **Restaurants.** Avoid the *10-minute* problems—the first 10 minutes with the bread basket staring at you and the last 10 minutes with dessert.

Skip breads altogether: Have a tomato juice or shrimp cocktail instead. For dessert, have sorbet...fruit...or cappuccino with skim milk.

Best: Have an apple...low-fat yogurt...or some other healthful snack before you go out.

- **Travel.** Do not eat desserts until the last day of your trip.

Airports: Stay away from newsstands—they stock high-sugar snacks.

Better: Bring your own fruit.

- **Watching TV.** Don't snack in front of the TV—sip hot or cool liquids instead.

Effective strategies wherever you are: Resist cravings for 10 minutes—they may go away.

Also: Avoid going longer than three or four hours without a healthful snack or meal. Eating at regular intervals will keep your blood sugar stable and keep cravings at bay.

10,000 Steps to a Better Life

The late Robert N. Butler, MD, founding president of the International Longevity Center at the Mailman School of Public Health, Columbia University, New York City. He won the Pulitzer Prize for *Why Survive? Being Old in America* (Johns Hopkins University Press). *www.mailman.columbia.edu/academic-departments/centers/international-longevity-center*

When I lived in Washington, DC, in the 1960s, I began participating in one of the most effective and enjoyable forms of exercise I know. Early each morning, a friend and I met for a fast, invigorating walk.

I didn't have to take lessons or join a gym, and it was a great way to start the day. Those early morning walks were the beginning of a valuable lifelong habit.

MIRACULOUS BENEFITS

Walking for exercise has a long tradition. Thomas Jefferson, who lived to be 83 at a time when average life expectancy was about 40, walked four miles every day. He wrote that the purpose of walking was to "relax the mind."

Now we know that walking briskly for 30 to 60 minutes each day also can help people live longer, healthier lives. Fast walking burns about the same amount of calories per mile as running, and it doesn't pound the joints. It builds endurance, enhances muscle tone and flexibility and strengthens bones. It also helps prevent heart disease, hypertension and diabetes.

In a study of Harvard graduates, the Mayo Clinic discovered that men who burned 2,000 or more calories a week by walking lived an average of one to two years longer than those who burned fewer than 500 calories a week walking.

GETTING STARTED

The only equipment a walker needs is a comfortable pair of canvas or leather shoes designed specifically for walking.

I've found it helpful to do simple stretching exercises before and after a walk.

Example: I raise my left leg on a tabletop, pointing my toes toward the ceiling. I hold the position for a minute. Then I repeat the stretch with my right leg. If a table is too high, use a chair or sofa.

Some people prefer to walk on a treadmill. Or you may choose to take advantage of day-to-day opportunities to increase your walking.

Examples: Walking up flights of stairs instead of riding the escalator or elevator...parking far away from store entrances...or even walking to the store.

The rule of thumb when you're walking is to break a sweat. Aim to reach your target heart rate (THR).

To determine THR: Subtract your age from 220. Multiply by 0.8 (80%).

10,000 STEPS

Jefferson shipped from Paris to his home in Virginia a cumbersome device that accurately counted every step he took. Today, we have a more portable version known as a pedometer, which can be clipped to a belt or waistband to count the number of steps taken. In fact, "steps per day" has become a standard unit of exercise measurement. Studies here and in Japan show that the average person needs to take at least 10,000 steps per day—what you would do in a strenuous 30-minute workout—to get maximum health benefits. You can buy a pedometer at the International Longevity Center at the Mailman School of Public Health, Columbia University (212-305-3927, *www.mailman.columbia.edu/academic-departments/centers/international-longevity-center*). Pedometers are also available at sporting-goods stores.

WALKING GROUPS

In recent years, hundreds of walking clubs have sprung up nationwide. You can find them by going online and typing "walking clubs" into a search engine.

Example: American Volkssport Association has 300 walking clubs. Go to *www.ava.org* or call 210-659-2112.

When I returned to New York City in 1982, I walked with a group of early risers on weekends. (During the week, I walked on my own.) We got together around 7:30 am, took a brisk turn around a six-mile trail in Central Park and then enjoyed a leisurely, healthy breakfast. Old friends and new got to meet and support each other's efforts to stay healthy. I credit my walking buddies with helping me reach my goal of 10,000 steps a day.

A Stronger Body in Only 30 Minutes a Week

Fredrick Hahn, president and cofounder of the National Council for Exercise Standards, an organization of exercise, medical and scientific professionals. He is owner of Serious Strength Inc., a Slow Burn strength-training studio in New York City, *www.seriousstrength.com*, and coauthor of *The Slow Burn Fitness Revolution* (Broadway).

We know the benefits of strength training. It restores muscle...increases bone density...improves balance, decreasing the likelihood of falls...and promotes weight loss and cardiovascular fitness. However, conventional strength training requires several hours a week and frequently causes injury to muscles and joints.

New, better way: The *Slow Burn* technique, in which weights are lifted and lowered with incredible slowness—about 10 seconds up and 10 seconds down. *The benefits...*

- **It's safer.** Slow lifting reduces injury-causing stress on ligaments, tendons and joints. This means that even the elderly can do it safely.
- **It's more effective.** Without the aid of momentum, more muscle fibers are exercised with each movement.
- **It's more efficient.** You can get a complete workout in 30 minutes each week—compared with at least three hours for conventional lifting.

HOW TO DO IT

In a Slow Burn workout, you complete a set of three to six repetitions of each exercise in 60 to 90 seconds. If you perform 10 exercises, you can complete your workout in approximately 10 to 15 minutes. Two workouts a week are all you will need.

To get the best results, raise and lower weights at the rate of about one inch per second. Allow a total of about 100 seconds for all repetitions of each exercise—push-ups, leg curls, etc. Breathe normally while performing each exercise.

Helpful: Use a metronome to maintain the one-inch-per-second rhythm.

Repeat each exercise until the muscles are fatigued and you can't do another repetition in perfect form. If you pass the 90-second point and feel as though you could keep going, the weights are too light. If you can't complete three repetitions in 90 seconds, the weights are too heavy. Experiment to find the right weight for you.

The following program stimulates all muscle groups. Do three to six repetitions of each exercise. For exercises that require switching arms or legs, do three to six repetitions with each arm or leg. You will need adjustable hand and ankle weights. Look for sets that can adjust from one to 20 pounds.

- **Push-ups.** Kneel on a towel with your hands on the floor in front of you, shoulder-width apart. Keep your back straight—don't let it sway or arch.

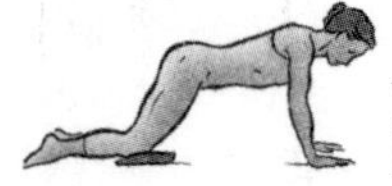

Take three seconds to lower yourself the first inch and at least seven seconds to lower yourself all the way, until your forehead almost touches the floor. Without resting at the bottom, reverse direction. Don't lock your elbows at the top. As soon as your arms are almost straight, reverse and go back down. If kneeling push-ups are too easy for you, do regular push-ups, with your toes on the floor.

- **Doorknob squats.** Open a door halfway so that you can grip both knobs. Place a stool or chair about two feet from the edge of the door. Stand an arm's length away from the door. Lightly grasp both knobs for balance, and slowly bend your knees and lower your body as though you were sitting down. Take three seconds to lower yourself the first inch and seven seconds to go all the way down, until your bottom just touches the stool. Then reverse and rise back up. Be careful not to pull yourself up with your arms—use the muscles of your buttocks and thighs.
- **Side-lying leg lifts.** Try this exercise without ankle weights at first. If it's too easy, start with five-pound weights. Lie on your left side

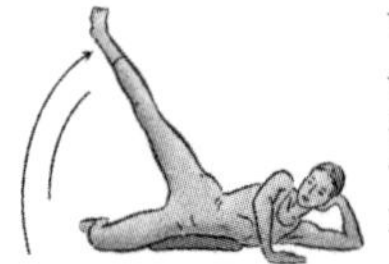

with your head propped on your left hand. Bend your left leg slightly so that your right leg rests on top of the calf. Slowly raise your right leg toward the ceiling, moving from the hip. Take three seconds to move it the first inch and seven seconds to raise it all the way. Pause at the top, tightly squeezing the hip and buttock muscles for a few seconds. Then slowly lower the leg back down. Repeat with the other leg.

- **Single-leg curls.** Attach a five-pound weight to your right ankle. The weight will probably be too light, but it's a good place to start. Lean forward and put both hands on a stool or chair...keep your right knee slightly bent and your spine straight.

Curl your right leg so that the heel approaches your bottom. Take three seconds to curl the leg the first inch and seven seconds to curl it the rest of the way. Pause at the top, squeezing the muscles in the back of your thigh. Then slowly reverse direction. Repeat with the other leg.

- **Side shoulder raise and overhead press.** This movement combines two exercises. Start with five-pound dumbbells. With a dumbbell in each hand, sit on a chair with your back straight and your feet flat on the floor. Slowly raise the weights away from your sides, taking three seconds to move them the first inch and seven seconds to raise them until they're parallel to the floor. Pause at the top for a few seconds; then slowly lower the weights.

Without resting, move on to the next phase of the exercise. With elbows bent, hold the weights at shoulder height, then slowly raise them overhead, taking three seconds to move them the first inch and seven seconds to go all the way up. Pause for a second; then slowly lower the weights until they're back at shoulder height. Don't lock your elbows at the top. Your muscles—not the joints—should support the weights.

• **Single-arm back pull-ups.** You need a stool or chair and a six- to eight-pound dumbbell. Hold the dumbbell in your right hand... face the stool with your left leg forward...and support yourself with your left hand on the stool. Let your right arm hang down beside the stool.

Slowly pull the dumbbell back and upward, taking three seconds to move it the first inch and seven seconds to raise it all the way. Your right elbow will be facing up and behind you. Pause at the top, squeezing the arm and back muscles for several seconds. Then lower the weight back down. Don't let your arm hang down at the end of the movement. Keep tension on the muscles all the time. Repeat with the other arm.

• **Biceps curls.** Sit on a stool or straight-back chair with a five-pound dumbbell in each hand. Tuck your elbows into your sides, and keep them there throughout the exercise. The only thing that should move is your lower arm.

Curl the dumbbells toward your shoulders, taking three seconds to move them the first inch and seven seconds to curl them all the way. Squeeze the muscles in the forearms and upper arms for a few seconds at the top of the movement; then slowly lower the weights back down.

• **Shoulder shrugs.** Sit on a stool or straight-back chair with a 10-pound dumbbell in each hand. Let your arms hang down away from your hips, with the elbows slightly bent.

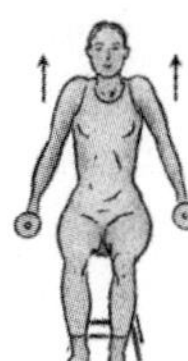

Raise the tops of your shoulders as though you're trying to touch them to your earlobes. Sit up very straight. Do not slouch forward or backward. Take three seconds to move your shoulders the first inch and seven seconds to raise them as far as they'll go. Pause at the top to squeeze the muscles in your shoulders; then lower them back down.

• **Abdominal crunches.** Lie on your back with your feet flat on the floor and your knees bent at a 90° angle. Tuck a rolled towel under your lower back...hold your arms straight in front of you...and keep your chin tucked into your chest. Curl your torso upward and forward, taking three seconds to move the first inch and seven seconds to move forward. Don't try to sit all the way up. Keep your lower back in contact with the towel. Pause and squeeze abdominal muscles at the top of the movement; then slowly lower your torso down. Don't rest your shoulders on the floor at the end. As soon as they brush the floor, repeat the exercise.

Illustrations by Shawn Banner.

How to Beat Osteoporosis

George J. Kessler, DO, clinical instructor of medicine and attending physician, Weill Medical College of Cornell University, and an osteopathic physician in private practice in New York City. He is author of *The Bone Density Diet: Six Weeks to a Strong Body and Mind* (Ballantine).

Who should be concerned about osteoporosis? The short answer is everyone. Your body builds all the bone density it will ever have by your late 20s. Bone density starts to decline after age 30, and this process accelerates as the body's synthesis of sex hormones slows.

Osteoporosis is especially prevalent among women, although 20% of its victims are men.

Until recently, it was thought that osteoporosis affected mostly Caucasian women, but new evidence suggests that these women are simply more likely to *report* breaks due to osteoporosis. All races are at risk.

NUTRITION AND EXERCISE

Bones *seem* stable as rock. In fact, they're made up of living cells. These are constantly being broken down and replaced by new ones.

Osteoporosis develops when breakdown accelerates and/or rebuilding slows. *But lifestyle strategies can keep the process in balance...*

• **Minerals.** Most of us are well aware that calcium is necessary for bone health. Premenopausal women and men under age 65 need 1,000 milligrams (mg) per day. For postmenopausal women and men over age 65, 1,500 mg is better.

Dairy foods are the classic source of calcium. One cup of milk contains 300 mg, one cup of plain yogurt, 450 mg. But you can also get calcium from beans (100 mg to 200 mg per cup)... kale (90 mg per cup)...and collard greens (350 mg per cup).

Calcium-fortified orange juice contains 300 mg per cup, fortified grapefruit juice, 280 mg per cup. Fortified breakfast cereals typically contain 250 mg per serving.

Soy milk, tofu and other soy products contain not only calcium but also *phytoestrogens* and other nutrients. These natural plant estrogens promote growth of new bone tissue and slow bone loss.

Bones need other minerals, too—notably magnesium and phosphorus—as well as vitamin D. Fortunately, plant sources of calcium also contain the other minerals. You can get all the vitamin D you need from 32 ounces of fortified milk...or from just 20 minutes of sunlight a day. (Skin makes vitamin D upon exposure to sunlight.)

• **Exercise.** The physical stresses to which bones are subjected during exercise stimulate new bone growth. Get at least 30 minutes of walking, weight lifting or another weight-bearing exercise, three times a week.

BONE ROBBERS

To slow the excretion of calcium from your body, it's essential to cut back on certain foods and activities. *Keep an eye on...*

• **Protein.** Each ounce of animal protein you eat causes elimination of roughly 25 mg of calcium. Most Americans get far more protein than they need.

• **Alcohol.** Have no more than three drinks per week.

• **Cigarettes.** Smoking doubles your risk for osteoporosis-related hip fracture.

• **Salt.** An eight-ounce serving of canned soup contains up to 3,000 mg of sodium chloride. Every 500 mg of sodium leaches 10 mg of calcium from your bones.

• **Caffeine.** Each cup of coffee pulls out 40 mg of calcium.

• **Soft drinks.** Phosphorus in sodas promotes calcium excretion.

DO YOUR BONES NEED HELP?

Bone densitometry is a 15-minute outpatient procedure that gauges bone strength. Most women should have the test at menopause—men, at ages 55 to 60. If it indicates a problem, doctors use one of the cross-linked collagen tests—N-Telopeptide (NTx) or deoxypyridinoline (Dpd)—to measure the rate of bone loss. Your doctor will use information from both tests to determine whether you need treatment for osteoporosis.

Depending on the degree of bone thinning, the rate of bone breakdown, your age, gender and other issues, your treatment may include hormones, bone-building drugs and/or medication for an underlying condition (such as an overactive thyroid).

HOW ABOUT HORMONES?

Although hormone-replacement therapy (HRT) may be effective against osteoporosis, for many women the risks of breast cancer, heart disease and stroke often outweigh the benefits.

Whether or not to go on HRT is a personal decision. A woman with a family history of heart disease or breast cancer may want to avoid it. Women should take HRT only if benefits outweigh risks.

Three alternatives to HRT...

• **Estriol.** This weak natural estrogen protects bone without increasing cancer risk. Sold by prescription as a pill or cream, it is not widely available. You may have to ask your doctor to find it for you. If he/she can't help, ask your pharmacist.

• **Natural progesterone.** Another bone-building hormone that declines at menopause or before, progesterone is less likely than estrogen to cause breast cysts, uterine fibroids and insomnia. It's sold over the counter.

• ***Raloxifene*** **(Evista).** This prescription drug and other *selective estrogen receptor modulators* are similar to estrogen. They have a real but smaller effect on bone density—and none of the cancer risk. In fact, they can *lower* your risk for breast cancer. Raloxifene may, however, cause blood clots and increased risk of stroke.

HORMONE ALTERNATIVES

For people who want to avoid hormones, four drugs are worth asking a doctor about...

• ***Alendronate*** **(Fosamax).** Available by prescription, alendronate is the drug of choice for men and for bone loss linked to steroid drugs. It slows bone loss.

• ***Risedronate*** **(Actonel).** This prescription drug is similar to alendronate but is less likely to cause digestive problems.

• ***Calcitonin*** **(Miacalcin).** This prescription drug is often the best choice for people who cannot tolerate alendronate or who prefer a natural rather than a synthetic product. It slows bone loss and decreases bone pain.

• **Ipriflavone.** This over-the-counter derivative of soy protein resembles estrogen. It can be used by women and men and is the only drug that slows bone loss and builds new bone.

Enlarged Prostate— It May Be Inevitable...but You Don't Have to Suffer

Kevin T. McVary, MD, professor of urology, Northwestern University Feinberg School of Medicine, Chicago. He is chairman of the American Urological Association's Benign Prostatic Hyperplasia Guidelines Panel, *www.auanet.org.*

For men, an enlarged prostate gland is a virtually inevitable part of aging. The condition affects half of men over age 50 and 90% of men over 80.

The good news: An increasing number of medications and surgical options are now available, making it easier than ever to manage this condition and reduce or eliminate the urination problems associated with it.

SYMPTOMS AND CAUSES

The medical terms for an enlarged prostate are benign prostate hyperplasia (BPH) and lower urinary tract symptoms (LUTS). These symptoms arise because of the prostate gland's location surrounding the urethra (the tube through which urine passes out of the body). A normal prostate is walnut-sized, allowing urine to flow freely. As the prostate becomes enlarged, however, it can press on the urethra, impeding urine flow.

Symptoms may include: Needing to urinate two or more times during the night...sudden urge to urinate...a weak urine stream...slow or delayed start of urination...dribbling after urinating ...incomplete emptying of the bladder...straining to urinate.

Almost all men will develop symptoms of an enlarged prostate if they live long enough. Several risk factors may hasten the process, however. The most important appears to be obesity. Recent studies have found that overweight men are at increased risk for prostate-related symptoms.

Studies also suggest that cigarette smoking may increase risk of symptoms, while exercise appears to decrease the risk slightly. In addition, stress can cause the prostate to grow more rapidly, and can also make symptoms worse even in the absence of new prostate growth.

DIAGNOSIS

If you're bothered by any of the urinary symptoms listed above, you should mention this to your doctor. He/she will then do a digital rectal exam to check the size of the prostate and will also order a urinalysis to check for infection, diabetes and kidney problems (all of which can cause urinary symptoms), and a prostate-specific antigen (PSA) blood test to rule out prostate cancer and serve as a marker for BPH/LUTS (since PSA levels tend to rise as the prostate enlarges).

If these tests indicate an enlarged prostate, you'll be referred to a urologist for further testing —possibly including an ultrasound scan of the prostate...a postvoid residual volume test, also done using ultrasound, to see how much urine remains in the bladder after urination...a cystoscopy, in which a tiny telescope is inserted into the urethra to examine the lining of the penis and the bladder for scar tissue or signs of bladder cancer (both of which can mimic symptoms of an enlarged prostate)...and a urodynamics exam, in which a catheter is used to measure bladder pressure and compare this against the patient's desire to urinate. This last test is done to spot bladder problems such as loss of muscle tone, which can produce symptoms similar to those of an enlarged prostate.

DRUG TREATMENTS

Once an enlarged prostate is diagnosed, the next step is to try medication to relieve the symptoms. One of two classes of drugs—or sometimes both together—may be prescribed for BPH/LUTS. Each is taken daily.

- **Alpha blockers** relax the muscles surrounding the prostate and bladder, reducing urinary symptoms. Studies have found these drugs to be effective for at least a year in 70% of men who take them, with results usually noticeable within a week. Potential side effects include dizziness, headache and a sudden drop in blood pressure upon standing. The most commonly prescribed alpha blockers are *tamsulosin* (Flomax) and *alfuzosin* (Uroxatral). Generic alpha blockers are also available, including *terazosin* (Hytrin) and *doxazosin* (Cardura), but their side effects tend to be more noticeable.

- **5-alpha reductase inhibitors** (5ARIs) work by deactivating certain male hormones, causing the prostate to shrink. These drugs are very effective in men with prostates weighing 35 grams or more (a normal prostate weighs about 25 grams). However, they take at least six months to produce any noticeable improvement in symptoms. In addition, about 3% of men taking a 5ARI report decreased libido, another 3% report decreased ejaculation and still another 3% report reduced erection quality. The only two FDA-approved 5ARIs are *finasteride* (Proscar) and *dutasteride* (Avodart).

One popular remedy that has not fared well in recent trials is the over-the-counter herbal supplement saw palmetto. Taken by millions of men for enlarged prostate, it's the third-best-selling herbal supplement in the US (after garlic and echinacea). However, a scientifically sound study of 225 men with enlarged prostate, published in the *New England Journal of Medicine*, found that saw palmetto did no better than a placebo pill in relieving symptoms.

SURGICAL TREATMENTS

If symptoms of enlarged prostate persist even with medication, surgery is the next option. Over the past 10 to 15 years, a number of minimally invasive procedures have been developed to widen the urinary channel by surgically removing excess prostate tissue.

The most common and effective procedure is *laser transurethral resection of the prostate* (laser TURP). The patient is usually given a general anesthetic, and a scope with an attached laser is inserted into the prostate through the urethra. The laser is used to destroy part of the prostate. Up to 95% of men who undergo TURP have a noticeable improvement in symptoms. It is estimated that about 10% of patients will require a second procedure some decades later.

Two other popular procedures are *transurethral needle ablation* (TUNA), in which a small scope inserted through the urethra uses radio waves to destroy prostate tissue...and microwave treatment, a similar but newer approach that uses microwaves to destroy prostate tissue. Both techniques work in about 70% of patients. Still, many men choose them over laser TURP since they can be done in a doctor's office under a local anesthetic.

The most invasive option is an open prostatectomy, in which the surgeon makes an incision and cuts out prostate tissue with a scalpel. Once widely used, this procedure has been eclipsed by the other, less-invasive alternatives, and now accounts for less than 3% of prostate operations performed.

Note: These procedures can result in sexual side effects, such as altered ejaculation and erection difficulties.

Hospital Smarts

Check the quality of care at over 4,600 US hospitals and other medical facilities. Sponsored by the Joint Commission of Accreditation of Healthcare Organizations. *www.jointcommission.org.*

Hospital Bill Self-Defense

Up to 90% of hospital bills contain errors. Three-quarters of the errors are in the hospital's favor and average about $1,400 per bill.

Self-defense: During your hospital stay, keep track of all services as best you can. Ask for an itemized bill each day so that you can track every expense.

Charles B. Inlander, health-care consultant and author of *Take This Book to the Hospital With You: A Consumer Guide to Surviving Your Hospital Stay* (St. Martin's).

Aspartame Has Side Effects

The popular artificial sweetener aspartame can cause symptoms that are identical to those associated with hyperthyroidism—which is also called Graves' disease.

Symptoms: Heart palpitations, anxiety attacks, headaches, hypertension, hair loss, enlarged eyes.

The symptoms appear most often in people who are dieting and on vigorous exercise programs.

Nan Kathryn Fuchs, PhD, nutrition editor and writer, *Women's Health Letter.*

Lower Stress in 5 Minutes or Less

Dawn Groves, Bellingham, Washington–based author of *Stress Reduction for Busy People* (New World Library).

No time to relax? Don't be so sure. *It can take five minutes or less to unwind and refresh your mind...*

- **Move around.** Take a quick trip through the halls of your workplace—or around the block. Walk up and down a flight of stairs. Do 15 jumping jacks.
- **Stretch while seated.** Lace your fingers under your knee, and draw it to your chest. Repeat with the other knee. This stretches the leg and lower back.

Next, stretch your arms above your head, palms up and fingers interlaced.

Drop your hands to your sides, then raise your right shoulder to your right ear, keeping your head vertical. Repeat with the left shoulder.

Finally, bend back the fingers of each hand. This is especially important if you use a computer for long periods.

- **Take 10 long, deep breaths.** Your belly should expand as you inhale and contract as you exhale.
- **Massage your eyes and ears.** Place your palms over your eyes. Slowly spiral your palms while applying gentle pressure. Do the same for your ears.

Blocking out sights and sounds, even for just a few seconds, is psychologically refreshing.

- **Try aromatherapy.** Put a drop of lemon-lime or orange essential oil in a saucer. These gentle scents relax you without making your home or office smell like an incense store.

Great resource: *www.aromaweb.com.*

You Don't Have to Put Up With Fatigue Anymore

Erika T. Schwartz, MD, internist in private practice in New York City. She is author of *Natural Energy: From Tired to Terrific in 10 Days* (Putnam).

You've tried getting more sleep. You've tried exercising and taking other steps to control psychological stress. Yet you're still feeling tired and run down. You know it's unwise to prop yourself up with caffeine. But what else can you do to boost your energy levels?

Once anemia, heart disease, thyroid disease, hepatitis, mononucleosis and other medical causes of fatigue have been ruled out, the average physician is at a loss as to what to do next.

"You'll just have to learn to live with it," he/she might say. Or, "Well, you *are* getting older."

Not true. *These nutrition-based strategies can be very effective...*

DRINK MORE WATER

Many cases of fatigue can be traced to the *mitochondria*, the microscopic "power plants" inside each cell of the body.

Mitochondria synthesize *adenosine triphosphate* (ATP), a high-energy molecule that's used throughout the body as a source of energy. But the chemical reactions that yield ATP also make free radicals and other toxins as by-products.

To flush out these toxins, the body needs at least 64 ounces of water a day. Less than that, and mitochondria are apt to become "clogged" with toxins, becoming inefficient at pumping out ATP.

RECONSIDER SALT

For many people with high blood pressure, salt deserves its status as a dietary no-no. But in healthy individuals, moderate salt intake boosts energy levels.

Salt helps the body hold on to the water it takes in. By boosting water retention, salt helps keep mitochondria free of toxins and functioning properly.

As long as your blood pressure is normal, it's safe to boost your intake of chicken stock, miso soup, salted nuts and other unprocessed sources of salt whenever you feel fatigued.

EAT SMALL, EAT OFTEN

Eating three big meals a day puts your blood sugar (glucose) levels on a roller-coaster. Low glucose can cause fatigue.

Eating every three hours helps keep your energy up by steadying your glucose levels.

Your goal should be to consume a mix of protein and fiber at each meal. Because fiber- and protein-rich foods are digested slowly, they provide a steady, reliable source of energy.

Eat plenty of vegetables, brown rice, whole-grain breads, grilled chicken or fish, nuts and dried fruits.

ENERGY-BOOSTING SUPPLEMENTS

Three nutrients are of proven value in the treatment of chronic fatigue...

• **L-carnitine.** This amino acid helps transport fatty acids into mitochondria, where they're used to make ATP.

L-carnitine is found in lamb, beef and other meats, but you would have to consume impossibly large amounts of these natural food sources to get the 1,000 mg of L-carnitine needed each day to boost your energy.

Ask your doctor about taking the prescription L-carnitine supplement *Carnitor*. The typical dosage is three or four 330-mg tablets a day.

• **Coenzyme Q10.** This antioxidant enzyme acts as a catalyst to "spark" synthesis of ATP.

Organ meats are the best source of this enzyme, but you would have to eat far too much to get the recommended 100 mg of coenzyme Q10 per day.

Coenzyme Q10 is sold over the counter in powder or gel form. The gel is more easily absorbed. The typical dosage is two 50-mg gelcaps a day.

• **Magnesium.** This mineral is needed for ATP synthesis. Unfortunately, chocolate, caffeine, soft drinks and highly processed foods tend to deplete the body of magnesium. As a result, magnesium deficiency is common in the US, and fatigue is a symptom of magnesium deficiency.

At special risk: Diabetics, people who consume lots of caffeine and people who take diuretic drugs.

Good sources of magnesium include wheat bran...brown rice...spinach...kale...chicken... turkey...pork...apricots...and curry powder.

Ask your doctor about taking a magnesium supplement, too.

How to Get a Good Night's Sleep

James B. Maas, PhD, professor emeritus of psychology at Cornell University, Ithaca, New York. He is author of *Power Sleep* (HarperCollins).

If you're having trouble sleeping, you are probably well acquainted with the basic recommendations for sound sleep...

• **Avoid caffeine and alcohol too close to bedtime.**

• **Avoid nicotine.** If you smoke, quit.

• **Take a warm bath or shower just before turning in.**

• **Get regular exercise and eat a wholesome diet.**

• **Avoid sources of stress late in the evening.**

If insomnia persists despite your best efforts to follow these strategies, the culprit could be your bedroom. *Here's how to set up your "sleep environment" for a restful night of sleep...*

• **Make sure your home is secure.** You will sleep better knowing that your family is protected against fires, burglary and other threats.

In addition to smoke detectors and good locks, consider investing in a burglar alarm.

• **Choose bedroom decor carefully.** Sky blue, forest green and other "colors of nature" are especially conducive to sleep. So are paintings of landscapes...or family photos taken on a favorite trip.

Bedroom office trap: Looking at stacks of bills or other paperwork makes it hard to fall asleep. If your home lacks a den or study, find a hallway or another place in your home to set up your office.

• **Eliminate light "pollution."** The easiest way to keep light from disturbing your sleep is to wear light-blocking eyeshades. You can pick up a pair at a drugstore.

If you find eyeshades uncomfortable, rid your bedroom of illuminated clocks, night-lights and other sources of light.

If streetlamps or other light sources shine in through your bedroom windows, fit your windows with light-blocking "blackout" curtains.

• **Silence environmental noise.** Any sound louder than 70 decibels (the equivalent of a dripping faucet) is disruptive to sleep. *If you cannot eliminate a particular sound, block it using these strategies...*

• Furnish your bedroom with heavy drapes and thick carpeting. If you're building a new home, make sure walls and ceilings have good sound insulation.

• Wear sound-blocking earplugs. Several types are available at drugstores. They are relatively inexpensive.

• Use a "white noise" generator. White noise is high-frequency sound like that produced by rainfall, surf, rustling leaves, etc. It masks other, more intrusive sounds...and helps lull you to sleep.

Low-cost white-noise generator: A bedside FM radio tuned between stations to static. Alternatively, you can play compact discs containing recorded nature sounds...or use an electronic sound-masking device.

• **Keep your bedroom cool.** An overheated bedroom can set off the body's wake-up call in the middle of the night. It can trigger nightmares, too.

Best temperature: 65° Fahrenheit.

• **Maintain ideal humidity.** Most people sleep best when relative humidity stays between 60% and 70%. Check it occasionally using a humidity indicator. This simple gauge is available at hardware stores.

If humidity regularly falls outside this range, a humidifier or dehumidifier can help. These devices are sold at department and hardware stores. They cost from $50 to $200.

• **Buy the best mattress you can afford.** If you like innerspring mattresses, spring count is crucial. A mattress for a full-size bed should have more than 300 coils...a queen, more than 375...a king, more than 450.

If you prefer the feel of a foam mattress, make sure the foam density is at least two pounds per cubic foot.

Whatever kind of mattress you pick, be sure to "test-drive" it at the store. You and your partner should have at least six extra inches of leg room.

Mattress maintenance: Once a month, rotate the mattress so that the head becomes the foot. Flip the mattress, too.

For more information on mattresses, contact the Better Sleep Council, 501 Wythe St., Alexandria, Virginia 22314. *www.bettersleep.org.*

• **Pick good sheets and bedclothes.** If you wear pajamas or a nightgown to bed, be sure the garment is soft to the touch—and roomy. Cotton and silk are more comfortable than synthetics.

When purchasing sheets, opt for cotton, silk or—best of all—linen. It feels smooth against the skin and absorbs moisture better than other fabrics.

• **Avoid overly soft pillows.** People often pick pillows that are too soft to provide proper support for the head and neck.

Down makes the best pillow filling. If you're allergic to down, polyester microfiber is a good second choice.

Some people troubled by insomnia find that a pillow filled with buckwheat hulls is particularly comfortable. These pillows are sold in department and/or health-food stores.

• **Don't be a clock-watcher.** The last thing you want during the wee hours is a visible reminder of how much sleep you're losing.

If you wake up in the middle of the night, don't even glance at the clock. If necessary, get rid of the clock...or turn it to face away from you before you turn in for the night.

• **Keep a writing pad on your nightstand.** To avoid ruminating on fears or "to do" lists as you try to fall asleep, jot them down as soon as they arise. Vow to deal with any problems or obligations the following day.

If worries keep you awake anyway, read or watch television until you feel drowsy.

New Way to Relieve Allergy Misery

A technique called *laser submucosal resection* permanently relieves nasal congestion in patients who haven't been helped by drugs and/or allergy shots.

The 15-minute treatment, often covered by insurance, decreases the size of *turbinates*, nasal structures that swell during an allergic reaction.

Result: Less congestion and allergy-related snoring and fewer sinus infections.

Information: American Academy of Otolaryngology—Head and Neck Surgery, 703-836-4444, *www.entnet.org.*

Rajiv Pandit, MD, otolaryngologist and former division chief, Department of Otolaryngology, Head and Neck Surgery at Methodist Dallas Medical Center.

Secrets of Youthful-Looking Skin

Nicholas V. Perricone, MD, adjunct professor of medicine at Michigan State University's College of Human Medicine, East Lansing. He is author of *The Wrinkle Cure: Unlock the Power of Cosmeceuticals for Supple, Youthful Skin* (Rodale). For more on skin care, see Perricone's Web site at *www.perriconemd.com.*

In their quest to keep a youthful appearance, growing numbers of men and women are using costly—but ineffective—wrinkle creams and undergoing painful procedures like face-lifts and dermabrasion.

There is an effective alternative. It's not a quick fix, but a science-based change in the way you eat and live.

OXIDATION AND INFLAMMATION

What we call "aging" of the skin—wrinkles, age spots, etc.—is *not* the fault of time. It's the result of inflammation. In fact, you might say that aging is inflammation...and that if you want to attack the first, you must defend against the second.

Inflammation is usually thought of as something obvious—the redness of sunburn, for instance, or painful swelling associated with infection. Actually, inflammation goes on invisibly—and constantly—at the cellular level.

Oxidation is a cause of underlying inflammation. You may have heard that this cell-damaging process is caused by highly reactive molecular fragments known as free radicals.

Ultraviolet radiation from sunlight creates free radicals in the skin. So does air pollution. And so do the natural metabolic processes that the body uses to convert food into energy.

The key to stopping or reversing "aging" is to minimize oxidation—and inflammation.

ANTI-INFLAMMATORY DIET

• **Cut back on sugar.** It's responsible for 50% of skin aging. Sugar molecules react with *collagen*, the protein that gives texture to the skin. That makes skin saggy instead of resilient. And each time sugar reacts with collagen, it releases a burst of free radicals.

In addition to cake, candy and other sweets, it's best to avoid pasta, potatoes, white rice, fruit juices, grapes and cooked carrots. These foods have a high glycemic index—meaning that they are converted into blood sugar very rapidly.

Most fresh fruits and vegetables like broccoli, eggplant, tomatoes and greens are okay because they are absorbed slowly.

3

The Bottom Line Guide to Practically Everything

How the War on Terror Is Invading Your Privacy

Identity theft is a serious crime that can make victims feel as if there is no way to keep personal information *private*. To make matters worse, new privacy concerns are arising from the war on terrorism.

Strong antiterrorism laws—along with credit card, discount card, telephone and E-ZPass databases—are allowing the government to monitor what you buy...where and what you eat ...what you read...where you travel...and more.

In the name of national security, Washington is scouring databases around the country. It can—and is—monitoring E-mail of specific people and checking some general traffic as well.

However, the government refuses to give details about its surveillance techniques.

Meanwhile, large corporations continue to collect, buy and sell a trove of personal data. These intrusions are cause for worry even if you have nothing to hide.

GOVERNMENT INTRUSIONS

The USA Patriot Act, passed shortly after September 11, 2001, permitted broader government monitoring of every American's activities.

Investigators at the Department of Homeland Security have much greater access to our financial information and credit reports. The Department of Justice used to need a judge's order for every phone it wiretapped. Now, it can apply for a roving wiretap that allows listening in on your phone conversations just because a suspect in an investigation lives or works near you.

Helpful: Modern wiretapping devices emit no sound. Call your local phone company if you think your phone is tapped. It will inspect for listening devices free of charge and alert you to an illegal wiretap. However, it will not tell you about a legal tap.

It remains to be seen whether any of these new government powers can foil terrorism, but

John Featherman, personal privacy consultant and former president of a Philadelphia firm that advised corporations on privacy needs, policies and data protection. He lectures around the country on identity theft and security.

it is clear that data collectors will know increasingly more about you.

Self-defense: It is much harder to be tracked if you use multiple Internet and *free* E-mail accounts, which don't require billing information. You can get free E-mail accounts through HotMail, Excite and other providers.

COMMERCIAL INTRUSIONS

Private companies are also collecting your personal data. Why be concerned? Because the information in many databases can hurt you. In addition, many of the entries in databases are wrong. Even if the information is correct, it's easy to draw the wrong conclusions from data. *Examples of information collected...*

Case #1: Supermarket and pharmacy loyalty cards earn you discounts. But your buying records are beginning to be sold to life and health insurance companies, which use them to evaluate your rates based on your food choices and nonprescription purchases. You might regularly buy something for a friend or relative, but the database logs you as the end user.

Self-defense: Avoid giving your full name when you sign up for "loyalty clubs." See if you can use just a first or last name. Many stores let you sign up anonymously as "Store Customer."

Case #2: E-ZPass technology was created to speed traffic flow and decrease congestion at highway, bridge and tunnel tollbooths. Several states now use it to issue speeding tickets if you travel too quickly between tolls on a highway. Moreover, E-ZPass records have been turned over to law enforcement to track people and have been subpoenaed in civil lawsuits, including divorces.

Self-defense: Use your E-ZPass selectively—remove it periodically and use cash at tollbooths. Or carry multiple E-ZPasses.

HOW TO CONTROL INFORMATION

Almost 70% of consumers complain that they've lost all control over how their personal information is collected and used by companies.*

Not every piece of data can be protected or is worth expending the energy to protect. Choose your battles. Decide what's most sensitive and when convenience or contributing to the collective security of the country makes sense.

Here are steps you can take to regain some control...

*According to a recent Harris poll.

- **Pay cash for purchases you want to keep confidential.**

- **Use a temporary credit card number.** To help reduce fraud, some companies offer free single-use numbers to account holders.

How it works: Use an online service to generate a disposable account confidentially linked to your real account. It will allow you to limit how much money an online merchant is able to get and the length of time the funds are available.

- **Keep your Social Security number (SSN) out of circulation as much as possible.** It has become the key piece of ID that unlocks access to your personal data, such as medical, insurance and driver's license records.

Self-defense: Avoid writing your SSN on checks or credit card receipts. Use an alternate ID number, either random numbers you select or the last four digits of your SSN. Tell the customer representative, "I'm concerned about my privacy, so I'd rather keep that information to myself."

Legally, you can refuse to use your SSN on any transaction other than those with tax consequences—such as getting a job or opening a bank account. For more information, contact Computer Professionals for Social Responsibility, *http://cpsr.org*.

- **Never confirm or provide personal information unless you called the company.** One of the most popular identity-theft scams is account "spoofing."

How it works: You get a call or an E-mail claiming to be from a major company wanting to update your security or billing information. You are directed to a Web site that looks just like that company's billing page, with blank boxes for your credit card number, SSN, etc.

The caller or E-mailer actually is a con artist who will use your personal information to open credit card accounts in your name and charge them to the limit. You won't be responsible for these charges, but straightening out the problem with all the credit card companies and credit-reporting bureaus will take huge amounts of time and trouble.

- **Maintain your Internet privacy.** Downloaded material that you thought you had deleted from your computer still remains on your hard drive. It can be accessed with widely available software.

Self-defense: Free computer programs that permanently erase files are available from *www.pcworld.com.* Search for "erase files."

PREVENTING INTRUSIONS AT HOME

- **Stop receiving unsolicited credit card offers by mail.** It will reduce junk mail and make identity theft harder for those who steal from your mailbox.

Self-defense: Contact the credit-reporting industry at the National Opt-Out Center, 888-567-8688, *www.optoutprescreen.com.* Specify that you wish to be *permanently* removed from preapproved credit card offer lists.

- **Stop telemarketers from calling your home** using mass-marketing lists filled with your personal information.

Self-defense: Use the federal "Do Not Call" registry. It will eliminate most telemarketing calls and provide stronger protection than most state registries.

If you don't block solicitors from calling, the registry requires them to exhibit their phone numbers on your Caller ID. Telemarketers who disregard the Federal Trade Commission (FTC) registry can be fined up to $11,000 for each call to a prohibited number.

Information: National Do Not Call Registry, 888-382-1222 or *www.donotcall.gov.*

Police Impersonator Self-Defense

The color of the flashing lights atop police cars are not standardized across the United States. While red flashers are common, many police forces use combinations on their vehicles, such as blue-and-red and blue-and-white. Other police forces use just blue lights.

Self-defense: To protect yourself from criminals impersonating highway police—without violating the law—turn on emergency flashers when an unmarked vehicle signals you from behind...stay on the road...slow down...then stop at the first well-lighted, populated area, such as a gas station.

Phil Lynn, manager, National Law Enforcement Policy Center, International Association of Chiefs of Police, Alexandria, Virginia.

Do-It-Yourself Home Security That Works

Ralph Winn, a 38-year veteran of the security industry and cofounder of the Home Security Store, which sells all major brands of home security products. He has worked for Honeywell Security's Government Division and served as a security consultant to foreign governments, including Russia and Ukraine. *www.HomeSecurityStore.com*

Many security companies advertise alarm systems for less than $100, including installation. But that requires that you sign a multiyear alarm-monitoring contract costing perhaps $25 to $35 per month, which promises that the monitors will alert police if the alarm is triggered.

You can avoid that monthly bill by installing your own unmonitored alarm system. Systems just like the ones supplied by security companies can be purchased for less than $300. Today's wireless technology makes them easy to install without having to drill holes and run wires through your walls.

IMPROVED SECURITY

While traditional security systems usually alert the security company when they detect a problem, self-installed alarm systems generally call the home owner's cell phone (or some other phone number), then the home owner calls the police. This not only saves the monthly monitoring fee, it often improves home security. The false-alarm rate with professionally monitored alarm systems is so high that busy police departments often make responding to alarm company calls a low priority. The police generally arrive faster when the home owner calls.

Professional alarm monitoring might make sense if you cannot always answer your cell phone quickly...if you feel more secure knowing a professional is monitoring your alarm, including smoke and carbon monoxide detectors...or if your homeowners insurance provider offers a substantial discount—typically 10% to 20%—for maintaining a professionally monitored security system.

There's no need to pay high security-company monthly rates, even if you want professional monitoring, however. There are companies that will monitor your alarm system for much less if you buy and install it yourself.

Example: Alarm Relay, Inc., charges $8.95 per month for monitoring services with a one-year contract. There is a onetime $35 start-up fee (800-624-6866, *www.AlarmRelay.com*).

WIRELESS SYSTEMS

A home alarm system should include alarms for both the front and back doors and a motion detector inside the home. Having two motion detectors is even better—most home owners put one in the family room and the other in the master bedroom, the rooms most often targeted by burglars. *Top choices...*

• **DSC PowerSeries 9047 wireless alarm kit** (888-888-7838, *www.dsc.com*)

• **Honeywell Lynx Plus wireless security system** (800-323-4576, *www.Security.Honeywell.com*)

• **Visonic PowerMax+ wireless home security system** (*www.Visonic.com*)

VIDEO MONITORING

If your goal is to identify trespassers and burglars so that they can be brought to justice or made to pay for damages, you'll also need a video-monitoring system.

The range and clarity of reasonably priced digital security cameras have improved dramatically in recent years. The digital recorders packaged with these systems typically can be set to record constantly, only when motion is detected or on a specific schedule. Some video systems can send images to your computer or even your cell phone. *Top choices...*

• **Lorex** (888-425-6739, *www.LorexTechnology.com*)

• **SVAT** (866-946-7828, *www.svat.com*)

These companies make excellent, affordable security camera systems. For around $400, you can purchase a kit from either company featuring two cameras capable of crisp night-vision images at up to 40 feet, a digital recording device and an LCD monitor.

EVEN LESS EXPENSIVE ITEMS

For less than $100, it's possible to reduce the odds that a burglar will target your home. *Among these low-cost security products...*

• **Motion-activated floodlights.** Burglars generally steer clear of homes that light up as they approach. It's worth paying $70 to $80 for solar-powered LED floodlights that don't need to be wired into the electrical system. *Top choice...*

• Maxsa 80 LED solar floodlight sells for about $75 (703-495-0661, *www.MaxsaInnovations.com*).

Avoid bargain-basement solar-powered floodlights, which may be dim.

• **Fake TVs.** These produce a flickering colored LED light that effectively replicates the light emitted by a television. One of these should convince anyone lurking outside at night that someone is home, awake and watching TV. It costs just $30, has a built-in timer and consumes far less electricity than leaving on an actual TV (877-532-5388, *www.FakeTV.com*).

• **Security company yard signs and window decals.** The security industry doesn't like to publicize this, but you can reduce the odds of break-in by perhaps 50% just by posting signs warning that you have an alarm system, even if you don't really have one. *Example...*

• An alarm company yard sign with a solar light and eight window decals are available for $29.95 on my Web site (*www.HomeSecurityStore.com*) or by calling 888-501-7870.

SECURITY WHEN YOU'RE HOME

Most alarm systems primarily protect property when the home owner is away. *Two products that offer effective security when you are at home...*

• **Driveway alarms.** These sound a chime inside the home when someone walks or drives up the driveway, giving the home owner a chance to see who's approaching before the person arrives. *Examples of ones that work well and sell for around $130...*

•Dakota Alert Wireless Motion Alert 3000 (605-356-2772, *www.DakotaAlert.com*)

•The Optex Wireless 2000 Annunciator System (909-993-5770, *www.OptexAmerica.com*)

• **Front-door video/intercom systems.** The intercom allows easy two-way conversation, while the video camera and monitor provide a better view than a peephole could.

Example: The Optex iVision wireless two-way video intercom has a portable, handheld monitor so you can see and speak with someone who rings your bell without even walking to the door. It has infrared capabilities for nighttime viewing, and it records pictures of strangers that can be shown to the police. It sells for around $300.

Safeguard Your Home Against Hidden Health Hazards

Alfred Moffit, director of site assessments and compliance services, Environmental Waste Management Associates, LLC, a full-service environmental consulting company that tests soil, air and water quality, Parsippany, New Jersey.

Buy a home that has hidden health hazards and you could lose your life savings to a massively expensive cleanup. Ignore the problem and you might be the target of a lawsuit by a neighbor or the home's next owner. Also, as time passes and environmental regulations tighten, problems may become even more expensive to fix.

Here are five major environmental risks and what to do about them...

UNDERGROUND OIL TANKS

Buried fuel tanks often leak as they disintegrate. Tank removal can cost $1,200 to $2,000, depending on the size and where the tank is located. Fixing a significant leak that impacts soil and ground water can cost $50,000 or more. If neighbors test their well water and discover that it is contaminated because of your leak or there are oil vapors in their homes, you can be sued.

The only clue that a tank is leaking is a dramatic, unexplained increase in your heating bills or a heating failure due to water entering the system.

Helpful: Some homeowner's insurance policies cover cleanup costs. Some insurers and tank-installation companies sell tank insurance. Or check with your state's department of environmental protection—it might have programs that help pay for cleanups.

Example: New Jersey has a "Petroleum Underground Storage Tank (UST) Remediation, Upgrade and Closure Fund."

- **Home sellers.** To expedite a sale, present contractor certification from your town that proves your tank has passed a pressure test to detect leaks...or the permit documentation that a former owner removed or properly buried a tank and filled it with sand.

- **Home buyers.** The purchase should be contingent on removal of a buried oil tank or passing of a pressure test.

Cost for a pressure test: $400 to $500.

ASBESTOS

Homes built before 1980 may have asbestos fibers in floor tiles, pipe insulation, roof material, sheetrock—even caulking. Asbestos can cause potentially lethal lung diseases, including asbestosis, mesothelioma and lung cancer. Professional removal costs up to several thousand dollars, depending on the amount of asbestos present.

You might not need to act. As long as asbestos-containing tile or insulation is intact, there's no immediate health risk. If items containing asbestos begin to deteriorate and must be removed, hire a licensed asbestos abatement contractor.

- **Home sellers.** Disclose to potential buyers that you have removed asbestos and whether any asbestos remains.

- **Home buyers.** If the home was built before 1980, make sure the deal is contingent on an asbestos test.

Cost: About $750.

LEAD PAINT

Homes built before 1978 usually have lead paint on walls, doors, trim and window frames. Lead in paint chips or dust can cause developmental problems in children. In adults, it can cause anemia, kidney damage, sterility and damage to the central nervous system.

If lead paint is in good condition, it usually is sufficient to paint over it.

Caution: Repainting is less effective on edges of doors and windows. It might be necessary to remove lead paint from these high-wear areas. Sanding kicks up a huge amount of lead dust, so it's best to hire licensed lead abatement professionals if paint is flaking throughout the home.

Cost: Up to several thousand dollars, depending on the extent of contamination.

- **Home sellers.** You must disclose the presence of lead-based paint in a home built before the year 1978.

- **Home buyers.** If a seller claims not to know about the existence of lead-based paint, make the deal contingent on a lead paint inspection.

Cost: $400 to $700, depending on the home's size and age.

UNDRINKABLE WATER

Nonpotable well water can dramatically affect quality of life—not to mention a home's resale value. Many water-quality problems can be corrected with a contaminant filter, which costs from a few hundred to several thousand dollars, plus monthly maintenance. If the problem can't be corrected, it might be necessary to drink only bottled water.

• **Home sellers.** Few states require sellers to test well water, but if you know of a problem, you should inform buyers.

• **Home buyers.** Make the purchase contingent on a water-quality test by a reputable environmental firm.

Cost: $350 to $500.

RADON

This naturally occurring radioactive gas is linked to increased risk of lung cancer. Homes sometimes have dangerous levels of this colorless and odorless gas in the basement or on the first floor when there is no basement. The problem can be alleviated with a venting system, but retrofitting one into an existing home can cost up to $10,000, depending on the size of the house and the concentration of radon.

• **Home sellers.** You can present proof that your home has a safe level of radon. However, the buyer probably will perform his/her own inspection. Most mortgage lenders require this test.

• **Home buyers.** A home inspector can test for radon for as little as $50. Do-it-yourself tests are available in home stores, but follow instructions to make sure that the house is "sealed" properly. A reading of more than 4 picocuries per liter of air means that action is required.

How to Spot a Ponzi Scheme

Dan Brecher, JD, securities attorney in New York City who specializes in claims against brokerage firms.

Bernard Madoff, a widely respected money manager and former chairman of the Nasdaq Stock Market, was arrested for securities fraud in December of 2008 and sentenced to 150 years in prison on June 30, 2009.

Operating a classic Ponzi scheme,* Madoff fleeced an estimated $65 billion from banks, charities, 401(k) plans, a US senator and many individual investors by using funds from new clients to pay off older ones. Faced with mounting losses, he confessed to perhaps the biggest scam in Wall Street history, prompting investors everywhere to wonder just whom they can trust.

Red flags that Madoff's clients should have been alert to—and that no investor should ignore...

• **Profits that sound too good to be true.** Even Warren Buffett loses money sometimes. Madoff's fund returned about 1% to 2% every month. Such a steady performance should have raised eyebrows—but it opened wallets instead.

• **Fuzzy investment strategy.** Madoff reportedly would say, "It's a proprietary strategy. I can't go into it in great detail." Investors who cannot decipher a fund's methodology on their own should ask a fee-based adviser whether it makes sense. If the adviser can't make sense of it, stay away. While the independent review may cost $500 or more, it can save you a fortune.

• **Obscure accountants.** The accounting firm that Madoff used was a little-known company that reportedly operated from a tiny office staffed with only three employees.

Trap: A big-name accounting firm is no guarantee either. In fact, it can lull investors into a false sense of security. Feeder funds, which market investments from other companies, may retain a major accounting firm to audit their own books—but not necessarily the books of the investment managers they "feed" into. Investors should find out who is auditing the company where the money ends up.

• **Promise of exclusivity.** Madoff's clients were invited to join an exclusive circle. Not just anyone could invest. The marketing approach was, "It is a privilege to invest with us." It is not unusual for exclusivity to be based upon a minimum required investment of a substantial amount, but in Madoff's case, you typically had to know someone to get in.

*Ponzi schemes are named for Charles Ponzi, who swindled thousands of New Englanders in a 1920s postage stamp speculation scheme.

- **Unwillingness to answer questions.** Investors who asked too many questions were actually kicked out of Madoff's fund. At the least, you should be given sufficient detail to allow you or your adviser to understand the investment strategy being used and how results are calculated, reported and audited.

Other self-defense strategies...

- **Allocate wisely.** Don't put all your money in just one or two investments. Anything can go bust. But also beware of too diversified a portfolio. Tracking more than 15 or 20 investments is difficult.
- **Don't invest solely on the say-so of a friend or colleague.** The recommendation may be well-intentioned but naïve. It's your money. Do your own due diligence.
- **Review monthly or quarterly statements.** In some cases, the statements from Madoff's firm did not even contain the names of any securities—which should have raised eyebrows, at least.

Wise Ways to Protect Yourself from Muggers, Carjackers, Pickpockets and More

Roger B. Shenkle, president, Survival Solutions, a security consulting firm, Box 476, Gambrills, Maryland 21054. He is a former US Army counterintelligence agent.

There are almost a half million robberies in the US each year—and that figure doesn't include the 150,000 stolen purses and wallets...or 30,000 carjackings. There are nearly 250,000 rapes, attempted rapes and sexual assaults. These numbers add up to almost 1 million victims. *How to protect yourself...*

MUGGERS AND RAPISTS

Maintaining "situational awareness"—that's military-speak for paying attention to what's going on around you—is the best way to avoid street crime. People get so caught up in their own lives that they don't spot danger until it is too late.

Situational awareness is especially important in places *between* the places where you spend time—the deserted parking lot you traverse to get from the mall to your car...or the empty stairwell you descend to get from your office to the street.

When you leave a building and enter a parking lot or garage, look for lingerers. If you see anyone suspicious, go back and ask someone to walk you to your car. If no one is available, call the police and ask them to send a cruiser. It's usually a mistake to try to rush to your car because there often isn't time to unlock the door, start the engine and drive away.

When you're in a potentially dangerous area, walk with a quick, confident gait. This makes you less appealing to criminals.

Caution: If the choice is between, say, walking confidently through a dangerous-looking group of teens or reversing course—reverse course.

Other high-risk situations...

- **Jogging.** Don't wear headphones unless you are certain your jogging route is safe. Headphones reduce your ability to hear danger. When jogging on a sidewalk, go against the flow of traffic so a vehicle can't follow behind you. On city sidewalks, stay close to the road, not near buildings, to make it harder for a predator to jump you from a doorway. Always avoid secluded areas.
- **ATMs.** After dark or in crime-prone areas, go to an ATM that is located inside a store—not one that is visible from the street. Don't assume that an ATM is safe just because it is in a locked bank vestibule accessible only with an ATM card. Muggers carry stolen cards so that they can buzz themselves in and corner victims.
- **Unfamiliar areas.** If you do not know whether a certain part of town is safe, call the local police department's non-emergency number. They'll tell you what neighborhoods to avoid.

Important: If you're mugged, hand over your money immediately. Try to escape only if your instincts tell you that you might be attacked even if you do turn over your cash. If you decide to flee, try a diversionary tactic. Throw some cash so that the mugger has to choose between pursuing you or retrieving the money. If your assailant tries to force you into a car in a public place, you're usually better off resisting right there rather than being driven to a more deserted site.

CARJACKERS

Most carjackings occur when vehicles are stopped at red lights or stop signs. If you're driving in a neighborhood that makes you uncomfortable, lock your doors and roll up your windows. Turn off the radio to cut down on distractions. When you come to a stop, leave enough room between your car and the one ahead so that you can maneuver quickly. Choose the lane farthest from the curb—you'll have more warning if someone on the sidewalk heads toward your car.

If you think you're about to be carjacked and no other cars are around, run the red light, blast your horn and flash your lights. If a carjacker is beside your vehicle with a gun drawn, let him/her have the car—aside from the engine block, no part of a car is likely to stop a bullet.

If confronted when you're unlocking your car, throw your keys to the side and run so that the pursuer must choose between following you and taking your car.

Carjacking gangs sometimes use a "bump-and-rob" technique—they cause a minor car accident, then steal the victim's car when he/she gets out to exchange insurance information.

Self-defense: If you're involved in a minor accident in a solitary area, stay in your car, keep the engine running and yell through the closed window for the other driver to follow you. Drive to the nearest police station or a well-lit, crowded area—an open gas station is a good option.

If possible, jot down the other vehicle's license plate number and call the police on your cell phone to report the accident and inform them where you're heading.

PICKPOCKETS AND PURSE SNATCHERS

A wallet is best kept in a front pants pocket. If you wrap a thick rubber band around it, you're more likely to feel friction if someone tries to slide it out. A purse should be held firmly against the body, not allowed to dangle freely. A fanny pack should be worn in front, with the zipper closed and secured with a safety pin.

Backpacks are the least secure and should be held against the chest when in high-crime areas.

The most secure spot to keep credit cards, passports or other light valuables is in a flat pouch worn under your shirt attached to a chain or string around your neck.

The most common place to have one's pocket picked is on a train or subway car while it is stopped at a station. The thief takes the wallet and makes a quick escape before the train departs. The victim is usually miles away before he notices his wallet missing.

From the time you board a train or subway until the doors close, keep a hand in the pocket that contains your wallet.

Diversions are another common technique employed by pickpockets.

Example: Someone bumps into you—or stops short in front of you so that you bump into him—while a partner picks your pocket.

Whenever you're jostled, always check for your wallet.

Notorious Ex-Hacker Reveals the Latest Scams

Kevin D. Mitnick, formerly one of the world's most notorious hackers. He spent five years in prison for computer hacking–related charges and began promoting computer security after his release in 2000. He is cofounder of Mitnick Security Consulting LLC, a computer security consulting firm, Las Vegas, *www.mitnicksecurity.com*, and coauthor of *The Art of Deception* (John Wiley & Sons).

A favorite department store calls to confirm your credit card number, or a Web site asks you to select a user name. Both are perfectly common situations—and potential cons.

Every day, high-tech con artists trick some of us into revealing personal account information, computer passwords—even secret corporate files. In 2010, nearly 13 million Americans fell victim to identity theft. *Here are the latest high-tech cons to watch out for...*

• **Caller-ID con.** Paul receives a call from a credit card company saying that he has been preapproved for a great credit card offer. Paul just assumes the call is legitimate because his phone's caller ID confirms the source, so he provides his date of birth, mother's maiden name, Social Security number and other confidential information.

Problem: Using a widely available telephone switch, a con artist arranged for Paul's caller ID to display the name of the credit card company. The con artist just as easily could have made it Paul's bank, a store he frequents—even the White House. Surprisingly, the ability to post phony caller IDs is an unethical but not illegal use of the technology.

How to protect yourself: Don't trust caller ID. When someone asks for sensitive information, insist on calling him/her back and look up the number.

• **Bogus Web site con.** Susan receives an E-mail at work that includes an attractive offer for a popular piece of merchandise. The E-mail includes a link to a Web page that prompts her to select a user name and password.

Problem: Like many people, Susan uses the same password for all of her online accounts. The offer and site turn out to be bogus, but the con artist who sent the E-mail now has Susan's password. With that and her work E-mail address, he can access her company's computers. He also might gain access to Susan's Web-based investment accounts or other password-protected personal data.

How to protect yourself: Use a different password for each Web site and online account. Make sure all passwords incorporate letters and numbers. This makes it difficult for hackers to guess them with programs that run through the dictionary. Never keep a list of passwords in an obvious place, and if you use *Windows*, don't let it save your passwords.

Note: The closed padlock image that appears at the bottom of your Web browser when you log on to a Web site means that the site has been certified as secure. This is a good sign that the site administrator has been vigilant about security.

• **Mislaid disk con.** Michael spots a computer disk on the floor of his office's restroom. The label says "Confidential Payroll Data" and carries the company logo.

Problem: Such a "mislaid" disk can be a computer-age Trojan horse left deliberately by a hacker employee or visitor. Once Michael loads the disk on to his computer, the hacker can gain access to his files. Worse, the disk unleashes a virus that crashes the company network.

How to protect yourself: Assume that a "lost" disk was left deliberately. Never put such a disk in your computer. Throw it away, or turn it over to your firm's information services department.

• **Stolen data.** Alan gets a call from his company's payroll department. There has been a computer problem, and his paycheck will be delayed by a week unless he can help replace the lost information.

Naturally, Alan is willing to help. He is asked for his Social Security number, whether he uses direct deposit and, if so, the name of his bank and his account number. This con is especially prevalent at large corporations—hackers realize employees are unlikely to know the names of everyone in the payroll department.

Alan wouldn't give such information to strangers, but the caller knows his name and seems to work for the company. Such information is available from company directories. Hackers can find the directories online or even by digging through the company's trash.

How to protect yourself: If you receive such a call, take the caller's name and say you'll call right back. Then dial your company's switchboard, and ask to be connected to the person in question. Consider it a red flag if the caller won't provide a name and call-back number. If you can't find the caller, notify your office manager so that he can alert everyone at your company.

If you own or manage a business, make it clear to all employees that it is always okay to say *no* to a phone request for confidential information.

Important: Hanging up and calling back might not be enough to stop the most sophisticated con artists. They might be savvy enough with phone systems to have your call rerouted to their phones. For greater certainty, get up from your desk and speak to the caller in person or ask to speak with someone you know in that department.

• **Helpful technician con.** Karen is at her desk when she receives a call from someone in her company's information services department. Would she read him the number on the jack to which her computer is connected? Most large companies label all Internet access ports. Of course, she complies.

Days later, after Karen has forgotten about the first call, someone else calls to see if her

Internet connection is working and leaves his number. She soon does have problems and calls back—and gives the man her user name and password.

Problem: Karen's helpful computer technician has just stolen her confidential information. It was he who caused her computer problem by calling her company's information services department and asking for her port to be shut down temporarily for testing. Most information services departments wouldn't question such a request. Once the con artist has Karen's user name and password, he calls the department back and has her port turned back on.

How to protect yourself: When asked to confirm confidential information, ask the caller to read the requested number in his file to you. If he says he doesn't have it handy, say you'll get back to him in a minute with the information. Then call your information services department to make sure you're talking to a real technician. Never let down your guard.

Even if you work from home, this con can be used by someone posing as a technician with your Internet service provider.

When Upgrading a Computer Is Smarter

Should you upgrade a computer...or purchase a new one? In general, upgrading a single component, such as the graphics card or hard drive, is quicker and cheaper than buying a new PC, setting it up on your network, removing and reinstalling all your data and reconfiguring your programs. But if you are looking for a complete overhaul—a new processor, more memory and a new graphics card and hard drive—then a new PC may be the better choice.

Rule of thumb: If you are thinking of replacing three parts that have a combined cost of $400 or more, instead put the money toward a new system.

PC World, 501 Second St., San Francisco 94107. *www.pcworld.com.*

When a Phone Call Is Better Than E-Mail—And How to Do It Right

Susan RoAne, networking expert based in the San Francisco Bay area. She is author of several books on networking, including *Face to Face: How to Reclaim the Personal Touch in a Digital World* (Fireside). *www.susanroane.co*

E-mail and text-messaging have their place, but an old-fashioned phone call often is your best communication option. *How to do it right...*

- **Write a one- or two-sentence summary of the reason for your call.** Writing this "note to self" forces you to think through what you want to say. It also keeps you focused during the call.

- **Be prepared to speak to a person or voicemail.** Not being prepared for both possibilities is a common cause of flubbed calls.

  - If you reach voicemail...succinctly explain the purpose of your call, but speak slowly, particularly when you provide your phone number. If you want a call back, say so. "I'd appreciate hearing from you" is my choice of words.

  - If you reach the person and it's not someone you know well, provide your name and a one-sentence explanation of why this person should trust you and speak with you. *Example:* "Sally Johnson suggested I call."

- **Ask, "Is this a bad time to talk?"** This question sounds like a polite attempt to consider the other person's schedule, but it also is a great way to obtain tacit permission to take up this person's time. If the answer is "no," then you have permission to proceed with the call now. If the answer is "yes," ask, "When would be a better time?" When he/she provides a time, he essentially has agreed to speak with you then.

- **Determine whether chattiness or straight-to-the-point is most appropriate.** The response you receive to the "Is this a bad time to talk?" is a clue. A friendly "Not at all, how can I help?" usually means a little conversation would be welcomed, but a terse "I can spare a minute" suggests that it is probably best to keep it brief.

• **Imagine that you're speaking to a friend** if you're calling someone you don't know well. Act as if the person is already open to talking to you and he's more likely to be so.

Use Your Camera Phone To Save Time and Money

Bruce Pechman, known as the "Muscleman of Technology." He is a popular TV personality specializing in consumer technology and appears regularly on major news programs. *www.mrbicep.com*

Most cell phones now come with built-in digital cameras, which can help you in a variety of ways...

SHOPPING

• **Take pictures of items you might want to purchase.** Make sure the full names and prices of the products are legible in your photos. Refer to the pictures when you see the item in other stores or when you shop for it online, to confirm that you are looking at exactly the same one...and to track which retailer offers the best price.

• **Record decorating ideas.** Take pictures of furniture, appliances and fabrics that you like when you see them in stores or other people's homes. Show these pictures to your spouse or your interior designer to confirm that everyone is on the same page. Or show them to clerks in stores to see if they have anything similar—perhaps at a lower price than that charged by the high-end store where you took the picture.

• **Remember a great wine.** Enjoy a bottle of wine at a restaurant? Taking a picture of its label will make it easier to find the same bottle in a wine store.

DRIVING AND PARKING

• **Find your parked car quickly.** When you park in a large lot, take a picture of the nearest identifiable landmark or nearest lot section sign. When you park on a city street, take a picture of the street sign at the nearest intersection.

• **Document your traffic accident.** Photograph the damage to each vehicle, and get a picture of the other driver's license plate. Take a few pictures that show the entire accident scene as well. Later, if there's a dispute over what happened or how much damage was sustained, your pictures could settle it.

HEALTH HELP

• **Send a photo to your doctor.** Are those harmless bug bites on your arm or a rash that requires medical attention? Your doctor might be willing to take a quick look at a digital picture and provide an opinion, saving you the expense and inconvenience of an office visit.

More Uses for Google and Yahoo

Get movie times, stock prices and weather information for free by sending a text message to Google (466453) or Yahoo (92466) requesting what you want.

Example: "Weather 10012" will return a forecast for that zip code. Information will be sent to your cell phone as a text message.

For instructions: *www.google.com/sms* or *http://mobile.yahoo.com/search.*

SmartMoney, 1755 Broadway, New York City 10019.

You Can Stop Those Annoying E-mails

Jason Catlett, PhD, former executive vice president of Guidescope Inc., a privacy advocacy group that fights spam, Brookside, New Jersey. He testified on the problem before the Federal Trade Commission, the US House of Representatives and the US Senate.

Unsolicited E-mail, or "spam," represents about 65% of all E-mail. The average computer user spends 25 hours a year deleting it.

WHO IS DOING THIS?

Spammers are usually individuals who send out millions of advertisements a day, swamping

Internet service providers (ISPs). About 7% of the spam sent results in sales.

Spammers usually work on commission, getting, for example, $50 for each mortgage lead or $85 for each cell-phone sale.

HOW THEY FIND YOU

Legitimate E-mail marketers send E-mails to their customers or rent lists of E-mail addresses. They also allow you to opt out of receiving their mail.

Illegitimate marketers don't adhere to the opt-out rule. They try to prevent anyone from recognizing and blocking their messages. They do this by constantly changing the false return addresses they use and the subject lines on their E-mails.

Some even use software programs to steal E-mail addresses from legitimate chat rooms and newsgroups.

Others legitimately buy address lists from Web sites that collect addresses from visitors.

SPAM DEFENSES

• **Use two E-mail addresses if you receive a lot of spam.** Give your primary E-mail address only to business colleagues, friends and family members.

Use the second address for chatting and shopping online and visiting Web sites that don't have privacy policies. Change this E-mail address when it attracts too much spam.

Free E-mail addresses are available from such sites as *www.yahoo.com* and *www.hotmail.com.*

• **Be careful when signing up for freebies or entering online (or offline) contests** that require personal information. These contests often exist only to collect and sell E-mail addresses. Your chances of winning are minuscule.

• **Decline any requests from your ISP** to list your E-mail address in a member directory.

• **Use a mailbox filter.** Most E-mail applications and services let you block specific E-mail addresses as well as particular words or phrases in the subject line or body of the text, such as "free money" or "X-rated."

In Microsoft *Outlook Express*, for example, click on "Tools," then "Rules," then "New Rule." Then you can create rules for the words and addresses that you want blocked.

• **Buy antispam software.** It is more sophisticated than the free security tools that are in your E-mail application.

Favorite: *McAfee Internet Security*, available at *www.mcafee.com.*

• **Complain.** Forward fraudulent and deceitful spam to the Federal Trade Commission at *spam@uce.gov.*

WHAT THE GOVERNMENT IS DOING

A federal law to regulate spam went into effect on January 1, 2004, making it illegal for anyone to send unsolicited commercial E-mail using a false return address or misleading subject line...collect addresses off Web sites...or fail to use a mechanism that allows recipients to opt out of getting future mailings. The penalties include fines and jail time.

In August 2004, Attorney General John Ashcroft announced that federal and state law-enforcement agencies had arrested or charged dozens of people with crimes related to junk E-mail, identity theft and other online scams.

Better E-mail Solicitations

Be sure that your E-mail solicitations include postal contact information.

If they don't, your company could face stiff fines under the Controlling the Assault of Non-Solicited Pornography and Marketing Act (CAN-SPAM) of 2003. The Act requires that all unsolicited E-mail include the sender's valid physical postal address. It imposes penalties for each violation, up to $11,000.

Be especially careful if you use a third-party E-mail provider—you may still be held liable if that provider fails to include contact information on your E-mails.

Alan Fisch, JD, technology law expert and partner, Kaye Scholer, LLP, Washington, DC.

Best Way to E-mail Your Résumé

Don't attach your résumé to an E-mail, unless you are asked to submit it that way. Instead, copy and paste it into the body of your E-mail message.

Reason: Like most firms, employment agencies are reluctant to download documents that might carry computer viruses.

Be sure to correct any type styles that might be lost in the copy-and-paste process, such as boldface or underlined text.

Katie Yeakle, executive director, American Writers & Artists Inc., Delray Beach, Florida. *www.awaionline.com*

Job Interviewers' Sneaky Tricks

Job hunters beware. Questions that seem like friendly small talk during or immediately after a job interview might be part of the screening.

- **If the interviewer notes your previous places of employment** and says, "I can understand why you left. I've heard complaints about the upper management there," don't take the bait.

Be either positive or neutral when asked about your relationship with previous employers, coworkers, neighbors, family or anyone else.

- **If an interviewer asks, "What do you do for fun?"** avoid giving answers that center entirely on you.

Rather than say, "I like to golf and watch baseball on television," say instead, "I like to golf with good friends and watch baseball games with my children."

The interviewer may be trying to determine if you enjoy socializing. The appropriate answers indicate that you are more likely to work well with others.

John McDorman, managing partner, Transition Consulting, a search and outplacement firm in Dallas.

Over 50 and Out of Work: Beat the Age Barrier

Jean Erickson Walker, EdD, CMF professional effectiveness coach, Pathways/OI Partners, Inc., which specializes in coaching people at midlife, Portland, Oregon, *www.oipart ners.net/pathways*. She is author of *The Age Advantage: Making the Most of Your Midlife Career Transition* (Berkley). For more information, go to *www.theageadvantage.com*.

Finding a new job isn't easy. It can be especially hard for people over age 50 because of age discrimination. Employers tend to believe younger candidates are more familiar with new technology, and they can pay younger employees less.

Discrimination is generally subtle and not always deliberate, but the result is brutal. It takes people over age 50 nearly 40% longer to find new jobs as those under 35.* The Age Discrimination in Employment Act of 1967 is intended to protect most people age 40 and older from discrimination in hiring, layoffs, salary, promotion, assignments and training.

Victims of age discrimination can sue employers or prospective employers—but these cases are difficult to prove. The employer can say that the candidate simply wasn't the best person for the job.

The best strategy is to *outsmart* age discrimination. *Here's how...*

- **Confront technology-skills stereotypes head-on.** When a 25-year-old applies for a job, everyone assumes he/she has computer skills. When a 55-year-old applies, many assume he/she does not.

Self-defense: Mention technological expertise during interviews. On your résumé, list computer programs you know or any special certifications you may have.

Example: Ken, 56, agreed to take early retirement after 27 years at his job. For four years, he searched unsuccessfully for a similar management post. At my suggestion, he got his project management certification. Then he positioned himself as an up-to-date telecommunications manager with extensive experience. Now he has a great new job.

- **Select appropriate companies and industries.** If possible, visit the company to get a sense of its culture. If it doesn't feel like a good fit, look elsewhere. If you have been laid off

*Study by the human resources consulting firm Drake Beam Morin.

from a youth-focused industry, emphasize your transferable skills or, if necessary, leave the industry. The technology, telecommunications and advertising sectors tend to favor younger hires.

The banking, government and utility sectors frequently hire younger employees and promote from within. An older job applicant in these industries should angle for a consultant's role rather than a promotion-track position.

Each year, AARP compiles a list of the top companies for older workers. To see the most recent list, go to *www.aarp.org/work.*

• **Dress for success.** Match the culture you're hoping to join, but also look sharp. Clothes are only as good as the body wearing them. Get in shape. Managers want to hire people who look like they could run—and win—a race.

• **Show flexibility.** A common stereotype holds that an older worker thinks his way is the only way to do things and that he won't even consider new ideas.

Self-defense: Design a résumé that reflects a range of positions and changing responsibilities. This is especially important if you have worked for the same firm for many years.

Example: Mention occasions when you implemented cutting-edge strategies.

• **Play the role of "possibility thinker" in interviews.** Mention a possible scenario, and run through the company's options should it actually occur. When young people do this, they come off as loose cannons trying to fix things that aren't broken. When older, more experienced people do it, they appear adaptable and innovative.

• **Don't abbreviate your résumé**—contrary to standard advice. Some older applicants include only their most recent experience.

Let your résumé run two or three pages, so long as each description is succinct and demonstrates your accomplishments. Don't try to hide your age by withholding employment dates. Emphasize how your experience can help the firm deal with problems.

For information on your rights...

• **AARP,** 888-687-2277, *www.aarp.org/work.*

• **US Administration on Aging,** 202-619-0724, *www.aoa.gov.*

• **US Equal Employment Opportunity Commission,** 800-669-4000, *www.eeoc.gov.*

Best Places to Retire

Kenneth A. Stern, CFP, founder and CEO, Asset Planning Solutions, San Diego, California. He is author of *50 Fabulous Places to Retire in America* (Career Press).

If relocation is part of your plan for retirement, don't rush into it. *Before making a decision, consider the "four Cs" that make a place suitable for your particular lifestyle...*

Crime: Is the community safe?

Climate: What kind of weather and seasonal changes do you enjoy? Don't assume that the place you love to visit in summer will be equally agreeable in the winter.

Cost of living: Can you afford to live there? Can you find work/business opportunities there if planning on a post-retirement career?

Culture: Do the local residents share any of your interests?

Where people are retiring to now...

NORTHWEST

• **Eugene, Oregon.** Located 110 miles from Portland, it's close to the ocean and the mountains. It has a moderate year-round climate and offers a variety of outdoor activities, including world-class skiing, river rafting, hiking and fishing. Local colleges provide great continuing-education programs.

Drawbacks: Occasional air-quality problems ...above-average living costs, including taxes and medical expenses.

• **Medford, Oregon.** Located about 170 miles from Eugene, Medford is a small, laid-back town with plenty of outdoor recreational opportunities, including golfing, skiing, fishing or just enjoying the mountains or picturesque Oregon coast. The world-renowned annual Shakespeare Festival in Ashland runs from mid-February through the end of October.

Other advantages: Below-average living costs...affordable housing...part-time jobs and start-up entrepreneurial business opportunities.

• **Bellingham, Washington.** About halfway between Seattle and Vancouver, it offers outdoor recreation in the nearby Pacific Ocean and Cascade Mountains, including fishing, skiing, kayaking and golf—as well as many trails for jogging and walking while enjoying the spectacular natural beauty of the Pacific Northwest.

This small, relaxed community also offers the cultural amenities of a university town (Western Washington University).

Drawbacks: Very wet—170 rainy days a year...limited job opportunities.

FLORIDA

• **Ocala.** Located in north central Florida, about 40 miles from Gainesville, it's one of the world centers for thoroughbred horse breeding. It offers plenty of outdoor recreational activities without crowds of tourists.

Other advantages: Below-average housing and living costs.

Drawbacks: No public transportation, limited shopping.

• **Kissimmee.** Located in central Florida—18 miles from Orlando, so your grandchildren won't need any urging to come visit you. Apart from nearby Disney World and other attractions, Kissimmee offers boating and fishing on the Chain of Lakes, and lots of wildlife.

Drawback: Floods of tourists.

LAS VEGAS

The self-styled entertainment capital has no income tax, inheritance tax or estate tax. Las Vegas has more than 320 days a year of sun and low humidity, year-round golf and tennis, and nearby state and national parks and skiing, hiking and canoeing. There are also many cultural offerings, along with excellent health care and senior services.

Drawbacks: July and August temperatures often exceed 105°F...heavy traffic...high crime rate.

THE SOUTHWEST

• **Austin, Texas.** The state capital of Texas is a rapidly growing metropolis with year-round outdoor recreation, a rich cultural environment and impressive health-care facilities.

Drawback: Hot summers.

• **Brownsville, Texas.** Located in the Lower Rio Grande Valley in southeast Texas, it has a Mexican heritage and a multicultural lifestyle. The cost of living is well below average. Matamoros, Mexico, with even lower prices, is a much larger city within walking distance.

Other advantages: Superb hunting, fishing and exceptional bird-watching.

Drawbacks: Hot, humid summers...heavy cross-border traffic and a high crime rate—particularly car theft.

RETIREMENT ABROAD

If you don't mind a major culture change and really want to stretch your retirement dollars, consider moving abroad...

• **Costa Rica.** San José, the country's capital, has much to offer, including a climate milder than Florida's, the lowest crime rate of any foreign community that's popular among US expatriates, and friendly people—most of whom speak English.

• **The Bahamas.** Nassau, a tropical paradise, is now an offshore banking haven attracting an increasing number of retirees. You don't need to worry about learning a new language in this English-speaking nation.

Caution: Medicare will not pay benefits if living in a foreign country so consider how you are going to pay for health care.

THE RELOCATION DECISION

Even if a particular community seems ideal on first sight, don't buy until you have spent time there on several occasions—and during different seasons. If it still appeals to you, rent for a year before you buy a new home to make sure you are in the right place.

Avoid Challenges to Your Will

Following are a few things you can do while you are alive to prevent your will from being contested after you're gone...

• **Use a *living trust* to handle the estate.** The longer the trust is in operation, the less likely a challenge will be successful.

• **Videotape the situation surrounding the signing of the will,** to show that you are competent.

Trap: A no-contest clause disinherits anyone who contests the will. But such clauses are invalid in many states and are useless if nothing is bequeathed to the person in the will.

Caution: If anyone is disinherited in the will, the document should explain why. Be sure that the explanation is factually correct.

Example: A child has not been in contact for 10 years.

Stanley Hagendorf, estate and tax attorney in private practice with offices in Nevada and California, and manager of The Hagendorf Law Firm in Las Vegas. He is a former professor of law in the estate-planning program at the University of Miami School of Law and author of numerous books on various aspects of estate taxes. *www.hagendorflaw.com*

What to Do If Your Dentures Don't Fit Comfortably

Do not use extra denture cream if your dentures fit poorly. Some denture creams contain zinc, and ingesting too much zinc can lead to serious blood and nervous system disorders linked to copper depletion.

Self-defense: See your dentist if your dentures do not fit comfortably. Consider using Secure Denture cream (available at drugstores and health-food stores), which does not contain zinc. If you do use denture cream containing zinc, use the smallest amount possible—two to four small dots on each plate, once a day. A 60-gram tube of denture cream should last at least one month.

Sharon Nations, MD, associate professor of neurology, University of Texas Southwestern Medical Center, Dallas.

How to Get Your Health Insurer to Pay Up

William M. Shernoff, JD, senior and managing partner of the law firm Shernoff Bidart Echeverria LLP, Claremont, California. The firm represents policyholders who have been treated unfairly by insurers or HMOs. Shernoff established the consumer law program at the University of Wisconsin, Madison, and is author of several books, including *Fight Back and Win: How to Get HMOs and Health Insurance to Pay Up* (Capital). *www.shernoff.com*

You pay your health insurance policy premiums without fail—but that doesn't mean your insurance company will be as reliable when you make a claim. It is very possible that your claim will be improperly denied.

Very few people bother to fight these denials. That's unfortunate, because policyholders who intelligently contest health insurance claims denials often get them reversed.

If a seemingly valid health insurance claim you make is denied in whole or in part, ask the insurance company to send you a full explanation of why it was denied (or accepted for only a lesser amount). *Then follow these steps to get your claim covered...*

Step 1: **Enlist support.** If you have a group health policy, ask the group benefits administrator to help you contest the denial. If you purchased an individual policy through an independent insurance agent, ask this agent to help. Not only do benefits administrators and insurance agents have experience with these matters, they have clout with the insurers. An insurance company might relent to an administrator's or agent's request to pay a claim simply to avoid losing future business.

Step 2: **Write a letter to the insurer** requesting a formal review of the denial and explaining why you believe it is incorrect. Get the name of the person to write to from your benefits administrator or agent. Send this letter via certified mail, return receipt requested.

Cite the insurance company's own literature if it seems to contradict the argument made in the denial. If the policy literature is vague or confusing—it often is—do not accept the insurance company's position that it means what it says it means. In most states, the courts interpret insurance policy provisions as a layperson would understand them, not as a corporate lawyer would interpret them.

Example: Your insurance company refuses to pay for your home care following a serious accident, arguing that the care you received was "custodial" care, which is not covered, rather than "skilled" care, which is. If you received what the average person would consider skilled care and your policy does not specifically define these terms in a way that defends the insurer's position, the law is likely on your side.

Some common reasons for claims denials and possible responses...

•**The procedure was not medically necessary.** Ask your doctor to write a letter to the insurer explaining why the procedure was necessary in your case.

•**The procedure was experimental.** Ask your doctor to write a letter to the insurer noting that Medicare or other insurers cover the procedure or citing statistics showing that it is widely used.

•**There was a filing error, such as a missed deadline.** In most states, the insurer cannot legally deny your claim because of a technical filing mistake unless it can show that it was harmed by this mistake.

•**The bill exceeds "reasonable and customary" charges.** Ask your doctor if there were special circumstances in your case that would justify higher costs. If there were, have him/her write a letter to the insurer describing them. Another option is to call other medical facilities in the region and ask what they charge for the procedure. Insurers often rely on old data or data from other parts of the country when they set these "reasonable and customary" estimates. If you can establish that your doctor did not charge more than others in your region do, the insurer might back down.

Step 3: **If your letter doesn't work, repeat your argument in a letter to the manager** or supervisor of the insurance company's claims department. Get the name of the individual from your claims representative. Work your way up the corporate ladder. You may need to convince only one person to agree with you for your denial to be reversed.

Remain calm and polite. Contesting an insurance claim denial is frustrating, but insurance company employees are more likely to take your side if they like you. Write down the name of any person you speak to, as well as the date and time and what you were told.

Step 4: **Contact your state's department of insurance,** and ask what it can do to help you. The quality and power of state insurance departments vary significantly. Some help policyholders stand up to unfair insurance company practices or conduct independent reviews of denied claims.

Example: California's Department of Insurance and Department of Managed Health Care offer "independent medical reviews" of denied health insurance claims. Approximately 40% of those reviewed are decided in the patient's favor.

Simply involving your state's department of insurance may be enough to convince an insurer that it is easier to pay your claim than fight it.

Step 5: **Call the media.** Local TV news programs and newspapers love stories about people being treated unfairly by big health insurance companies. Insurers despise this bad press and sometimes relent when reporters call. Determine which local reporters cover human-interest stories of this sort, contact them and ask if they would be interested in your story.

Step 6: **Go to court.** If your claim is in the low four figures or less, it might qualify for small-claims court. If it is larger, you will need to hire an attorney. If your case appears strong, there will be plenty of attorneys willing to take it on a contingency basis (they get paid only if they win or settle).

Hiring an attorney makes the most sense when the insurance company's unfair claim denial has interfered with your medical treatment and endangered your health. Juries often award substantial damages when this occurs.

First Aid for Air Travelers

Air travelers should pack a bottle of baby aspirin in their carry-on baggage. Aspirin isn't always included in the medical kits aboard commercial airliners—even though its clot-busting effect can be lifesaving in case of a heart attack. If you think you're having a heart attack, chew one of the 81-milligram (mg) tablets while seeking emergency medical assistance.

Victor S. Sloan, MD, clinical assistant professor of medicine, University of Medicine and Dentistry of New Jersey, New Brunswick. His suggestion was published in the *Annals of Internal Medicine..*

Better Hotel Stays

When registering at a hotel, ask for something specific, such as a room with a view or one closer to the elevator, etc. This eliminates the chance that you will get stuck with an undesirable room. If you have stayed at the hotel before, mention that when you check in. Never settle for an unacceptable room—instead, call the front desk and ask for a reassignment. If you are planning to stay a week or more, write the hotel manager personally at least one week ahead of time and ask for a "space-available" upgrade, price break or extras such as restaurant credits or free shoe shines or free high speed internet access. At check-in, ask to meet the manager to say hello.

Chris McGinnis, editor of *Expedia Travel Trendwatch*, *www.expedia.com*, and author of *The Unofficial Business Traveler's Pocket Guide* (McGraw-Hill).

Wrinkle-Free Packing

Book of Everyday Solutions (Bottom Line Books).

If your travel is more than overnight and the occasion calls for multiple dress-up outfits, you will want to pack a single suitcase as efficiently as possible.

According to the authors of *Packing: Bags to Trunks* (Knopf), the tissue or plastic bag method is effective...

- **Place tissue paper or plastic bags between each layer of clothing.** This lets garments slide rather than rub.
- **Interlock belts and run them along the circumference of the suitcase.** Place trousers waistband to waistband with the legs left to hang outside the case. Add a layer of tissue to the surface.
- **Place blouses and shirts facedown folded,** using a long fold to turn up the bottom of the garment a third to avoid a mid-belly crease. Add more tissue.
- **Turn suit jackets inside out.** Roll up ties and tuck them inside jacket pockets. Add another tissue layer.
- **Now the pant legs.** Fold them over the top. Add more tissue. On top of that add sweaters and socks laid out flat, not rolled.
- **Shoes, stuffed with underwear,** go into bags (plastic or fabric) and get stuffed in the sides of the bag along with the toiletry kit.

Insider's Guide to Slot Machines

Frank Legato, founding editor of *Strictly Slots* magazine, 8025 Black Horse Pike, Pleasantville, New Jersey 08232. Author of *How to Win Millions Playing Slot Machines!...Or Lose Trying* (Bonus Books). Legato is also senior editor of *Global Gaming Business* magazine, 6625 S. Valley View, Las Vegas, Nevada 89118.

Josephine Crawford of Galloway Township, New Jersey, didn't believe the casino employee when he told her that she had just won $10 million. But when bells kept ringing and people gathered around her, the 84-year-old former waitress soon realized that the employee at Harrah's Atlantic City was right. Her bet on the Megabucks nickel slot had paid off.

The odds are infinitesimal that you'll ever duplicate Crawford's success at the slots, but you can still have lots of fun. And who knows? You just might get as lucky as she was—especially if you know the ropes in playing slot machines.

Besides, playing slot machines requires little or no skill. You can play at your own pace and bet as little or as much as you want. *What you need to know...*

THE ODDS

Casinos try to take your mind off the odds. They introduce a constant stream of new slot games and offer eye-catching jackpots, such as new cars displayed on turntables in full view of the machines.

Regardless of the enticements, the majority of slot machines give an edge of 1% to 10% to the house, a term used for the owner of the machine, whether it's a casino or a convenience store in Nevada. This means that most slot players "win" back only 90 cents to 99 cents of every dollar they play.

These payback rates are calculated over the long run, which can be many thousands of games. So don't be misled when you see a player win several times during an hour's play at a particular machine. There eventually will be enough losses to bring the odds back in the house's favor. And you never know when those losses will occur.

The more it costs to play a slot, the higher the payback rate usually is. Games that cost $5 or $10, for example, might pay back 99%, while nickel games often return no more than 90% and penny games pay even less.

Caution: Slot games on the Internet are becoming popular.

My advice: Stay away from Internet slots. They're illegal to play in the US, and there's no way of knowing what the payback rate is.

Also, keep in mind that even the best odds at slots aren't as good as the odds with other games, such as blackjack, that require skill, concentration and a good memory.

IMPROVING YOUR CHANCES

The best slot machine odds are in Las Vegas—but not on the city's famous Strip. Casinos on the Strip—including Bally's, the Mirage, the Stardust and the Tropicana—don't need player-friendly slots because they enjoy a steady stream of tourists. The payback on 25-cent machines at Strip casinos is 93% or 94%, and on dollar games, it's 95% or 96%.

Casinos off the Strip rely more on local residents who demand the incentive of better odds to play the slots. That's particularly true in the suburbs of Henderson and North Las Vegas, where the payback at such casinos as Sunset Station, Fiesta Station and Green Valley Ranch is one or two percentage points higher than it is on the Strip.

In Atlantic City, nickel slots usually have a payback rate of only 90%, while 91% or 92% is typical for quarter games and 94% for dollar slots. Casinos elsewhere in the country have similar payback rates.

Slots at most casinos pay out bonuses to players who bet two or three coins at a time.

Example: If you put one quarter in a classic Double Diamond slot and three "wild" symbols come up, you'll win 1,000 quarters. But if you bet three quarters and the same symbols line up, you'll win 15,000 quarters—15 times the payback for three times the bet. Each slot machine has a written explanation of its winning combinations and prize amounts for various sizes of bets.

Today, video slots are popular, and they have the same payback rates as traditional mechanical machines, known as reel slots.

Some of the worst paybacks are at Nevada's airports and convenience stores, where the payback rate can be as low as 75%.

To find slots with the best payback rates, look at one of the gaming publications that regularly report on them. Two magazines with monthly payback reports are *Casino Player* (800-969-0711, *www.casinoplayer.com*) and *Strictly Slots* (800-969-0711, *www.strictlyslots.com*).

In any one casino, all slots that cost the same usually have the same payback rate. This is regardless of the particular game that's featured on the machine.

Example: If you put $1 in a Blazing 7s slot machine, you'll get the same payback rate as you would by putting $1 in a machine that features Tabasco, another popular game.

Nevertheless, many players believe that some games are luckier than others, and *Strictly Slots* regularly polls players to find out which games have that reputation. Be aware, however, that these polls are based on anecdotal evidence, and there are no statistical data to back them up.

Biggest game in town: Progressive slots, a game where machines are connected to one another and the jackpot rises as more people play. A huge overhead meter lets players keep track of the jackpot, which has reached more than $20 million in some cases. Two of the most popular wide-area progressive slots are Quartermania and Megabucks.

While prizes continue to rise, the odds of winning them remain long—very long. Ms. Crawford, for instance, was playing the nickel Megabucks slot, where the odds of winning the jackpot are about one in 40 million.

Important: To win the top prize, you must put the maximum number of coins in the slot, usually three. If Ms. Crawford had been playing with fewer coins, she would have won a few thousand dollars instead of $10 million.

MAKE THE SLOTS MORE FUN

Set a limit on how much to wager during any one session at the machines. Then stop playing when you've reached your limit or—if luck is with you—when you've won more than the amount you started with.

This exercise in self-discipline makes sense because no matter how long you play the slots, you're likely to lose many more games than you win. By quitting when you're ahead, you'll avoid the risk of a losing streak that takes away your winnings. Remember that the odds always favor the house. If you play long enough, you're certain to lose more money than you win.

Guidelines to establish a spending limit: At 10 spins a minute, it costs about $9 an hour to play a nickel machine with a three-coin maximum. A quarter machine would cost about $45 an hour and a dollar machine $180 an hour.

If setting a limit is difficult, remember Ms. Crawford. On the day she won, she had set a limit of $40 for the session and was down to her last $5. But if she had gone over her limit on the previous day, she might never have played on the day she struck it rich.

Winning Strategies for Texas Hold 'Em

Phil Hellmuth, Jr., 11-time World Series of Poker champion and one of the most respected Texas Hold 'Em tournament players. He is author of *Phil Hellmuth's Texas Hold 'Em* (HarperTorch) and *Play Poker Like the Pros* (HarperResource). *www.philhellmuth.com*

Texas Hold 'Em, the poker game favored by professional poker players, is rapidly becoming the favorite game of amateurs as well.

The rules of Texas Hold 'Em are simple. Each player receives two cards facedown. After a round of betting, three cards are dealt face up for players to share (called the "flop"). There's a second round of betting, a fourth card up (the "turn"), a third round of betting, a final up card (the "river"), then one more round of betting.

Players make their best five-card hands out of their two "pocket" cards and the five "community cards" face up on the table. While the rules are easy to learn, those who know Texas Hold 'Em only from watching TV tournaments often run into trouble when they try to play. *Here, winning strategies...*

- **Start tight.** When you watch poker on TV, the professionals seem to play lots of hands. That's because TV coverage shows only key hands. In most home games, the bets are small, so the best strategy is to play extremely "tight," folding most of the hands you're dealt. Play only when dealt one of the 10 best two-card starting hands—pairs of 7s or higher, or an ace-king or ace-queen. When you do get one of these great starting hands, always raise or reraise—don't just call (match a bet).

Exception: If a very conservative player already has made a big bet in front of you and you have a pair of 7s, 8s or 9s, you should fold.

Playing only strong hands will boost your odds of survival while you learn and perfect your game, and you will earn a reputation for playing only great cards, which will make bluffing easier later on.

- **Raise after the flop even if it didn't help you.** The flop is the first three community cards turned over. Often, they won't be the cards you want—but your opponents may not want them either. Rather than not betting on a disappointing flop, make a bet to find out where you're at. Maybe your opponents will fold or call rather than raise, indicating that you might not be in such bad shape after all. (If a raise and a reraise are made before it's your turn to bet, fold if your hand isn't strong.)

Example: You hold 10-10, and the flop comes king-queen-2. With two cards on the table higher than your 10s, someone might have hit a higher pair, putting you at a big disadvantage—or then again, maybe no one was holding a king or queen. If you don't bet, someone else likely will—and you'll have to assume he/she made his hand and fold. If you do make a small bet and no one raises, it may tell you that you're still ahead and may confuse your opponents.

- **Learn to read your opponents.** Even after you fold, time at the poker table shouldn't be wasted. Pick one or two of your opponents and try to guess what cards they're holding based on their behavior and bets. Watch for patterns. Do they only raise on big hands? Do they act especially confident when they have nothing?
- **"Slow play" the occasional big hand.** Once your opponents get used to you betting big on great hands, throw them a curve. If you have ace-ace or king-king, call before the flop. You might make the other players believe that your hand is weak and win a bigger pot.

Even if you don't, you'll make it harder for them to figure out what you have later.

In no-limit or pot-limit Hold 'Em, in which pots can grow large, it might be worth seeing a flop (matching a bet before the flop) with a small pair if you can do so cheaply. The odds of hitting three of a kind still are against you, but if you do hit, you might be able to build a big enough pot to make it worthwhile.

How to Get Out of Embarrassing Situations

Letitia Baldrige, renowned expert on manners who in the early 1960s was Jacqueline Kennedy's White House chief of staff. She is author of several books, including *Letitia Baldrige's New Complete Guide to Executive Manners* (Scribner).

When you make a mistake in a social setting, it is usually awkward for everyone there. But, the damage can be controlled if you know how to gracefully wriggle out of sticky situations. *How to handle highly embarrassing moments...*

• **Someone gives you a holiday gift—but you don't have one in return.** Be effusive in your thanks, and talk about how thoughtful the gift is. Do not apologize for your lack of a gift. It will only draw attention to the awkwardness of the situation.

As soon as you can, write a thank-you note stressing how surprised you were and how much you are enjoying the gift.

If it is from a business associate, you can refuse it by referring to company policy. However, be gracious.

Important: Don't rush to buy the person a gift. It looks phony, and you'll have to buy that person a gift next year. Give presents only to those close to you.

• **You suddenly must introduce someone whose name you've forgotten.** If it is someone you've just met, an easy way around the problem is to gently touch the person's arm and say, "Forgive me, I didn't catch your name." Avoid saying, "Sorry, I've forgotten your name." It is less embarrassing not to have heard the name than to have forgotten it. If it is a person you've met before, put your hand to your forehead and say, "I'm an absolute idiot. Today, I can't even remember my own name."

Everybody forgets names. The person who gets most upset is the person who forgot the name, not the person whose name has been forgotten.

Key: Get beyond the mistake quickly.

• **You make a remark and realize that you have unintentionally hurt the person with whom you're speaking.** This happens frequently, especially when people feel comfortable enough to express themselves honestly.

Solution: Don't try to undo the remark—just move on to the next topic as quickly as possible. Then, when the person starts to leave the group, go up to him/her and humbly apologize. If you act genuinely upset and your apology is heartfelt, most people are eager to forgive you. In fact, at this point, most will be more concerned about your discomfort than about their own.

Use the same approach when your child makes a disparaging comment about someone's appearance. As you leave the room, whisper to the person, "I hope you can forgive my child."

• **You show up at a dinner party with an uninvited date—only to discover that your role was to be the eligible man or woman.** This is a real gaffe and it is something that usually becomes apparent by your host's immediate and obvious discomfort.

Solution: Take your host or hostess aside and whisper your apologies. Don't tell your date about the mix-up. Otherwise, your date could feel uncomfortable.

The next day, send flowers to your host with a note thanking him for the evening. Say that you're sorry and that you did not understand he wanted you to come alone.

Important: Never ask to bring a date to anything other than a cocktail party or large buffet. If the invitation reads "and guest," be sure to let your host know your date's name before the gathering takes place.

• **You get caught in a white lie.** You've canceled a dinner engagement with a colleague, claiming urgent business.

In reality, it was the only night that you could dine with someone else. The problem occurs when a friend of the colleague spots you and tells your colleague.

Strategy: Apologize to your colleague the next day, preferably in person. Say, "If I had told you the truth up front—that this was the only night that I could see this person—I know you would have understood. I was just too embarrassed to tell you."

• **A disparaging remark you make gets back to the person about whom it was directed.** You called a colleague "a jerk" without realizing that his spouse was at your elbow.

Solution: Everything that follows is about damage control. If possible, preempt the problem by immediately taking the spouse aside to apologize before she leaves the group. If she has already left, call their home immediately and speak to both spouses. Be sure to state that you're sorry and that you were nasty without cause. Then explain that you've learned your lesson.

If you have told a lie about the person, send a disclaimer to everyone present when you told the lie.

Gift-Giving Dos and Don'ts

Peggy Post, great-granddaughter-in-law of the etiquette pioneer, Emily Post. She is spokesperson for the Emily Post Institute in Burlington, Vermont, and author of *Emily Post's Etiquette* (HarperCollins). *www.emilypost.com*

Every holiday season, we receive hundreds of letters at the Emily Post Institute asking about gift-giving etiquette. *Here are the questions we get most often...*

• **Is it OK to "regift"?** Sometimes—but proceed cautiously and follow these guidelines...

• The item must be brand new and in its original package.

• The gift should be something the recipient would love.

• It should not be something the original giver took great care to select or make for you.

• Regifting a nice bottle of wine to a wine lover is fine. Regifting a crystal vase that your mother gave you is not. When in doubt, don't do it.

• **Someone with whom I wasn't planning to exchange gifts gave me one. Do I have to reciprocate?** No. Just thank the gift giver warmly and leave it at that. Otherwise, you may start a new gift-giving tradition that is difficult to break. Of course, if that's what you would like to do, reciprocate!

• **My parents gave me a very expensive television—but it is not the one I wanted. Can I ask them if I can exchange it for a different one?** Just be honest, especially since the gift was extravagant and your parents will expect to see you use it.

First, thank them enthusiastically for the very generous gift. Try to point out something specific that requires you to return it. For example, if it's missing a feature that you were hoping for, gently suggest an exchange. Say something like, "Mom, Dad, this is an amazing gift—but this model doesn't have the surround-sound feature that I think we would really enjoy. Would you mind terribly if I exchanged it?"

• **I've been invited to a holiday party. Should I bring a gift for the host?** Yes, but don't bring anything that distracts the host—food or flowers that need to be taken care of immediately are not the best choices.

Keep the gift simple and the cost below $20—a bottle of wine...a small potted plant...a flower arrangement already in a vase...or perhaps a holiday ornament.

There is one exception. An open house is an informal way to celebrate and doesn't require a gift for the host, though you can certainly bring one if you choose.

• **I mail my grandchildren their holiday presents, but they never send thank-you notes. This really bothers me. Should I talk to my son?** Start by calling and asking your son or daughter-in-law—or better yet, ask your grandchildren directly—whether the gifts arrived safely. If the answer is yes, drop a hint with, "Well, I'm glad to hear that. Since I didn't hear from you, I was starting to wonder if the packages made it there. Did you like the gifts?"

If you don't think you got your message across, you'll have to be more direct. Talk frankly to your son—or if the grandkids are age eight or older, speak to them. Tell them politely that it's important to you that they express appreciation.

If this doesn't work, you may choose to stop sending gifts. That should get their attention—and teach your grandchildren that thank-you notes mean a lot.

• **Should I give my boss a holiday gift? What about the people who report to me and other coworkers?** Generally, you shouldn't give a gift to the boss. It could be seen as an attempt to win favor. However, an inexpensive gift that isn't too personal from you and other employees is fine. If you and your boss have worked closely together for years, it's OK to give a small gift.

When you're the boss, it's up to you whether or not to give gifts to your staff. It's certainly a nice gesture and a great way to acknowledge those who work for you.

If you do decide to give gifts, give across the board—don't give to only one department head but not the other two.

Good gift ideas include a nice bottle of wine, gift certificates, CDs and food items.

As for coworkers, a Secret Santa (in which each employee draws a name and gives a gift to that person) or a holiday grab bag are two of the easier ways to handle gift giving.

Food gifts are also a good idea—bring in a batch of homemade cookies or a box of chocolates to share with colleagues.

Nancy Samalin Tells How to Help Your Kids Build the Right Kind of Friendships with the Right Kind of Kids

Nancy Samalin, founder and director of Parent Guidance Workshops, 180 Riverside Dr., New York City 10024. She is author of several books on parenting, including *Loving Your Child Is Not Enough: Positive Discipline that Works* (Penguin). *http://samalin.com*

Parents have much more influence than they think over their children's choice of friends.

But in our attempt to protect our children, it is important to recognize that peer relationships are vital to our children's development. It's the arena in which they learn to make decisions, to lead or follow, to become considerate and loyal and to recover from mistakes.

How to have a positive influence over your children's choice of friends...

• **Deemphasize popularity.** Many parents unwittingly push kids to make friends. They fret if their children aren't invited to every birthday party. They are devastated whenever their kids are rejected by the "in" crowd.

But when you push for more popularity, your children get the message there is something wrong with them.

Encourage quality over quantity. The number of friends your children have is less important than if they have one or two good friends. And if you emphasize popularity or being part of the clique, your children may become followers who go along blindly with the crowd.

If children are left out—or picked on by their peer group—help them recognize that it is not necessarily their fault. Instead, reassure them that it is normal, though painful, to be "in" one week and "out" the next.

I've found that these popularity contests are more upsetting to parents than to kids. Most kids are more resilient than we give them credit for. Try to ride the waves of friendship fads, remembering that kids are fickle and peer groups are constantly in a state of flux.

• **Don't interfere without good reason.** Unless your children's friends are leading them into potentially hazardous situations, resist meddling in their relationships.

If you suspect that risky behavior is involved, remind your children about your clear, firm rules.

Example: When my kids wanted to go along with peer pressure, a phrase we used was, "Safety is a nonnegotiable issue in this family."

Otherwise, allow children opportunities to negotiate their own issues and differences. Kids need time among themselves to learn how to develop their own rules, to share and take turns, to play fair and square, to recover from bruised egos.

Certainly there are times and places for adult supervision, but try to intervene selectively.

• **Listen to your child.** The stronger your children's self-confidence, the better they'll be able to resist negative influences of peers.

Help strengthen children's egos by listening attentively when they say they're having trouble with friends.

Don't jump right in with ready-made solutions or criticism. Invite children to tell you what happened before you overreact...and then listen. They're not likely to open up if you go through the roof.

Example: Your son comes home in tears because his friends ridiculed him for backing out of a scheme to shoplift.

Don't immediately yell, "You're not spending time with those kids ever again." Instead, listen to his anguish about being ridiculed. Encourage him to talk about his feelings, and praise him for being strong and taking an unpopular stand.

You might say, "I know that was tough. It took a lot of courage not to go along with the guys. I'm wondering, though, if these are kids you really enjoy being with."

Try to determine whether your child is afraid of being left out. If that's the problem, help build up his/her self-confidence by praising him when he shows independent thinking.

- **Encourage individuality.** Keep in mind that you and your child have different tastes and opinions.

He may be attracted to people to whom you don't relate at all, just as you and he probably don't share the same tastes in food, music or movies.

Try to respect your children's differences even when you don't like the friends they keep.

Helpful: Encourage children to make choices and solve problems...ask their opinions about people you meet, TV shows and articles and books you read together.

When your child mentions a new best friend, don't grill him with lots of intrusive questions. Withhold your judgment.

Even if you don't like his choice of friends, don't automatically denigrate him, especially without any evidence of harmful behavior.

- **Encourage children to stick up for themselves.** Help your children practice this skill by allowing them to disagree with you in reasonable ways.

That doesn't mean tolerating sassy back talk or outright defiance, but it does mean supporting their self-expression.

Example: When your daughter insists that she must have a pair of expensive sneakers because all her friends are wearing them...or when she begs you to let her stay out with peers past her curfew... give her a chance to express her reasons for asking.

You don't have to agree, but show respect for her opinions. You might say, "Well, I'm ready to listen—try to convince me..." or "Let me hear your point of view..."

Even if you disagree with her, you are giving her opportunities to think for herself and evaluate her options.

If you decide that your child should not stay out past her curfew or that you cannot afford to buy her those expensive sneakers, reassure her that she can still be part of the group.

Point out that the other kids will still invite her to play basketball in her old sneakers or that she'll be able to go off with her friends on other excursions —even though she must be home by 9 pm on this particular night.

By supporting children in voicing and defending their opinions, you help them practice a skill that they can also use with their peers.

They will become more confident about saying no the next time friends try to lead them toward misbehavior or toward values that are unacceptable to you.

How to Get Back on Schedule When You're Always Running Behind

Stephanie Winston, time-management consultant and author of *The Organized Executive: A Program for Productivity* (Norton).

Even the most efficient people frequently feel as if they are constantly running behind schedule.

Here's how to overcome the diversions that prevent you from accomplishing as much as you would like to each day...

- **Catch your breath and start to plan.** One of the biggest enemies of good time management is poor planning.

The more rushed you feel, the less productive you'll be. The more frantic you are, the less decisive you will be.

Helpful: Go into the office one hour earlier than usual one day a week...or stay one hour later. Spend the time writing down your three most important priorities. Then set deadlines for each of them and create a manageable to-do list that prioritizes the tasks.

• **Use peak time wisely.** Tackle your toughest or least pleasant projects when you are feeling your most productive.

The best time of day for most people is early in the morning, when they are least distracted and most motivated.

Your hardest tasks should be slotted for the early hours. Once this work is out of the way, you can make better use of the remaining hours of the day.

• **Know when to run and hide.** Sometimes you need absolute silence to concentrate on what needs to get done. Sitting in your office—with the door open or closed—isn't always the best solution.

Better: Commandeer an empty conference room or head out to a coffee shop. Distraction-free time—even if it's just 15 minutes to a half-hour—is powerful when used to refocus on what needs to be done.

• **Just say *no*—very politely.** Interruptions by people who need your help can throw you off track. While you can't stop these requests, they can be controlled.

Helpful: Learn to deflect assignments when you're too busy. Try saying, "I'm just snowed under right now." If you really can't say no, take on only part of the assignment—and not all of it.

• **Delegate down—and down.** Some of my clients would be less overwhelmed if they identified and delegated the less important areas of their jobs.

The key is to start thinking of the people who work with you—and this can include your boss—as your helpers. They are there to help you get things done so that you can be more efficient and productive.

Don't be so obsessed with setting things right that you can't let go of an assignment.

Never feel guilty about backing off and using resources to reach your goals at work.

• **Keep track of interruptions.** Some people are overwhelmed when they are at work because subordinates ask them for more guidance than they should.

Others spend too much time talking to friends or family members. Some may pay too much attention to the stock market.

Helpful: Keep a running list of interruptions, the topic and how long you were distracted. Review this list every day to see where you can limit your availability and willingness to give up precious time.

• **Cut down on business travel.** Most business travel is a waste of time.

While it is important to travel to make a presentation or close a deal, many of your trips away from the office and home aren't as critical as you think.

Before you agree to attend a conference or to go out of town to meet with people, ask yourself what you could accomplish if you remained at the office.

Unnecessary business travel and "networking" actually make you less efficient and distract you from what's truly important—your staff's needs and your company's goals.

Protect Yourself from Kitchen Sponges

Kitchen sponges harbor large numbers of germs. To avoid contact with these potentially infectious microbes, use paper towels...or rinse the sponge, wring it out and microwave it for 30 to 60 seconds.

Dean O. Cliver, PhD, professor emeritus of food safety, School of Veterinary Medicine, University of California, Davis.

Spill Something In the Oven?

Immediately sprinkle an oven spill with a mixture of one part cinnamon to six parts salt. This mixture will absorb the spill and eliminate the burnt odor. Once the oven has cooled, wipe up the mixture.

Graham and Rosemary Haley, household task experts, Toronto, and authors of *Haley's Cleaning Hints* (New American Library).

Cleanliness Is Next to...

Toilet seats are up to a million times cleaner than dish cloths. Chopping boards, sinks and kitchen countertops are also dirtier than toilet seats—which are too dry to support a thriving population of bacteria. To clean a dish cloth, soak it for 10 minutes in diluted bleach (one cup in a sinkful of water).

Pat Rusin, PhD, research scientist, department of soil, water and environmental science, University of Arizona, Tucson.

When to Buy Gas

Buy gas early in the week. In times of rising prices, service stations typically raise the cost per gallon on Friday so they can profit from weekend traffic.

Buying at the beginning of the week should get you the lowest price of that week.

Geoff Sundstrom, spokesman, AAA, Heathrow, Florida

Stores Are Cracking Down on Returns

Sue Goldstein, founder of Underground Shopper, a 37-year-old company focused on bargain-shopping tips. Goldstein has written more than 70 books on shopping over the past four decades. She hosts a morning call-in radio show on radio station KVCE-AM in Dallas/Fort Worth.

It used to be that shoppers could indulge their buying habits and then take advantage of liberal return policies, especially around the holidays, to take back what no longer seemed worth the expense. But stores have severely tightened those policies, making it harder to splurge and then repent.

Tricky return policies and how to deal with them...

• **Blacklisting of serial returners.** These days, stores monitor how often you return items, typically by checking your driver's license or credit card when a return is made, and store the information in a computer. If you exceed the store's established limit, your return is denied even if you have a receipt. Criteria usually include the frequency of your returns and the dollar amounts involved. Consumer rights vary from state to state with respect to product returns, but generally, a store can set up any return policy that it wants as long as it discloses the policy and agrees to replace or refund defective items that are returned.

Examples: Clothing stores such as Express and The Limited allow shoppers only five returns within any 90-day period. The returns must include receipts, and the original tags must still be attached to the items. Requiring that tags be attached is to prevent "wardrobing"—buying an item, wearing it once and returning it.

Some stores have strict policies on returns without receipts.

Examples: Target tightened up its policy and now allows only two receiptless returns a year and only for items that cost less than $20.

Walmart's cash register system automatically flags customers who try to return more than three items without receipts within a 45-day period. If you surpass that limit, the store usually will not accept your returns, though a manager may approve the transaction. The flag on your account will disappear if there are no more receiptless returns within six months. Retailers with similar policies include The Home Depot, KMart, The Limited, Lowe's, Sports Authority and Staples.

Self-defense: Check a store's return policy —it usually can be found on the company's Web site, or call customer service. Don't buy too many items that you know you might return. Ask the store manager to allow an exception if your transaction is denied. Check your return history, and correct mistakes by E-mailing the

Retail Equation, a company that monitors returns for select retailers (*returnactivityreport@theretailequation.com*). The report is free.

Note: Retailers do not share information with one another about your returns. Blacklisting does not appear on or affect your credit report.

• **Special return restrictions on some electronic or seasonal items.** These restrictions can severely limit your return window.

Examples: The Home Depot's standard 90-day return window drops to 30 days for gas-powered equipment, such as lawn mowers and snowblowers. At Walmart, you have 90 days to bring back most merchandise, but only 30 days for camcorders and digital cameras and 15 days for computer hardware, Global Positioning System (GPS) units and digital music players. Around the holidays, retailers may extend their return policies for gift items, but be sure to confirm this before making a purchase.

Self-defense: Ask to speak with the store manager if the time limit has lapsed. Most companies allow their managers to override store policies. When you ask for an accommodation, prove to the manager that you're a good customer by bringing along sales receipts for previous purchases you made at the store. Some retailers also may be able to pull up your purchase history if you don't have the receipts.

Also, many credit cards offer 30-day satisfaction-guaranteed coverage. If you charged the item, tell the manager that you intend to dispute the charge with your card company and have the payment stopped. Managers sometimes let you return or exchange merchandise rather than go through the hassle of dealing with a credit card company.

• **Restocking fees.** Stores may charge 15% to 20% of the item's purchase price if you opened the package.

Example: Best Buy and other sellers of electronics, music and software have restocking fees.

Self-defense: Don't snip off the tags or open packaging unless you're sure you want to keep an item. If you do open the package, ask to see the manager to find out if he/she will waive the restocking fee. He might if you are a good customer or if the packaging looks barely touched.

Important: If the merchandise is flawed or damaged, you should get it replaced or your money back with no restocking fee.

• **Different rules for in-store and online purchases.** Policies for making returns of online items to retail stores vary widely.

Examples: Online orders from Toys 'R' Us can be mailed back for a refund but only exchanged for credit in stores. The Home Depot doesn't allow store returns at all for online purchases. You must ship them back. Other stores with different rules for in-store and online purchases include Kohl's, Macy's, Victoria's Secret and Pottery Barn.

Helpful: All Sears stores accept Land's End Internet and catalog mail-order returns, as well as Sears' own merchandise.

Self-defense: Make sure you follow a retailer's specific rules carefully. You can find them on the retailer's Web site or ask in the customer service department.

Surprising Ways A Chiropractor Can Help You

Karen Erickson, DC, chiropractor in private practice in New York City and a spokesperson for the American Chiropractic Association. She is author of several academic texts on the role of chiropractic in integrative health care and is on the board of trustees at New York Chiropractic College, New York City.

Well-designed studies have shown that chiropractic care (often just called "chiropractic") is at least as effective —and sometimes more effective—than traditional medicine for treating certain types of physical complaints.

Emerging research indicates that chiropractic affects more than just the spine and surrounding muscles. It has been used to successfully treat a variety of conditions, including digestive complaints and ear infections.

Ways chiropractic can help…

DIGESTIVE DISORDERS

A survey of 1,494 patients found that 22% reported digestive relief following chiropractic treatments, even though the majority had never mentioned digestive issues to their chiropractors.

Many of the spinal nerves that are affected by chiropractic manipulation control digestive functions. Patients who undergo routine manipulations may experience changes in their levels of digestive fluids, the speed at which food moves through the intestinal tract or the strength and/ or frequency of intestinal contractions.

We're often told by patients that manipulations for neck or low-back pain not only helped their musculo-skeletal complaints but also resulted in improvement in constipation, irritable bowel syndrome and other digestive issues.

Digestive problems need to be medically diagnosed first, but the most effective treatments involve an integrative approach, which can include chiropractic. I often get referrals from medical doctors of patients with constipation, colitis or irritable bowel syndrome.

Help for colic: A study published in *Journal of Manipulative and Physiological Therapeutics* found that colicky babies treated with chiropractic cried about three hours less daily than they did before, compared to a one-hour reduction in those given the drug *dimethicone*, a standard treatment. The manipulations given to children are very gentle. Many have a reduction in colic after just one or two treatments. Look for a chiropractor who specializes in problems that affect children.

TENSION HEADACHE

The headaches that we all get from time to time often are related to the cervical spine in the neck. Known as *cervicogenic headaches*, these occur when vertebral misalignments cause muscle tightness or spasms. The tension begins in the neck but can radiate through the occipital nerves that rise upward from the base of the skull.

A study that compared patients receiving chiropractic care for tension headaches with those who were treated with the antidepressant *amitriptyline* showed reduction in both the frequency and pain intensity of these types of headaches. Most important, the chiropractic patients sustained these improvements after the treatment period, unlike patients who were treated with medication.

In a typical treatment, the chiropractor attempts to realign the cervical joints by manipulating the neck and head. The main goals, apart from adjusting the vertebrae, are to increase the range of motion, relax the surrounding muscles and decrease pain and inflammation.

People who have only recently started getting headaches often will improve after one or two sessions with a chiropractor. Those who have suffered from headaches for years probably will require multiple treatments before they start to notice a significant improvement.

Also important: The chiropractor will take a detailed history to learn why there is excess misalignment in the neck. This usually is due to lifestyle issues. For example, many of us look down at our computer monitors, which puts excessive tension on the neck. Raising the monitor to eye level can correct this. Women may be advised to carry a handbag rather than a heavy shoulder bag. Cradling your phone between your neck and shoulder also can cause problems. If you often find yourself doing this, get a headset.

It's not clear if chiropractic is as effective for migraines, but preliminary research suggests that chiropractic manipulations may affect nerves that control vascular expansion and contraction, a key component of migraines.

EAR INFECTIONS

Some adults and virtually all children accumulate fluids in the eustachian tube, the passage between the throat and middle ear. The fluid is a perfect medium for viruses and bacteria, which can cause *otitis media*, an infection or inflammation of the middle ear.

Many studies have shown that chiropractic can relieve and prevent ear infections without antibiotics. The treatments, which include chiropractic adjustment and massage of the lymph nodes along the neck and around the ear, help drain excess fluid. The adjustment helps regulate the nervous system, which in turn drains the eustachian tube and promotes long-term drainage.

SINUSITIS

People with *chronic sinusitis* (inflammation of the mucous membranes in the sinuses) rarely get long-term relief from antibiotics or other types of conventional medicine, such as antihistamines and decongestants. Chiropractic can sometimes relieve all or most of the typical symptoms, such as facial pain and nasal congestion.

People with chronic sinusitis often have a misalignment in the cervical vertebrae. Chiropractic adjustments may help sinuses drain more efficiently. The treatment for sinusitis also includes applying pressure to the sinuses near the eyebrows and on either side of the nose.

REPETITIVE STRESS DISORDERS

Most repetitive stress injuries, including tennis elbow, are caused by *tendonitis*, an inflammation of the fibrous tissue that connects muscles to bones. *Carpal tunnel syndrome*, another type of repetitive stress injury, is caused by nerve inflammation in the wrist.

Doctors usually treat these conditions with anti-inflammatory drugs, including steroid injections in severe cases. For carpal tunnel syndrome, surgery to "release" pressure on the nerve is sometimes recommended.

Chiropractic, a more conservative approach, is effective for virtually all types of repetitive stress disorders. Manipulations to realign joints and improve range of motion can reduce pressure on tendons and nerves. The movements also improve lymphatic drainage, which reduces inflammation, improves circulation and accelerates healing.

To find a chiropractor: Go to the American Chiropractic Association Web site, *www.acatoday.org*, and click on the "Find a Doc" icon.

What Debt Collectors Don't Want You to Know

Gerri Detweiler, credit adviser at the consumer education and financial services company Credit.com. An expert on consumer money matters, she has written or coauthored several books, including *Stop Debt Collectors: How to Protect Your Rights and Resolve Your Debts* (Credit.com).

More and more Americans are getting calls from debt collectors—for unpaid medical bills, mortgages, car loans, credit card bills, etc. In fact, nearly one out of four American families has a debt in collection. The Federal Trade Commission (FTC) says that it received more consumer complaints about the debt-collection industry last year than about any other industry. *What you need to know now...*

ASK FOR VERIFICATION

When you first get a phone call from a debt collector, don't give any information about yourself or your financial situation. Instead, politely ask for written verification of the debt, which the collector must send within five days. Written verification includes the name of the creditor, the balance due, original due date, your account number and what action you should take if you believe that you don't owe the money.

It's critical not to acknowledge the debt in that initial call. If you acknowledge a debt on which the statute of limitations has run out, the clock may start all over again. The statute of limitations is the period of time a debt collector has to sue you to collect a debt. It varies by state and type of debt, generally running between three and 15 years. Check with your state attorney general's office to see which period applies to your situation. (To find your state attorney general, go to the Web site for the National Association of Attorneys General, *www.naag.org*.)

After you get the written verification, you have 30 days to dispute the debt. If you don't believe that you owe the debt or you are sure that the statute of limitations has run out, send the collection company a letter explaining concisely why you don't owe the debt and requesting that the collector stop calling or writing to you. By law, a debt collector must stop contacting you when he/she receives your letter, although he is allowed to contact you one time to notify you of his intent or to say that there will be no further contact. This doesn't mean that the collector must stop pursuing payment. If he/she thinks you owe the debt, he must notify you of any legal action that he intends to take.

Warning: In certain cases, collectors can sue to collect a debt that's outside the statute of limitations, and you must respond to a legal notice or risk a judgment by default.

NEGOTIATE

If you do owe the debt but can't pay it in full, call the debt-collection agency and say that you can't afford to pay in full but would like to resolve the debt within your means. Decide what you can afford, then offer an amount 20% to 25% lower than that as a starting point.

Example: If you owe $1,200 and feel that you can pay $400, you might say, "I can pay $300 in a lump sum to settle the debt."

Debt collectors prefer single payments to installments. Politely hold your ground if the collector tries to insist on an amount that you can't afford. If he keeps insisting, tell him that you will contact him when you have more money.

If you're being contacted by several debt collectors, prioritize your debts by working to pay off secured loans first.

These are debts, such as mortgages and car loans, that are "secured" by collateral—namely, your house or car—which the lender could repossess.

Once you have agreed on payment, ask the debt collector to agree to remove the collection from your credit report after you have paid the debt. Collectors are not obligated to comply, but they may honor your request as a courtesy if the debt is settled to their satisfaction.

Do not pay anything until you receive written confirmation of the amount and the terms to which you and the collector have agreed.

Never send a debt collector a personal check or provide a credit card number. Use a bank-certified check or Western Union money transfer, which allows you to prove payment without revealing any personal financial information.

Keep copies and written records of all communications, and send any letters certified mail, return receipt requested. Such records can help you negotiate and will be useful if you wind up in court. You can download a free worksheet from *www.credit.com/credit_information/debt_help* to help you keep track of your interactions.

COLLECTION NO-NOs

Be aware that under the Fair Debt Collection Practices Act, collection agencies...

- **Cannot** threaten violence or use violence.
- **Cannot** use obscene, profane or abusive language, including racial slurs.
- **Cannot** call repeatedly with the intent of harassing you. (There is no set number of allowed calls—it has been left up to the courts to decide this in specific cases.) Debt collectors also may not call at "unreasonable" times, which usually means before 8 am and after 9 pm.
- **Cannot** send a letter that appears to come from a lawyer when it does not, or otherwise falsely claim to be initiating legal action.
- **Cannot** send a letter that shows on the envelope that it's from a debt collector.
- **Cannot** threaten to ruin your credit forever.
- **Cannot** tell your employer about your debt or threaten to do so.
- **Cannot** imply any affiliation with the government or with a law-enforcement agency.

If you believe that a debt collector is in violation of the law, file a complaint with the FTC (877-FTC-HELP [382-4357], *www.ftc.gov*) or with your state attorney general's office. Numerous consumer complaints about the same debt-collection company may prompt an investigation. You also may wish to retain a consumer-law attorney to see if suing the debt collector for actual and/or punitive damages is an option. This may make sense if the collector has broken the law or is suing you. A lawyer may be willing to take your case on a contingency basis (no fee unless you win). The first consultation usually is free, but be sure to ask in advance.

Latest Internet Scam

Beware of "spear phishing" fraud, warns cyber-security expert Michael Gregg. Scammers craft very specific e-mails pretending to be from a person or business that you know. Clicking on a link in the e-mail can give the scammer access to your online accounts. Self-defense: Let your pointer hover over a link in an e-mail. The status bar on the bottom of your Web page shows the link's Web address. Be suspicious if you don't recognize it or if it doesn't end in ".com" or ".org."

Michael Gregg is president of Superior Solutions, a cyber-security consulting firm in Houston, and author of 15 books on Internet security. *www.TheSolutionFirm.com*

4

Turn Recession Worries Into Recovery Riches

Break the Rules! And See Your Mutual Funds Take Off

For years, Sheldon Jacobs built up a treasure trove of investment rules to help small investors beat Wall Street professionals. In the past decade, however, the rules have changed dramatically because of the wrenching transformation of stock markets and the global economy. *Here's how Jacobs has adjusted his rules for today's investment climate...*

A LONG-TERM BEAR MARKET

For the next decade, I expect plenty of extreme volatility and annual returns that average perhaps 6% for US stocks. You can smooth out the ride and beat those returns if you follow my new rules.

FORGET 10-YEAR RECORDS

The old rule: Look at long-term returns, such as 10-year periods or longer, to judge actively managed funds (those that rely on a manager's decisions rather than tracking an index).

My new strategy: Focus on shorter-term performance periods—three months, six months and one-, three- and five years.

Why it's necessary: You want to find funds that have excelled in comparison to their peers under the challenging conditions of the past few years. That's because these types of conditions are likely to continue for some time. They have included the market collapse of 2008... the bullish rallies of 2009 and 2010...and the grinding, volatile markets of 2011 and 2012.

AVOID TARGET-DATE FUNDS

The standard rule: Rely on target-date mutual funds, which have been around since the early 1990s, to automatically shift your asset

Sheldon Jacobs, widely regarded as the dean of no-load mutual fund advisers. The newsletter he founded, *The No-Load Fund Investor*, won a first-place ranking over a 15-year period. He still is a contributing editor to the newsletter and is author of *Investing Without Wall Street: The Five Essentials of Financial Freedom* (Wiley).

mix to a more conservative stance as you approach and live through your retirement years.

My new strategy: There are better alternatives that allow you to adjust to changing conditions.

Why it's necessary: Target-date funds have inherent weaknesses in this extended bear market. First, many fund companies, striving to maintain high returns so they can beat the competition, keep as much as two-thirds of the typical target-date portfolio in stocks even as investors are just a few years from retirement. That's too aggressive if the market has a big down year. Second, the funds ignore current market conditions when deciding on allocations.

Better: "Asset-allocation" funds own both stocks and bonds but have more flexibility to vary allocations depending on market conditions. Funds can make changes if the market outlook shifts. This exposes you to less risk over the long run.

Important: Asset-allocation funds are best suited for tax-deferred or tax-exempt retirement accounts rather than taxable accounts because they tend to generate large amounts of taxable income.

Attractive asset-allocation funds now...

• **Fidelity Four-In-One Index** (FFNOX). This fund shifts allocations among four Fidelity index funds that give you broad exposure to large- and small-cap US stocks, foreign stocks and bonds.

Performance: 9.56%.* *www.Fidelity.com*

• **T. Rowe Price Balanced** (RPBAX) invests in a mix of stocks as well as actively managed in-house funds such as T. Rowe Price Real Assets and T. Rowe Price High Yield. The fund has about one-third of its portfolio in bonds and cash and the rest in US and foreign stocks.

Performance: 9.76%. *www.TRowePrice.com*

FOCUS ON EMERGING MARKETS

The old rule: Use foreign stock funds to diversify your portfolio and reduce your overall risk. The idea was that domestic and foreign funds moved independently of each other.

My new strategy: Continue to use foreign funds—especially those focusing on emerging markets—as potential growth engines in your portfolio, but don't expect to get as much diversification benefit as before or to reduce your overall portfolio risk.

Why it's necessary: As the world continues to grow more economically interconnected, returns in the US and overseas tend to move in the same direction. But annualized returns of emerging-market stocks, although more volatile, have been double those of developed-market stocks over the past 10 years, on average, and will continue to do better. I keep about 10% of my overall portfolio in developed-market foreign stocks and 5% in emerging-market stocks.

Attractive now...

• **iShares MSCI EAFE ETF** (EFA) invests in nearly 1,000 stocks from 22 developed markets outside Canada and the US.

Performance: 11.85%. *www.iShares.com*

• **Vanguard Emerging Markets Stock Index Fund** (VEIEX) tracks more than 800 stocks.

Performance: 17.8%. *www.Vanguard.com*

IMPROVE YOUR INDEXING

The old rule: Use traditional index funds as the core of your portfolio because of their unbeatable low costs.

My new strategy: If you want to use index funds, switch 50% of the assets that you hold in them to "fundamental" index funds.

Why it's necessary: These new index funds perform better in bear markets because they are relatively light on high-flying stocks that can easily plummet. If you own a traditional fund that tracks a well-known major index such as the Standard & Poor's 500 stock index, it is "capitalization-weighted," which means that companies whose overall stock market values are greatest and rising quickly tend to dominate the index. That's great in bull markets because the more that a stock price goes up, the bigger its presence in the index. But it can be risky in bear markets or when a particular stock that dominates the index goes sour. Apple, for instance, whose stock price

*All performance figures are three-year annualized returns as of September 29, 2012.

has soared, takes up a hefty 4.9% of the entire S&P 500 stock index.

Attractive now...

- **PowerShares FTSE RAFI US 1000 ETF** (PRF) is a large-cap index fund that currently is dominated by stocks such as AT&T and Exxon Mobil and allocates just 0.6% to Apple.

Performance: 11.37%. *www.InvescoPowerShares.com*

- **PowerShares FTSE RAFI US 1500 Small-Mid Portfolio ETF** (PRFZ).

Performance: 12.09%. *www.InvescoPowerShares.com*

- **Schwab Fundamental Emerging Markets Index (SFENX).**

Performance: 3%. *www.Schwab.com*

How to Invest Now To Cash In Big During the Recovery

Allen Sinai, PhD, chief global economist and strategist at Decision Economics, Inc., an economic advisory firm in New York City. Sinai has been the top economic forecaster in annual surveys in *USA Today* and *The Wall Street Journal*, and was chief global economist at Lehman Brothers, Inc., from 1983 to 1996, prior to starting his own firm.

Some financial analysts are warning that stocks are due for a big downturn. After all, the unemployment rate is still high, and the economy's recovery is only tepid. But those pessimists don't appreciate how resilient the markets can be.

Why the economic outlook still offers great investment opportunities...

EARNINGS, YES...REVENUE, NO

I expect S&P 500 earnings to climb on average, from the year before. Stronger earnings and healthier profit margins will result mainly from effective efforts by companies to reduce costs, rather than from any big jump in revenues. At the first indications of recession, many employers started to cut payrolls sharply. Businesses outsourced some jobs and began making more effective use of technology. All that has increased productivity and helped companies squeeze more profits out of anemic sales.

Moderate growth in the US economy also should start to slowly push up revenues and fatten bottom lines. This growth will come partially because of increases in population. Consumer spending on necessities, such as health care, housing, food and basic services, rises relentlessly, even during recessions. In addition, heavy spending by the federal government will help the economy as Washington continues to support state governments and pay for infrastructure projects. Increased revenue from overseas sales also should help.

In a typical cycle, stocks begin rising before the economy hits bottom, as was the case in early March 2009. This occurs because investors anticipate better days ahead and bid up share prices before the proof materializes. As stocks rise, consumers and businesses gain more confidence and begin spending more. As revenues increase, companies order more business equipment and eventually begin hiring. Gradually, the recovery gains momentum.

The current anemic recovery will limit earnings growth but not so tightly as to end the bull market in stocks. Bull markets have lasted an average of nearly five years but have ranged from three to 10 years. The current bull market began on March 10, 2009, and I expect it to last up to five years. The cycle will prove relatively short because economic growth this time very much depends on government spending, which is trailing off as the fiscal stimulus ends and federal debt mounts higher.

BEST STOCK SECTORS

To take advantage of this bull market, focus on stocks in these sectors...

- **Financials.** As the market continues climbing, there will be more activity on Wall Street, with organizations acquiring other companies and issuing new shares to raise money. The picture for banks will improve as consumers and corporations resume borrowing, although risks surrounding consumer and commercial real estate loans will limit the earnings gains of regional banks, and there will be additional bank failures.

• **Technology.** To operate efficiently in a challenging environment, businesses must spend more heavily on hardware and software. When companies do hire, they must outfit employees with computers and printers. These days, more and more employers consider it necessary to supply a BlackBerry and other wireless gadgets as well.

• **Health.** In past years, many health-care stocks have lagged as investors awaited Congressional action on health-care reform. A bill finally passed in March 2010, and it may increase demand for health-care goods and services of all kinds. And health care will remain one of the fastest-growing sectors in the US and globally.

• **Energy.** I do expect oil to increase. As the global economy recovers, demand for oil will put upward pressure on prices. Suppliers will restrict supply, trying to offset the effects of a weak dollar.

• **Foreign stocks.** I think overseas markets will outperform Wall Street. For investors, this means it will be wise to emphasize big US exporters that benefit from an expanding global economy. The outlook is especially bright for stocks from emerging markets, particularly in Asian and Latin American countries. As millions of consumers in emerging markets enter the middle class, many are buying cars, phones and other consumer goods for the first time, fueling economic growth.

WHAT'S AHEAD FOR JOBS

Even though stocks will thrive, the overall economy will be sluggish. Employers will remain reluctant to hire at a time when rising health-care and retirement costs make it too expensive to add many more workers.

After the recession of 2001 hit bottom, it took two years before significant job growth appeared, so economists talked about a jobless recovery. The current one could turn out to be the mother of all jobless recoveries.

Layoffs gradually will decrease. But the increases will do little to whittle down high unemployment. However, the weak job markets will not be severe enough to derail the stock market.

Check Up on Your Financial Adviser

BrightScope has data on the backgrounds of nearly 450,000 financial professionals. Go to *www.brightscope.com*, and type in your adviser's name to gain access. Information on advisers has been public for some time through the SEC and the Financial Industry Regulatory Authority (FINRA) but often has been difficult to find or confusingly presented. BrightScope makes data available more easily and clearly.

The Wall Street Journal, www.wsj.com

What a Weak Dollar Means for You

Kenneth Rogoff, Thomas D. Cabot Professor of Public Policy at Harvard University, Cambridge, Massachusetts. Formerly, he served as the chief economist and a director of the International Monetary Fund. He also is coauthor, with Carmen Reinhart, of *This Time Is Different: Eight Centuries of Financial Folly* (Princeton University). Find him at *www.Economics.Harvard.edu/faculty*

As stocks, gold and even junk bonds have soared over the past few years and the economy began to recover, questions lingered about a pillar of the US financial system—the dollar.

How much does a weak dollar really matter to you as a consumer and an investor? And is there much that the US can—or should—do about it?

To shed light on what the weak dollar means for readers, we interviewed Harvard professor and former International Monetary Fund economist Kenneth Rogoff...

Does the weakness of the dollar affect the average American's life on a daily basis?

It does. And in many ways that go beyond the obvious, such as the sticker shock you get when planning a vacation to Paris or Rio. For instance, a weak dollar makes imported products much pricier to buy here. Many products are getting more expensive in the US, including Italian olive oils, French wines and Japanese cameras. The falling dollar also is fueling speculation among investors in commodities, including crude oil and wheat, which drives up prices of gasoline and bread.

Why has the dollar gotten so weak?

Foreign investors are worried that we can't keep our fiscal house in order, due to our ballooning federal budget deficit...fears of inflation which have risen because of excessive government spending...and the expectation of continued US trade deficits, which the US is paying for by borrowing from the rest of the world. Another force undermining the dollar is the measures that we have taken to stimulate the weak US economy by decreasing our short-term interest rates to near zero. Investors are borrowing dollars cheaply, then speculating by selling them to buy currencies of countries where they think that stocks and bonds promise better returns.

Are there any benefits of a weak dollar?

Yes. By making American products cheaper for most foreign buyers, the dollar is helping many US companies boost their overseas sales. The weakening dollar also gives our domestic businesses a competitive edge at home, making their products cheaper than rival imports and increasing tourism here as more foreigners can afford to visit and spend money in the US.

The Federal Reserve and the White House would never put it this way, but they welcome the weak dollar now because it helps stimulate the economy.

If the dollar continues to weaken, what's the worst-case scenario?

Foreign powers could decide that they are tired of financing our current deficit by investing in US government assets, in which case they would demand a reduced price for our bonds and a higher yield to invest in dollars. That could lead to a sharp plunge in the value of the dollar, perhaps a 25% drop against the world's other major currencies over a few months. Any panicky sell-off of dollars would make it even harder for us to pay down our national debt and would increase our risk for another long, deep recession.

Despite much saber rattling from China about that possibility, though, I think it is unlikely. China currently owns a trillion dollars' worth of US government bonds. The collapse of the dollar would be economically catastrophic for China as well. The underlying dynamics of the US economy and the diversity and depth of US financial markets will generate a demand for dollars for many decades. It's still the most used currency for international transactions and constitutes more than 60% of other countries' official foreign-exchange reserves. During the global meltdown in 2008, for instance, many people around the world jumped into US Treasury securities even though the US economy was among those being battered.

What do you think will happen to the dollar in the future?

It will continue its long, very gradual slide against other currencies, with periodic rallies during times of world crisis, for the rest of our lifetimes. The long-term worry for our children and grandchildren is that the dollar will lose its central role in world financial markets. But with sound fiscal and monetary policy, the US dollar might slow down its slide considerably.

Best Investments When The Dollar Is Weak

Elizabeth K. Miller, CFA, CFP, founder and president of Summit Place Financial Advisors, LLC, in Summit, New Jersey. She serves on the board of trustees for the New York Society of Security Analysts. Her Web site is *www.SummitPlaceFinancial.com*

Here are the investments that I'm making right now to take advantage of the weak dollar...

• **Large US manufacturers that export globally.** A weak dollar makes our goods more attractive to consumers overseas and also helps boost revenue for US companies when their sales overseas in foreign currency are translated to greater amounts of US dollars.

My favorites: Caterpillar (CAT, recent share price: $84.60*), McDonald's (MCD, $101.42) and PepsiCo (PEP, $78.59).

• **Gold and oil.** Commodities such as gold and oil that are priced in dollars generally rise in price when the dollar weakens because

*Prices as of April 5, 2013.

global investors obtain the commodity with stronger currencies that translate to more US dollars. My favorite way to invest in these is with iShares COMEX Gold Trust (IAU, recent share price: $15.35), an exchange-traded fund (ETF) that owns gold directly...and iShares S&P North American Natural Resources Sector Index Fund (IGE, $39.22), an ETF that invests in stocks of companies involved in oil and other natural resources that trade in dollars.

- **Emerging-market stocks.** Emerging economies are leading the world out of the recession with strong economic growth and strengthening currencies. These are very risky markets, appropriate only for the most aggressive investors.

My favorite way to invest in emerging markets: iShares MSCI Emerging Markets Index Fund (EEM, $41.61).

- **A currency ETF.** You can invest directly in a declining dollar using the DB US Dollar Bearish Fund (UDN, $26.28). And just in case the dollar turns upward, I hedge my bets with a small investment in PowerShares DB US Dollar Index Bullish Fund (UUP, $22.45), an ETF that replicates the performance of the US dollar against a basket of currencies, including the euro, Japanese yen, British pound, Canadian dollar, Swedish krona and Swiss franc.

---

4 Big Trends from a Top Money Manager

Richard Bernstein, CEO of Richard Bernstein Advisors LLC in New York City, *www.rba-llc.com*, and manager of the Eaton Vance Richard Bernstein Multi-Market Equity Strategy Fund (ERBAX). From 1988 to 2009, he was at Merrill Lynch & Co. in several positions, including chief investment strategist and was selected to be on *Institutional Investor's* All-America Research Team 18 times. He is author of *Style Investing: Unique Insight into Equity Management* and *Navigate the Noise: Investing in the New Age of Media and Hype* (both from Wiley).

For Richard Bernstein, choosing specific stocks is not what is most important for successful investing. Throughout his more than 25 years as a Wall Street strategist with Merrill Lynch and other firms, he has spent most of his time looking at the big picture, figuring out what size companies were going to do best, which countries would shine and what industries would outperform each year. This approach to investing wound up making huge profits for his institutional and individual investors and helped to keep them out of trouble when the market plunged.

Here, Bernstein tells how this approach can work for our us...

START WITH THE BIG PICTURE

Different segments of the stock market tend to excel at different times, depending on powerful trends in the US and global economies. For instance, if throughout the past decade you owned shares of a variety of large-cap growth stocks—those issued from big companies with promising growth potential—you struggled no matter how talented a stock picker you were, while those investors who were positioned in commodity investments, such as gold, earned double-digit annual returns.

The secret is determining what the emerging economic environment is like and identifying overlooked and underestimated areas of the stock market that are best-suited for that new environment. That's where 90% of my mutual fund's returns are likely to come from.

Letting the big picture tell me where to invest helped me sidestep the bursting bubble of tech stocks in 2000 and the collapse of housing and financial stocks in 2008.

The problem with stock pickers who ignore economic trends is that they wind up chasing yesterday's story, investing in companies that have done well in the recent past, often just as the old trend that benefited them is on the wane.

Right now, there are four "Big Picture" trends that I think can lead us to the best areas of the stock market...

1—US STOCKS WILL SHINE

The market crash of 2008 has cast a long shadow, rattling many Americans so much that they still have little confidence in US companies, even though the stock market has posted two winning years in a row. With US unemployment still high, investors feel inclined to wait for signs of a stronger economic recovery before jumping in.

But by the time the US has regained its full economic strength and the unemployment rate is back to its historical average of 5% to 6%, the lion's share of the stock market rebound will have already passed.

Even though the US economic recovery is a weak one, it is no weaker than the recovery of 1991 or 2001. Many investors don't realize this and remain enamored with BRIC (Brazil, Russia, India and China) countries, even though the emerging-markets stock trend has run its course, leaving little room for further gains over the next several years.

BRIC inflation rates are rising rapidly, and their stocks have become very expensive over the past dozen years. In a sign that the BRIC stocks are fading, the Standard & Poor's 500 stock index far outperformed BRIC stocks over the past three years, on average.

What I am doing now: About 60% of my fund's assets are in US stocks now and less than 1% in emerging markets.

2—GOLD LOSES ITS LUSTER

In 2012, gold had its 12th consecutive year of gains, driven by investor nervousness over the $16 trillion US national debt and fears of a depreciating dollar and hyperinflation. But gold prices have fallen in 2013 and the dollar actually bottomed out in 2008, and inflation expectations remain well under control.

What I am doing now: I'm avoiding gold and investing in asset classes and sectors that have stronger fundamental bases. Even if you think gold is in a long-term bull market, it is trading on pure emotion and momentum these days.

Momentum markets can fall very quickly, as evidenced by frequent sharp pullbacks in gold prices.

3—ENERGY IS POWERFUL

As we enter the middle of the US economic recovery, the historical trend is for energy stocks to take leadership positions. That's happening now as increased global demand for oil, natural gas and coal—along with a pickup in industrial production—will likely drive up the price of energy stocks.

What I am doing now: I'm currently putting 17% of my portfolio in US and foreign energy stocks, including oil and gas producers.

4—EUROPE RECOVERS

Heavy pessimism still hangs over European markets, which currently are the cheapest in the world. But the new trend here is that European corporations are doing better, even if the government balance sheets of many countries that use the euro still are a mess.

What I am doing now: I have about 25% of my portfolio in the developed world outside of the US, much of it in Europe.

The World's Smartest Investor on 7 Ways to Protect Yourself in a Tricky Market

Alice Schroeder, former Wall Street analyst and former managing director at Morgan Stanley, New York City. She is author of *The Snowball: Warren Buffett and the Business of Life* (Bantam).

Over the past few years, I spent thousands of hours with legendary Nebraskan investor Warren Buffett, chairman and CEO of the conglomerate Berkshire Hathaway. While I was writing his biography, he gave me unprecedented access to his work, opinions, struggles, triumphs, mistakes and wisdom. Buffett's success on Wall Street has made him the richest man in the world. But in many ways, he's closer to Main Street than Wall Street, a careful investor like you and me who still lives in the house he bought in 1958 for $31,500.

Many Americans watch Buffett very carefully when the stock market plunges and the economy teeters on the edge of disaster. In these kinds of grim markets, he has been at his most brilliant and visionary. No one has a better record of protecting assets, making shrewd purchases—and inspiring the confidence we need to survive financial turmoil.

Advice Buffett is giving...

- **Invest in what you understand.** In the years 1998 to 2000, Buffett famously avoided buying Internet stocks because he didn't see how the companies could make enough money to justify their valuations. In 2002, he started warning against complicated "derivatives," including the subprime mortgage deals that have devastated such giants as the investment firm Lehman Brothers and insurer AIG—deals that are at the core of the current financial crisis.

If you want an understandable business, Buffett points to Coca-Cola, of which he owns a little more than 8%. After 129 years, the Coca-Cola Company still sells more than a billion beverage servings a day. He also is partial to Gillette, a division of Procter & Gamble (P&G). He holds a 3% stake in P&G. Gillette dominates US razor blade sales and will never run out of customers as it expands worldwide.

• **Decide on your investing values and criteria**—then maintain them no matter how good or bad the market is. When investors get in trouble, it is usually because fear or greed has made them ignore commonsense rules.

Buffett has strategies that he follows in bull and bear markets. He looks for quality companies with ethical, highly committed management teams in essential but often unexciting industries. Most important, he waits for a time when he can acquire these companies at a large discount, often 40% below what he considers their "fair values."

In fact, Buffett's relentless focus on getting bargains extends to every aspect of his life. As an example, he related the following anecdote to me. He had a friend who went to stay in a house owned by Buffett's business associate Katharine Graham, the late chairman of *The Washington Post.* Afterward, the shocked friend called Buffett to tell him that Graham kept an authentic Picasso painting in the guest bathroom. Buffett said that he had used that bathroom many times over the years but never noticed the painting. What he did appreciate was that the bathroom was well-stocked with shampoos and toiletries. Buffett loves freebies.

• **Have cash on hand.** Many investors feel that they need to be totally invested and that holding cash in their portfolio is a drag on returns. Cash, however, has its advantages when markets plunge. For several years, Buffett sat on more than $44 billion of cash in Berkshire Hathaway accounts. This allowed him back in September of 2008 to brilliantly and carefully pick up shares of preferred stocks in top companies in specially-negotiated deals with hefty dividends and at nearly half off the price they had been selling for a few months earlier.

• **Don't try to catch a falling knife until you have a handle on the risk.** Many investors get into trouble because they see opportunity but don't think about risk fully enough. Asking yourself, "And then what?" over and over can help you see all the possible consequences of an investment.

Let me give you an example from Buffett's life. In spring 2008, Buffett was approached about investing in, or perhaps even buying, Bear Stearns. Until it was badly damaged by the subprime mortgage debacle, Bear Sterns was one of the world's largest global investment banks and brokerage companies. Buffett could have practically named his terms, but he passed on the deal. He worried that the company had at least 750,000 derivative investments. He said that even if he cloned Albert Einstein and worked 12-hour days with him, they could never properly analyze the risk of that many investments. Rebuffed by Buffett, Bear Stearns raised billions in capital from sovereign wealth funds in China and the Middle East. Those funds lost most of their money as Bear Stearns unraveled and was eventually taken over by JPMorgan Chase.

• **Don't bet the ranch.** As an investor, leave yourself a margin of safety in case something goes very wrong. Buffet says that in the past 50 years, he never permanently lost more than 2% of his own personal worth on any investment position. He has suffered heavy losses at times, but only on paper, which is why he warns against using leverage (borrowing money to increase your bet on a stock pick).

• **You can't be just a little bit smart.** Buffett feels that if you try to be just a little bit smart, you're liable to be really dumb, especially in a treacherous market such as this one. Few people have the time or inclination to study enough to beat the market. Diversification is probably your best route. Choose a low-cost index fund, and put your money into it slowly and steadily over time. That way you don't buy everything at the wrong price or the wrong time.

• **Never sell into a panic.** Buffett isn't very worried about the big picture for America. He believes that the stock market does some very crazy things in the short run, but in the long run, it behaves quite rationally. Buffett's underlying belief now is that the American economy will do very well and so will people who own a piece of it. He knows that the economy might get worse for a while and even endure a long, hard recession. There are a lot of factors gumming up its potential now. But 10 years from now, he says, we will look back and see that, as investors, we could have made some extraordinary buys.

What Would Warren Buffett Do Now? How To Pick Stocks That Are True Bargains

Prem C. Jain, PhD, CPA, professor of accounting and finance at McDonough School of Business at Georgetown University, Washington, DC. He previously taught at The Wharton School, University of Pennsylvania, and is author of *Buffett Beyond Value: Why Warren Buffett Looks to Growth and Management When Investing* (Wiley).

Most investors would love to duplicate Warren Buffett's returns—increases of more than 20% per year, on average, since 1965 for shares of the billionaire's company Berkshire Hathaway. Including reinvested dividends, that means each $1,000 invested in the stock in 1965 is worth nearly $4 million today.

I have spent the past two decades studying every investment move that Buffett has made. In the MBA classes that I teach at Georgetown University, my students dissect his trades and deconstruct why they work. I find that Buffett's simple, homespun investment advice actually is much more appropriate for small investors than for professionals because it requires the ability to take a long-term perspective and the courage to go against the herd—attributes that most money managers lack.

Buffett's four favorite investment strategies, and how to apply them to your own portfolio today...

Buffett rule #1: **Stay within your circle of competence.** Buffett invests in companies only when he can confidently project how their businesses will fare for at least the next decade or two. He made his fortune with high-quality companies that provide easy-to-understand products and/or services, such as insurance, transportation, paint and carpeting.

How to use this advice: Invest 10% to 20% of the stock portion of your portfolio in a few stocks in one particular industry or subsector that you enjoy following and that you can get to know inside out. Put the other 80% to 90% in a diversified index fund, such as one that tracks the Standard & Poor's 500 stock index. Over time, you can add more stocks and reduce your holdings in the index fund.

Buffett rule #2: **Keep at least 20% of your money in cash.** Buffett has a war chest of money ready to snap up stock opportunities, and he waits for an opportune moment to deploy it.

How to use this advice: It is challenging for small investors to retain that much cash when the interest rates on bank accounts and money-market funds are low. However, buying stocks at bargain prices can be so lucrative that it makes sense to always hold some cash so that you can take advantage of these opportunities.

Note that Buffett lets his cash percentage grow anytime he cannot find investments that will earn returns sufficiently above the risk-free interest rates offered by US Treasury bills. Risk-free rates are so low now that you should be putting much, but not all, of your cash to work.

Example: Long-term investors can buy a conservative exchange-traded fund (ETF), such as SPDR S&P Dividend (SDY), which tracks companies that have increased their dividends annually for at least the past 25 years. You'll earn a yield of around 3.6% even if the price of the ETF's shares remains flat for some time.

Buffett rule #3: **Be fearful when others are greedy...and greedy when others are fearful.** Some of Buffett's most brilliant results come from his ability to remain rational in the face of market excesses. He famously avoided tech stocks in 1999, just before the Nasdaq Composite Index lost 78% of its value. He started scooping up blue-chip stocks at the end of 2008, when the US was just coming out of the worst recession since 1929.

How to use this advice: I expect the coming decade to be as volatile as the last one, but you can rely on simple mechanical measurements, such as price-to-earnings ratios (P/Es), to help you make rational, unemotional decisions in the face of mass optimism or pessimism. The P/E is the price of the stock divided by its earnings per share, a number that provides a snapshot of how the market expects the company to perform in the future.

Watching P/Es won't ensure that you will spot the bottom of a bear market or the top of a bull market, but they can save you from making big mistakes that take years for your portfolio to recover from.

When picking a specific stock, first check whether you are getting it at a bargain price by making sure that its current P/E is below its 10-year average. Second, determine whether the company is a good candidate to grow for many years by confirming that its earnings have grown faster than those of its industry and the broad market over the past 10 years.

Example: Throughout the 10 years prior to Buffett's purchase of Coca-Cola shares, the company's earnings per share grew at an average rate of 11.1% a year, compared with an average of 7.1% for the S&P 500 over the same period.

Helpful: You can find historical P/Es and growth-rate information on company Internet sites.

Buffett rule #4: **Look for outstanding, share-holder-friendly management.** Buffett puts an enormous emphasis on meeting and evaluating CEOs before he buys stocks in their companies.

How to use this advice: Most of us can't sit down for lunch with CEOs, but we still can vet them carefully...

- **A CEO should have a history of earnings predictability,** increasing earnings for at least seven of the last 10 years.
- **Be suspicious if a CEO offers excuses or avoids responsibility for the company's weak performance or pretends that there are only positives.** Read the CEO's annual letters, and listen in on teleconferences held by executives to talk about quarterly earnings. (Check the company's Web site for dates and phone numbers.) You can read transcripts of many of these teleconferences at *www.morningstar.com/earnings.*
- **Examine a CEO's compensation package.** The CEO should own stock in the company worth several times his/her base salary... and his compensation should be based on company results so that he receives less in years in which the company underperforms.

Stocks Warren Buffett Would Buy

John Reese, founder and CEO of Validea Capital Management, LLC in West Hartford, Connecticut, which provides research for stock investors and model portfolios based on the methods of greats, *www.validea.com*

Small investors can use Warren Buffett's investment style to choose a wider variety of companies with greater growth potential than Buffett can invest in today. *If Buffett were a small investor now, he would likely consider picking these stocks...*

- **Coach, Inc. (COH),** the specialty retailer with more than 400 stores worldwide that has found a lucrative niche in the leather accessories market. Its strong brand name will reap benefits in overseas markets that are recovering faster than the US, especially China, where Coach plans to open 30 stores this year.

*Prices and rates as of October 8, 2012.

Recent share price: $56.05.*

P/E: 15.88.

•**Johnson & Johnson (JNJ)**, the world's largest health-care company. A robust pipeline of new drugs and innovative surgical tools should boost the stock price by at least 13% annually for the next decade.

Recent share price: $69.44.

P/E: 22.06.

•**Varian Medical Systems, Inc. (VAR)**, the leader in manufacturing systems for treating cancer through radiation treatment and other X-ray products. Its high-tech systems, sold to hospitals, cancer clinics and health agencies, have captured almost 70% of the US market and 50% of the global market, which has created a wide protective "moat" against any possible competition.

Recent share price: $60.65.

P/E: 17.04.

Get a Second Opinion on Your Broker's Advice

Get a second opinion on investments if you aren't comfortable with your broker's recommendations. Financial professionals often have differing viewpoints.

Best: Go to a financial planner who charges a flat fee or hourly rate—as opposed to a broker, who may be compensated on commission. Find a planner through *www.acaplanners.org* or *www.garrettplanningnetwork.com*. A one-time assessment of your finances is likely to cost a few hundred dollars.

George Mannes, senior writer at *Money,* Time-Life Bldg., Rockefeller Center, New York City 10020, on the Internet at *http://money.cnn.com*

How to Handle Small-Company Stocks

Brad Evans, CFA, the co-portfolio manager for two small-cap-blend (growth and value) funds—the Heartland Value (HRTVX) and Heartland Value Plus (HRVIX) funds, based in Milwaukee. Check out *www.heartlandfunds.com*

Janet M. Brown, president of DAL Investment Co., San Francisco, and managing editor of *NoLoad FundX* newsletter. For more information, go to *www.fundx.com*

Since the stock market began to rebound in March 2009, the stocks of small companies have gained more than those in the Standard & Poor's Index of 500 large-cap stocks.

Small-cap stocks—a small-cap stock is one whose total share value is roughly $2 billion or below—are historically the best-performing stocks during an economic recovery, beating large-cap stocks in the first year following the last nine recessions. And after the 1973–1974 recession, small-caps beat large-caps in each of the following 10 years.

That is partly because smaller companies can adjust to downswings in the economy and take advantage of upswings more quickly than larger companies. They also have much less debt in proportion to their size, which means that they're less likely than larger companies to be squeezed by heavy interest payments during slow times.

But because small companies have far fewer shares held by the public than bigger, established companies, the movement of their stock prices can be much more volatile. That makes investing in them especially tricky at a time when the economic outlook is so uncertain.

To help choose the small-cap stocks and mutual funds that have the brightest outlooks now, we spoke with two leading specialists in small-cap investing...

SMALL-CAP STOCKS
Brad Evans, CFA

There are signs that the economy may be stabilizing, albeit at relatively depressed levels.

We will likely see tepid economic growth for some time as a result of more government regulation, higher taxes and higher debt. The overall stock market is likely to move up and down within a fairly narrow trading range. *I look for two kinds of small companies that can thrive in this type of scenario...*

1. Companies that have little debt that can continue to increase earnings and cash flow in slow-growth environments. I especially like those that pay shareholders a dividend—dividends tend to be paid by the most stable small companies, and those payouts tend to lower the volatility of shareholder returns.

My favorites now...

• **Chemed Corporation (CHE)** owns and operates two wholly owned subsidiaries—VITAS Healthcare, the country's largest provider of end-of-life hospice services, and Roto-Rooter, the leading provider of plumbing and drain-cleaning services. Both businesses have proved solid even in a weak economic environment, but this odd coupling has scared off shareholders and left the stock undervalued. When the US economy strengthens, a spin-off of either of these subsidiaries would benefit investors.

Risk: If the economy stumbles, Roto-Rooter's revenues, which are affected by the state of the housing industry and household discretionary spending, could lag.

Recent share price: $78.47.*

Yield: 0.9%.

Market cap: $1.5 billion.

• **Maximus, Inc. (MMS)** helps states manage and administer federal funding and social welfare programs, including Medicare, Medicaid and enforcement of child support. Skyrocketing unemployment has expanded the social safety net and increased the need for states to outsource these programs to save money. Recently, Maximus won a large contract with the state of Texas.

Risk: Maximus could lose some business in the short term from one of its largest customers, the fiscally ailing state of California, but this should not affect the company's long-term potential.

*Prices and rates as of April 5, 2013.

Recent share price: $77.40.

Yield: 0.4%.

Market cap: $2.3 billion.

2. Companies in out-of-favor sectors that have excellent long-term prospects. When investors sour on a sector, they tend to dump all the companies in that sector, making for bargains.

My favorite now...

• **Analogic Corporation (ALOG)** designs and produces equipment utilized in imaging systems, including MRI and CT scanners, ultrasound machines and airport security monitors. Like many health-care equipment stocks, it has been hurt by the decrease in hospitals' capital spending, but the company has little debt and a dominant market position that will serve it well when the economy recovers.

Risk: Health-care reform could curtail hospital spending and lower Analogic's revenues, but I don't think we will see draconian cuts.

Recent share price: $78.89.

Yield: 0.5%.

Market cap: $966 million.

MUTUAL FUNDS
Janet M. Brown

You need exposure to small-caps to get the most out of a recovery, but given their extreme volatility in recent years, I'm moving cautiously and sticking with widely diversified funds that blend both growth and value small-cap stocks. I am holding only 10% of my overall stock-fund portfolio in small-cap funds until I see more signs of economic improvement that results in better fund performance. I expect to increase this allocation month by month as long as the relative performance of small-caps remains strong.

Important: There is a wide gap in performance among small-cap funds. Keep an eye on the relative performance of your funds versus their peers. You don't want to hang on to an underperformer. *Two favorites...*

• **Gabelli Small Cap Growth Fund (GABSX).** Veteran stock picker Mario Gabelli holds more than 500 stocks in this fund, but he has managed to beat his peers and the benchmark S&P 500 Index for more than 15 years. "Growth" in this low-volatility fund's name is relative. Gabelli buys undervalued companies that have some kind of growth catalyst and tends to hold them for three to five years.

Performance: 8.42%.* 800-422-3554, *www.gabelli.com.*

• **The Skyline Special Equities Portfolio (SKSEX)** is a relatively aggressive fund that is willing to take a chance on companies with less-than-stellar balance sheets. This strategy hurt the fund in 2007 and 2008 but has led it to outperform in past economic recoveries.

Performance: 10.60%. 800-548-4539, *www.managersamg.com.*

*Fund performance figures are five-year annualized returns through April 5, 2013, based on research from Morningstar, Inc.

Technology Stocks Are Strong: How You Can Profit

Michael Lippert, manager of the Baron Opportunity Fund (BIOPX), New York City, which specializes in technology stocks, *www.baronfunds.com.* The fund ranks in the top 10% of its category over the past five years.

Janet M. Brown, president of DAL Investment Co., San Francisco, and managing editor of *NoLoad FundX* newsletter. The publication is ranked by *The Hulbert Financial Digest* as the best investment-picking newsletter over the past 25 years on a risk-adjusted basis.

Technology has evolved into an attractive stock sector, and there are good reasons why it likely will continue to lead the market.

To understand why tech stocks are doing so well and how to profit from the trend, we spoke with two leading investment experts...

TECH STOCKS
Michael Lippert

The allure of technology stocks is easy to understand. Tech firms are sitting on loads of available cash and have little debt, unlike many companies in other beaten-down sectors. Tech companies provide better, clearer growth prospects than other types of companies. That is because businesses today need state-of-the-art technology to remain competitive. Tech firms also do not have to fear that the government will tightly regulate their operations—a threat hovering over drug companies, banks, automakers and even food companies...and they do not have potential disasters, such as mortgage-backed securities, lurking on their balance sheets.

In 2008, tech stocks got beaten down more than stocks in industries that are typically considered good defensive havens for investors during a recession, such as consumer staples.

The sector suffered even though many tech firms remained healthy and profitable. That's partly because investors shied away almost indiscriminately from numerous industries and partly because they feared that many kinds of businesses would cut back on technology investments during the recession, cutting into tech-firm revenues. These factors have created many bargains in the tech sector.

I do not know when the economy will get back to normal or even what that new normal will look like, but the technology sector is in the best position to lead the recovery.

Here are the tech companies that I believe have strong competitive advantages and whose stocks are likely to soar when the next bull market takes hold...

• **EnerNOC, Inc. (ENOC)** is an energy-management company that works as a middleman between utilities and their large corporate customers to help those customers both reduce their electricity use and pay less for the electricity that they do use. For example, it helps these customers set priorities for energy use in industrial plants. The stock price shot up in 2009, thanks to the Obama administration's push for energy efficiency, as well as billions of dollars in stimulus funding for upgrading the nation's electric grid. It took a hit at the end of 2011. But I believe EnerNOC still will see years of good growth that will push up its stock price.

Recent share price: $16.48.*

*Prices as of April 5, 2013.

• **SBA Communications Corp (SBAC)** manages and owns approximately 9,200 wireless communication towers in the US and Puerto Rico. There is tremendous pent-up demand for wireless communication that will benefit certain stocks. SBA isn't a sexy story, but it's a dependable, less volatile infrastructure stock that is especially attractive as voice and data traffic grow and telecommunication giants, such as AT&T, Sprint and Verizon, continue to expand their networks.

Recent share price: $72.94.

• **WebMD Health Corp (WBMD)** is the dominant company among all the health-information Web sites that allow users to obtain detailed information about a disease or condition, analyze symptoms and locate doctors. The firm also operates a site for physicians and other health professionals that allows them to stay abreast of the latest medical information. And it runs private Web portals, in association with employers and health insurance providers, with information and services that enable health-plan members to make better medical decisions. I believe that it is in the sweet spot of two powerful trends—a demographic trend because more people are looking for medical information online as the older population increases...as well as a business trend because busy doctors and hospital administrators no longer have the time to meet with salespeople face-to-face.

Recent share price: $23.00.

MUTUAL FUNDS
Janet M. Brown

Technology companies are doing better because they have been more resilient in this economic downturn, thanks to lessons they learned after tech stocks crashed in 2000. The companies that survived back then realized the importance of holding large amounts of cash and being able to cut capacity and liquidate inventory quickly when the economy and markets dive.

Some technology stocks are attracting investors now because they also have become solid sources of dividend income—and those payouts appear to be considerably more secure than dividends from traditionally reliable companies, such as banks.

Even so, investors who want to add a tech mutual fund now need to have a different mind-set than in the 1990s, when the tech bubble grew wildly and many technology companies appeared attractive even if they did not have profits or realistic business plans.

To design a shrewd strategy for adding technology funds to your portfolio, first look at the growth funds in which you already hold shares. Using a Web site such as Morningstar.com, you can check what percentage of each fund's holdings are in particular sectors. If the funds you hold already provide you with a heavy investment in technology stocks, you many not need to add a fund that is specifically focused on technology. Keep in mind that technology makes up about 19% of the Standard & Poor's 500 stock index.

Second, a specific tech fund should not be more than 5% of your overall portfolio. Sector-specific funds, by their nature, tend to be much more volatile than diversified funds and to move in and out of favor.

Here are the most highly rated tech funds that are best positioned to outperform the overall market now...

• **Janus Global Technology Fund (JAGTX),** which was one of the favorites during the late 1990s—scoring a triple-digit return in 1999. Then it collapsed in the bear market that followed. This fund has reinvented itself with a more conservative portfolio that concentrates on mature, dividend-paying tech organizations, such as IBM, Microsoft and Oracle. The fund identifies high-growth sectors of technology, finds leading companies in those sectors and tries to buy them at reasonable prices.

Performance: 7.38%.* 800-525-3713, *ww4.janus.com*

• **The Fidelity Select Technology Portfolio (FSPTX).** This is a more aggressive fund that favors the smaller tech companies with robust earnings. It benefits from Fidelity's deep research staff and one of the lowest expense ratios in its category—0.81% per year.

Performance: 8.39%. 800-544-6666, *www.fidelity.com*

*Mutual fund performance figures are based on five-year annualized returns as tracked by Morningstar, Inc., through April 5, 2013.

Stocks That Turn Top Trends into Big Money

Robert Male, senior vice president at Kornitzer Capital Management in Shawnee Mission, Kansas, which manages more than $5 billion in investments. He is comanager of the Buffalo Small Cap Fund (BUFSX). Go to *www.KornitzerCapitalManagement.com* for more.

If only you had known 10 years ago just how important the following words and phrases would be to investors—iPhone... Google...organic foods...emerging markets. Forecasting the trends that these words symbolize might have helped you to take advantage of the most rewarding investments of the last decade.

Most of the stocks held by the mutual fund that I co-manage with two other managers tapped into these lucrative trends and others, including the growth of e-commerce and increased spending on healthier lifestyles and leisure activities by baby boomers. Focusing on those trends helped narrow our universe of stock choices and deliver strong investment returns.

Here are trends we see ahead and how investors can take advantage...

ECHO BOOMER SPENDING

The spending habits of baby boomers have influenced US business for several decades. But now their offspring—a "demographic echo"—have become a substantial factor in the economy. About 80 million adults in their 20s and early 30s, members of the nation's second-largest generation, were raised on a model of conspicuous consumption and will hit the prime of their careers in this decade. By 2015, these echo boomers will account for $2.45 trillion in annual spending.

Stocks likely to benefit...

• **Align Technology, Inc. (ALGN)** is a global medical-device company that has revolutionized the orthodontics market with clear, removable, mouth guard–like appliances for straightening teeth, available through dentists. More than one million patients, mostly adults, have used the product, which is much more aesthetically pleasing than traditional metal braces.

Recent share price: $31.04.*

• **Urban Outfitters, Inc. (URBN)** is an edgy fashion retailer that sells brand-name apparel, accessories and house-and-garden furnishings in more than 300 stores in the US. Its chains, including Urban Outfitters, Anthropologie and Free People, have outperformed competitors in good times over the past decade and also proved practically recession-proof. The target audience—women in their 30s with ample disposable income—puts it right in the sweet spot of the echo boom. The company opened its first non-US Anthropologie store in London in 2009 and plans to expand aggressively overseas.

Recent share price: $39.97.

ENERGY EFFICIENCY

Energy and commodity prices will continue to be volatile and wildly unpredictable in the next decade as the world's voracious demand for oil clashes with environmental concerns and geopolitical maneuvering. That makes it impossible to forecast reliable growth in these sectors and difficult to profit as a buy-and-hold investor. No matter where energy prices head, however, there will be massive business and government interest in getting more efficiency out of the energy we use. Investments in productivity are expected to grow by 17% annually through 2020.

Stocks likely to benefit...

• **Covanta Holding Corp. (CVA)** is the leading provider of energy-from-waste services in the US, Europe and Asia. Its 44 facilities convert garbage and landfill gases into enough electricity to power a large American city. A potentially enormous joint venture with the government of China and interest by other governments in reducing greenhouse gases should create double-digit annual growth over the next decade.

Recent share price: $19.74.

• **Hexcel Corp. (HXL)** develops and manufactures lightweight composite materials that improve aircraft design and dramatically lower fuel costs for the defense and commercial aerospace industries. Hexcel has won major contracts to provide products for the new Airbus A380, the largest airline passenger plane in the world. Hexcel's ancillary business—wind-turbine blade manufacturing—is growing by more than 15% a year as governments around the world introduce greater incentives to create wind-generation farms.

Recent share price: $28.24.

RETRAINING AMERICA

The US unemployment rate will remain stubbornly high throughout most of this decade. As the country's economy grows increasingly service-based, millions of manufacturing workers will need to go back to school to be retrained. Many service jobs, such as working in health care or information technology, require post–high school education.

A stock likely to benefit...

• **Capella Education Company (CPLA)** is an accredited online adult-education company that offers bachelor's and master's degrees and doctoral programs for professions where demand is high, such as behavioral health and human services, technology and education. This fast-growing company has more than 39,000 students, mostly older working adults. It is in superb financial health with zero debt and $115 million in cash.

Recent share price: $29.10.

US COMPANIES OPERATING IN EMERGING MARKETS

Developing economies around the world will grow two to three times as fast as the US economy. That's great news for large US companies that can export their innovative, well-known franchises and expertise to millions of new middle-class consumers in foreign markets—and replicate the success that they've had here.

A stock likely to benefit...

• **Yum! Brands, Inc. (YUM)** is one of the largest quick-service restaurant operators in the world, with $13.6 billion in annual sales and more than 37,000 franchises, including KFC, Pizza Hut and Taco Bell, in more than 110 countries. While Yum! will be lucky to grow revenues 5% annually this decade in the US, growth of sales at its restaurant franchises is poised to jump 20% a year in China.

Recent share price: $66.97.

CAUTION: OTHER REQUIREMENTS

Just because a company taps into one or several powerful trends doesn't mean that it will thrive. *We insist on seeing the following characteristics in a stock before we invest...*

• **Little or no long-term debt and substantial free cash flow.** In an environment where credit may stay tight for a while, companies have to pay a very high rate to borrow money. A business that can finance its own growth has a huge advantage.

• **Leading market position and a sustainable competitive advantage.**

• **Sales and revenue growth higher than the company's five-year average...**and stock valuations, such as the price-to-earnings ratio (P/E), lower than the company's five-year average.

How a Small-Town Fund Manager Gets Big Returns in *Any* Market

Frank James, PhD, founder and chairman of James Investment Research, Alpha, Ohio. He oversees $3.5 billion in assets, including the James Balanced: Golden Rainbow Fund (GLRBX), which had 9% annualized returns over the past 10 years, putting it in the top 2% of its Morningstar category. *www.JamesFunds.com*

You might call Frank James *The King of Balance.* Over the past 20 years, the fund manager has shown an uncanny ability to get strong returns while avoiding big drops. His insights are especially valuable at a time when investors are trying to balance the potential for stock market gains with a heavy dose of caution.

We spoke with James, who is based far from Wall Street in rural Alpha, Ohio (population less than 500), to find out how you can benefit from his simple strategy...

THE SECRETS TO BALANCE

I got my start investing mutual fund assets for the trust department of a tiny thrift bank, so my style always has been to protect against big losses but figure out a way to get high, single-digit returns most years. I don't go in for fancy alternative investments or complex hedging strategies. Instead, I start with a balance of about 50% stocks and 50% bonds. Then, every few months, I adjust my allocations slightly up or down depending on more than 100 risk indicators and my forecast for the economy and stock market. In January 2008, I told clients that an extended recession was likely. As the 2008 market crash approached, I positioned my portfolio with approximately 25% stocks and 75% bonds, keeping my losses to just 5.5% that year, compared with a 37% loss for the Standard & Poor's 500 stock index.

I take as little risk as possible with the bond portion of my portfolio, holding mostly US Treasuries. I don't worry about yield because I use bonds mostly as shock absorbers against volatility.

That allows me to take an added element of risk with stocks. Unlike many balanced-fund managers, I normally tend to keep more than half of my equity allocation in micro-, small- and mid-cap companies that are growing as fast as their peers but are unloved or overlooked by Wall Street analysts, so they sell at much steeper discounts. It's like buying an insurance policy. When the market turns downward, these smaller-cap, undervalued stocks fall less than stocks that have had bigger run-ups.

A CAUTIOUS OUTLOOK NOW

I have grown quite cautious about the stock market because of continuing troubles in Europe. It's not so much the possibility of countries such as Greece or even Spain and Italy defaulting on their debt but something less dramatic and far more plausible—Europe falling into a long, severe recession that could upset our own fragile recovery. A European recession will exacerbate China's slowdown in economic growth, drag down global growth and hurt our markets, especially stocks of large multi-national companies that depend on global exports for the bulk of their revenues.

Moves to make now...

- **Raise bond allocations.** Slightly over 40% of my portfolio now is in bonds. About half of that is in US Treasuries. Despite the amazing performance of Treasuries last year, I think that they will continue to appreciate as long as the European crisis persists and the world treats Treasuries as a refuge from investment uncertainty. However, I am using new cash and capital that I get from selling stocks to buy government agency bonds (Ginnie Maes)... very high-quality corporate bonds...and even municipal bonds. Like Treasuries, munis appreciate when the rest of the world looks for safety, and they offer better valuations than Treasuries after last year's run-up.

- **Reduce bond maturities.** The prices of longer-term bonds are severely hurt by rising interest rates, so I am gradually shortening maturities of the bonds that I buy to lower my average to five to six years.

- **Reduce stock allocations.** I'm holding close to 60% of my portfolio in stocks and avoiding companies that derive significant revenue from selling overseas because I think slower global growth and a strong dollar will hurt their export businesses. In this environment, companies will have a hard time passing along cost increases, which will hurt their profit margins.

- **Include large-cap dividend stocks—but make sure they are bargains.** Although I continue to hold small- and mid-cap stocks, it is time also to invest in large-caps with strong balance sheets and cash flow and hefty annual dividends. They offer the best overall value now. They also will hold up better than the overall market if the US economy takes a downturn. For most investors, I would recommend placing about half the assets in a stock portfolio in large-caps and about half in mid- and small-caps. *My favorite large-cap now...*

  - **BCE (BCE)** is the largest communications company in Canada. The stock is cheap because investors dismiss BCE as a boring utility and worry that its landline phone business of roughly nine million customers will continue to suffer attrition year after year. But the company, whose dividend recently yielded 4.9% and has grown steadily, has considerable strengths, including the largest satellite-TV business in Canada...the country's number-one television network...and thriving cell-phone and high-speed Internet services. *Recent share price*: $45.42.

• **Focus on importers and companies with high domestic sales.** I look for firms closely tied to positive trends in the US economy rather than dependence on the global economy...retailers that can import cheap inventory because of the strong dollar...and discount retailers that appeal to price-conscious consumers still worried about the recovery. *My favorites now...*

• **Big Lots (BIG).** The nation's largest close-out retailer operates more than 1,450 stores in 48 states. The fast-growing company purchases brand-name items in bulk, then resells them at steeply discounted prices. *Recent share price*: $35.38.

• **Dillards (DDS).** Wall Street has written off many brick-and-mortar retailers due to online competition. But Dillards, a well-managed company with more than 300 department stores that sells moderately priced goods in small shopping centers, is having a resurgence. *Recent share price*: $80.43.

• **Hi-Tech Pharmacal Co. (HITK)** manufactures more than 100 generic and branded medicines sold over-the-counter and through prescriptions. With the bulk of its sales in the US, it has found a lucrative niche in liquid and spray products such as its generic version of Flonase. *Recent share price*: $34.54.

• **Sturm, Ruger & Co (RGR).** One of the largest makers of firearms, this company is benefiting from strong sales due to political factors. Some gun owners are buying additional weapons now out of fear that restrictions on firearms could be enacted by Congress or state legislatures. *Recent share price*: $34.54.

Gold in Your Portfolio

Allan S. Roth, CPA, CFP, president of Wealth Logic, LLC, a financial advisory firm in Colorado Springs that serves clients with investments ranging from $10,000 to $2 million. He is author of *How a Second Grader Beats Wall Street: Golden Rules Any Investor Can Learn* (Wiley). His Web site is *www.daretobedull.com*

Are you ever tempted to invest in gold but frightened by its intense ups and downs? Some gold investing experts will tell you that gold is the one safe place left to invest your money...and that it will hit $5,000 per ounce within a few years. Skeptics claim gold is much too volatile. For instance, it soared by nearly 50% to $1,000 an ounce between October 2008 and February 2009 and then pulled back to $907 by early July 2009. In April 2013, it was around $1,400 an ounce.

There are good reasons to put a portion of your assets in gold—if you do it the right way.

GOLD PROVIDES DIVERSIFICATION

Stocks, bonds and real estate are all very dangerous for investors now. Historically, gold has done well when the economy gets shaky and stocks and bonds seem too risky.

Example: In an economically troubled period from 1973 to 1980, the price of gold rose by 2,300%, from $35 to $850 per ounce.

That doesn't mean you should buy gold because you think you can make a killing. Gold prices are notoriously hard to predict. Investors cannot analyze gold like they can a company, which has quarterly earnings.

The truth is that, as an investment, gold's average annualized returns have only barely kept up with inflation. For example, back in 1979, I used my college graduation money to invest in 10 ounces of gold coins at $664 per ounce. I was sure gold prices would quickly soar to $2,000 per ounce because of high inflation. But after three decades, the value of my gold coins gained less than 50%.

Where gold does shine, however, is as a terrific way to diversify your portfolio. Its price has so little correlation with stock and bond returns that adding just a little gold can lower your overall volatility and protect you in bad times. Gold held its value in the credit crisis of 2008, rising 4% when almost every other major asset class plunged in value. In the past decade, gold has increased by about 13% annually, on average, compared with a 3% annualized drop for the Standard & Poor's 500 stock index.

INVEST FOR THE LONG-TERM

Gold is only for those who can stay invested for 10 years or more and can accept wild, short-term swings in gold prices. *Guidelines...*

• **Devote a maximum of 3% of your overall portfolio to gold.**

• **Invest fixed amounts at regular intervals,** maybe once a month over the next year. That way you are likely to buy during periods when gold pulls back, which happens often.

• **Rebalance gold holdings at least once a year.** If gold rises further, you will want to take some profits at the end of the year and trim back to your original 3% target.

FOR CONSERVATIVE INVESTORS

Avoid buying into gold mines or gold futures contracts. Invest directly in the mineral, which gives you the most control.

• **Gold bullion coins.** This is pure gold metal cast as coins. Buy only from a dealer found through the Professional Coin Grading Service (800-447-8848, *www.pcgs.com*) or at the Numismatic Guaranty Corporation (800-642-2646, *www.ngccoin.com*), whose members have to abide by stringent standards and procedures. Both organizations offer a money-back guarantee for grading accuracy and authenticity.

Select one-ounce coins, either South African Krugerrands, Canadian Maple Leafs or American Eagles. These are the easiest to sell if you want or need to. Prices are based on the market price of gold (which you can find at *www.kitco.com*) plus a 3%-to-5% dealer charge.

Drawbacks: The IRS classifies gold coins as a "collectible," which means that capital gains on the sale of this type of gold are taxed at a flat 28% rate—not at the usual rate for most other capital gains, which is a maximum of 23.8%. Also, you may have to pay to store your coins in a bank safe-deposit box. Another option is to store your coins in a home safe. Check to see what your homeowner's insurance policy will cover, or consider becoming a member of the American Numismatic Association for coverage.

• **SPDR Gold Shares (GLD).** This gold exchange-traded fund (ETF) may be a better option if you don't want the drawbacks of actual physical possession of your gold. The fund now is the second-largest ETF on the market. The gold backing the shares is kept in vaults in Europe and audited regularly. Keep in mind that the 0.4% annual expense ratio will take a bite out of your account every year.

Recent share price: $152.81*

FOR MORE AGGRESSIVE INVESTORS

If you are willing to take more risk, consider investing in stocks of precious-metal firms and gold-mining companies. Whenever the price of gold rises, these stocks tend to gain even more because the cost of producing gold doesn't necessarily increase, which means much higher profits for the company. This is especially true if a company finds new reserves or develops more cost-effective mining technology.

• **To dampen volatility, use a mutual fund focused largely on gold.** Gold-related stocks can plunge a lot faster than gold itself because a company's profitability can disappear quickly—and the stocks carry the additional risks that come with an investment in any company.

I like Vanguard Precious Metals and Mining Fund (VGPMX) because of its low volatility and low fees. The fund invests in stocks of companies that mine for gold and other precious metals (877-662-7447, *www.vanguard.com*).

10-year annualized performance: 11.46%.

• **If you prefer a passively managed fund that tracks an index** and whose expenses likely are lower than a fund whose managers choose the investments, consider Market Vectors Gold Miners (GDX), an ETF that owns shares in the world's leading gold-mining companies.

Recent share price: $35.06.

*Prices and rates as of April 5, 2013.

Retire Richer with Your HSA

Roy Ramthun, president of HSA Consulting Services, LLC, a consulting practice specializing in consumer-driven health-care issues. *www.HSAConsultingServices.com*

More than 13.5 million people now use Health Savings Accounts (HSAs) to set aside pretax dollars for their medical expenses. But because you don't have to use the money in an HSA by any particular deadline, HSAs also can serve as powerful savings tools to supplement your retirement accounts or to provide some emergency cash.

One of the greatest advantages is that, unlike the more popular Flexible Spending Account (FSA) that requires employees to predict their medical spending for the year in advance and contribute a defined amount, the IRS allows you to fund your HSA with pretax dollars after a medical expense* has occurred, then immediately reimburse yourself. In fact, you have until April 15, 2014, to fund your HSA for 2013 expenses.

Smart strategies for using HSAs...

• **Pay insurance premiums.** You might know that if you change jobs or lose your job, you still keep your HSA and have access to all the money you have contributed. That means that even if you aren't eligible to make contributions because you are no longer enrolled in a high-deductible health insurance plan, the money still can be withdrawn tax-free and penalty-free to cover medical expenses.

But you might not know that if you get fired, laid off or quit your job, the IRS allows you to use HSA money to pay premiums for temporary COBRA health insurance coverage.

*HSA money can be used tax-free for only "qualified" medical expenses, which include most ordinary procedures, treatments and prescribed medications but not over-the-counter medications, vitamins or cosmetic surgery. HSA contributions are deductible for federal income tax and for state income tax in all states except Alabama, California and New Jersey. If you withdraw HSA funds for unqualified medical expenses before age 65, you are subject to a 20% penalty plus income tax on the amount withdrawn.

Moreover, if you are receiving federal or state unemployment benefits, you can tap your HSA to pay the premiums for any health-insurance coverage.

Once you turn 65, HSA flexibility increases even further. At that point, the IRS allows you to withdraw your HSA money tax-free and penalty-free to cover your premiums for Medicare and long-term-care insurance.

• **Supplement your nest egg.** You might know that the money in your HSA account can be invested and can grow tax-deferred just like your IRA assets in investments such as certificates of deposit, stocks, bonds and mutual funds, depending on which kinds of investments your HSA provider offers.

But you may not know that once you turn 65, HSA money can be used—without paying a penalty—for any reason, medical or otherwise, although if you use it for purposes other than qualified medical costs or insurance premiums, you have to pay income tax on the withdrawn amount.

That makes the HSA so attractive that I often recommend that while someone is employed, he/she should fund it to the maximum allowable amount year after year—even before fully funding IRAs and even if he doesn't expect to spend nearly that amount in the same year he makes the contribution.

I also recommend that if someone can afford to, he should consider paying for all or a portion of medical expenses with non-HSA money in years when he is contributing to his HSA. That way, HSA investments can grow tax-free, as they would in an IRA, for many years.

• **Leave your HSA to your spouse.** When you die, your HSA can be transferred to your spouse tax-free, and it becomes his/her HSA. The surviving spouse can continue to make contributions if otherwise eligible to do so and can use the HSA money to pay for qualified medical expenses or for other purposes outlined above. However, if your HSA is left to a beneficiary other than your spouse, it converts to a regular bank account upon transfer and loses any tax advantages.

5

Spend Like a Miser, Live Like a King

Money-Saving Rules for The New Economy

This new economy requires some new approaches for managing our money and our lives. *Here are my favorite money-saving strategies for right now...*

1. Conduct a financial fire drill. Don't wait to be blindsided by an unpleasant financial event. Spend a Sunday afternoon conducting a financial fire drill. Brainstorm various worst-case scenarios—job loss, continued declines in the stock market, loss of health-care insurance—and how you would handle each of them. For scenarios that seem the most thorny, you can decide to research solutions either online, at the library or by talking with a financial professional.

Be sure to involve your family in your discussions. I have always found that when you get things out in the open, they generally are not as scary as they seemed before—and you tend to sleep a lot better because of it.

2. Barter. Bartering is the ancient practice of swapping goods and services rather than paying for them. Check out the swapping going on at Web sites, such as Craigslist.org, or join one of the increasing number of online bartering clubs, such as BarterBart.com. Recent online swaps include a used laptop computer traded for a cache of home-brewing supplies...a Web site designer trading her services for a week's stay at a vacation cottage on the Gulf Coast...and two radial tires for a pair of concert tickets.

Many online bartering clubs will allow you to trade goods and services for club "credits." Then you can trade the credits—instead of specific goods or services—with club members offering something you want.

Jeff Yeager, dubbed "The Ultimate Cheapskate" by NBC's *Today* show, honed his cheapskating skills during 25 years working with underfunded nonprofit agencies. He lives in Accokeek, Maryland, and is author of *The Ultimate Cheapskate's Road Map to True Riches* and *The Cheapskate Next Door* (both from Broadway). His Web site is *www.ultimatecheapskate.com*

Caution: Consult IRS Publication 525, *Taxable and Nontaxable Income,* to determine the tax consequences of your bartering. (Go to *www.irs.gov* to download the publication for free or call 800-TAX-FORM.)

3. Always put off until tomorrow what you could buy today. Here is where procrastination pays off. Studies have shown that most of us eventually regret more than half of all the discretionary purchases we make. Wait at least one week between the time you are first tempted to buy an item and when you go back to buy it. Odds are good that you'll never go back to buy it.

Also, make a list of things that you bought recently that you could have done without. Take a look at the list before you go shopping—it might curb your impulse buying.

4. Grow your own. It is time to bring back victory gardens, those small vegetable gardens that helped families through the two World Wars. Even a 4' x 4' raised-bed garden in the backyard can produce lots of fresh produce in a season. A few dollars' worth of seeds easily can quadruple your investment. If you don't have space for a garden, consider growing a pot or two of herbs on the kitchen windowsill and patio-variety tomatoes and cucumbers in containers out on the deck.

More and more cities and towns have community gardens, where you get your own little plot for the season for a nominal fee. To find a garden near you—or to learn how to start one—go to *www.communitygarden.org.*

Community Supported Agriculture (or CSA) programs allow you to buy shares of the harvest from local farms. CSA shares sometimes can be expensive—and veggie quantities overwhelming—so research the options and consider splitting one share with your neighbors. Many CSA farms also offer volunteer opportunities to help with the gardening. For farms near you, go to *www.localharvest.org.*

5. Ask and you might receive. In difficult times such as these, customers gain bargaining muscle when it comes to negotiating better prices on goods and services. A study by the Consumer Reports National Research Center found that more than 90% of those who got up the nerve to ask for a discount on purchases (such as electronics, appliances, furniture and even medical expenses) reported receiving a price concession at least once—and the average saving was $50 or more.

The key is always to be friendly and polite when asking for a better price or other concession. Even if you're unhappy with the service that you have received or the condition of the merchandise, ask nicely.

Also, go into the store knowing the price that you are willing to pay. Don't be afraid to say "No, thanks" and look elsewhere if need be.

---

5 Big Ways to Save $20,000 a Year

Jeff Yeager, dubbed "The Ultimate Cheapskate" by NBC's *Today* show, honed his cheapskating skills during 25 years working with underfunded nonprofit agencies. He lives in Accokeek, Maryland, and is author of *The Ultimate Cheapskate's Road Map to True Riches* and *The Cheapskate Next Door* (both from Broadway). His Web site is *www.ultimatecheapskate.com*

Nearly all of the talk these days about economizing focuses on how to get what we want but pay less for it. It's all about how to get more for less.

For those of us who are longtime advocates of the "simple living" movement, it seems as if most Americans are missing what could be the golden opportunity of these hard times—coming to appreciate that less can often be more. In other words, we shouldn't be—worrying so much about "How can we afford it?" Instead, we should be asking ourselves, "Do we really need it?"

Here are five lifestyle changes to consider. They may seem fairly radical to you when you first think about them—but if you adopt even one or two, you'll not only save some serious money, you just might be happier in the end.

1. Cancel your cell phone.

Yearly savings: $1,000 per phone.

The idea is surprising, I know, but just consider it for a moment. Only 20 or so years ago, cell phones were virtually nonexistent, and the world seemed to work okay. Now cell phones are considered a necessity, even though surveys show that we dislike our cell phones more than any other device that we own (including the alarm clock). So if that's truly how we feel, how can giving them up be a bad thing? The average cell-phone plan costs about $80 a month, and a study recently released by Utility Consumers' Action Network found that the actual average cost of using a cell phone is more than $3 a minute if you don't use up most of your minutes and about $1 per minute even if you do use all of your minutes. As a fairly successful author and national media personality, I am the poster child for this cause—I have never owned a cell phone, and I get by just fine.

If you can't imagine not having a cell phone, consider a prepaid phone plan. Watch for sales at such stores as Target, Walmart and Radio Shack.

2. Get rid of your second or third car.

Yearly savings: $9,000.

The average American household now owns two or three vehicles. That compares to about one car per household in 1960. AAA estimates that it costs $8,588 per year to own and operate a medium-sized sedan that is driven 15,000 miles annually. The national average cost per mile is 58.5 cents by the time you factor in depreciation, insurance, repairs, gas, taxes, etc. If your family owns more than one car, what's the worst thing that could happen if you give up one? You could easily save thousands of dollars a year by sharing a single car, coordinating trips, taking public transportation and so on. And Mother Earth will thank you.

3. Prepare more meals at home.

Yearly savings: $2,000.

According to the Bureau of Labor Statistics, the average US family spends $2,668 on eating out each year. I would estimate that you could prepare the same meals at home for about 80% less, or an annual savings of roughly $2,134. The other upside is that old-fashioned family time around the dinner table may make a comeback. An article in *Archives of Pediatrics & Adolescent Medicine* reported that frequent family meals are associated with a lower risk for smoking, drinking and using marijuana among adolescents, as well as a lower incidence of depressive symptoms and suicidal thoughts. And the kids were more likely to have better grades.

4. Wear out your clothing.

Yearly savings: $1,800 per family.

A small fraction of the clothing we throw away in the US is truly "worn out," meaning that it's threadbare, torn or badly stained. Many of us donate unwanted clothing to charity, but even charities have more donations than they can handle, and much of the clothing eventually ends up being thrown away. The problem is that we rarely wear out our clothing—or much of anything else—these days. According to some government reports, the average family in America spends roughly $1,800 on shoes and clothing per year. Clearly most of us have more than enough in our closets to go for six months to a year, or even longer, without needing to buy anything new.

5. Give up college room and board.

Yearly savings: $9,000 per student.

The average cost of student room and board at colleges and universities is about $9,000 per year. A generational shift has occurred here in the US over the past few decades when it comes to kids living with their parents while they attend college. Back in my college days (the 1970s), lots of us—myself included—lived with our parents and attended a local university or community college. Today that arrangement is fairly rare—it's just not "cool" to live with your folks. Of course, in my day, student loans were uncommon, in part because we didn't need to borrow money to pay for room and board. The irony is that these days, many kids graduate with so much debt—tens of thousands of dollars in student loans—that they have no choice but to move back home with their parents after college. Now, back in my day, living with your parents *after* you graduated really was uncool.

How Money Experts Bill and Mary Staton Trimmed Their Budget By $10,000

Bill Staton, CFA, a money coach and economic historian based in Charlotte, North Carolina, and Mary Staton, CEO of Staton Financial Advisors LLC, also in Charlotte. They are authors of several books on financial topics. Bill Staton's latest book is *Double Your Money in America's Finest Companies* (Wiley). Go to *www.statonfinancial.com* for more.

Financial advisers have plenty of suggestions for trimming the family budget—but what savings strategies do these financial pros follow in their own lives?

We asked Bill and Mary Staton, the married pair of professional money advisers who co-wrote the book *Worry-Free Family Finances*, what they have done to trim their budget in these challenging times...

• **We don't go shopping without a list.** We used to wind up with a full cart every time we went to the grocery store for just a few items. Now we don't set foot in a store of any kind without a shopping list, and we don't buy anything that isn't on that list. This has kept us from making impulsive, unnecessary purchases.

Estimated savings: About $1,000 per year.

• **We stopped using most credit cards.** Credit cards are a convenient way to shop—too convenient. They made it easy for us to buy things that we really didn't need and really couldn't afford. We started using debit cards instead so that we can't spend more than we have in our bank account, and we never get stuck paying huge credit card interest charges.

Exception: We do use an American Express card to purchase electronics and appliances, because the card provides extended warranty protection. We also use the card to rent vehicles, because it provides rental-car insurance.

Estimated savings: By using debit cards primarily, we calculate that the reduced spending and elimination of interest charges save us between $3,000 and $5,000 per year.

• **We "shop" in our closets.** There was a fancy fund-raiser for the arts in October. Rather than buy a new gown as she might have done in the past, Mary "shopped" for something to wear among the gowns and shoes already in her closet. New clothes are almost never a necessity, and shopping can be a very expensive form of entertainment.

Estimated savings: At least $1,000 every year.

• **We use our car's cruise control.** When we drive on the highway, we set the cruise control. We select a speed close to the speed limit that balances our need to get where we're going in a timely fashion and our desire to maximize our mileage.

Exception: Cruise control wastes fuel on hilly terrain because it keeps gunning the engine to get up the hills.

Our vehicles display miles per gallon (mpg) right on the dash, so it's easy for us to choose a fuel-efficient speed. If your vehicle does not display your mpg, experiment with different highway speeds until you find the speed that best stretches your fuel. Fuel economy generally drops by at least 1% for every one mile per hour (mph) over 55 mph.

Estimated savings: Several cents per mile, which adds up to $200 or more per year.

• **We favor retailers with liberal return policies.** Getting stuck with an ineffective or inappropriate product because a retailer won't take it back is a major money waster. Now we try to shop only at stores that are good about taking things back.

Estimated savings: Potentially hundreds of dollars a year, depending on what we need to return.

Important: Many stores have toughened up their return policies, so ask before you take anything home that you think you might want to return.

• **We combine our errands.** We work from home, so we used to jump in the car whenever we had an errand to do. We would drive to the bank, come home, then go out again a few hours later to the dry cleaner. Those short trips ate up our free time and increased our gasoline bills.

Now we coordinate trips, thinking through everything we need to do and everywhere we need to go in a particular direction before we get in the car. We have greatly reduced the total number of trips we take to town. Each round-trip we avoid saves us about 14 miles of driving and at least a half-hour of time. If we eliminate an average of one trip to town per day, that's 180 gallons of gas saved per year.

Estimated savings: About $400 per year in gas...as well as the wear-and-tear those short trips took on our vehicles.

• **We learned to make fancy coffee drinks.** Bill used to go to a local coffee shop almost every day to treat himself to one or two large lattes (espresso with steamed milk), which cost about $4 each. Rather than give up this indulgence to save money, he bought a latte maker for $399 and learned to make his own lattes.

The machine paid for itself in less than a year and now saves Bill around $1.50 per latte, plus time, gas and wear on his car.

Estimated savings: At least $500 per year.

• **We cut down on eating out.** We used to eat out somewhat regularly, but we've both learned to cook a range of meals. Bill really enjoys cooking. Now we try to go out only on special occasions.

Estimated savings: About $2,000 per year on restaurants.

• **We gave up trying to cool the hottest room in our house.** In the summer, our son's bedroom was always much hotter than the rest of our home. We never realized just how much it was costing us to keep that room cool until our son left for college and our electricity bill fell by 20%.

In retrospect, we could have saved all that money long ago by having our son sleep in a cooler room on the hottest summer nights.

Estimated savings: $400 to $500 per year.

• **We rely less on automatic bill payment.** Instead of having monthly payments automatically deducted from our checking account, we sit down and pay our bills together, writing out the checks by hand. This is more time-consuming but well worth it because it forces us to think about the money we're spending. Did we need to make this purchase? Was there a way we could have paid less?

Example: We used to pay our health insurance automatically—we didn't want to miss a bill and lose our coverage. As a result, we failed to pay close attention as the cost of our policy increased over the years. When we finally got around to shopping for new coverage, we discovered that we could have paid thousands less per year all along. We would have shopped around years ago if we'd been paying the bill by hand each month.

Estimated savings: Potentially in the thousands each year.

• **We are taking fewer overseas trips.** We are going to our one-bedroom cabin in the mountains more often. It is a three-hour drive each way. Considering the hassles of air travel, local vacations can be more relaxing than distant ones anyway.

Estimated savings: Thousands of dollars per vacation.

How to Cash In Big With Coupons

Susan Samtur, editor of *Refundle Bundle*, a newsletter about coupon and rebate opportunities, *www.refundlebundle.com*. She also operates the online grocery coupon Web site SelectCouponProgram.com and is author of *Cashing In at the Checkout* (Warner).

Coupon use has recently surged as consumers try to trim their budgets during this recession.

Coupons easily can trim 10% to 20% from your grocery bill—and it is possible to save much more if you're willing to put in a little time and effort. I recently used coupons and rebates to purchase $211 in groceries for a total of 42 cents.

Supermarkets are no longer the only places to save. Pharmacies, hardware stores, home stores and online retailers are offering big savings, too. *Some of the best offers...*

ONLINE COUPONS

The most attractive of coupons often are available only on the Internet, not in Sunday newspaper circulars. Some Web sites—including Coupons.com...RetailMeNot.com...and my Web site, SelectCouponProgram.com—offer you a wide range of coupons.*

Also visit the Web sites of the companies that make the food products, over-the-counter pharmaceuticals, health and beauty products, household products and other consumer products that you buy. Many of these companies are likely to provide printable coupons on their Web sites, or they will mail or e-mail coupons to consumers who sign up for their e-letters.

Most consumer product companies list their Web addresses on the packaging. If not, try using the company's name followed by ".com," or search for the company's name on Google.com.

Once on a company's Web site, look for a link along the lines of "sign up," "newsletter," "promotions," "special offers" or "coupons." If a company's Web site is very complex, it might be easier to search for the product name on Google rather than the company name.

Example: At Bayer.com, it is not easy to locate coupons...but at Aleve.com—the Web site for Bayer's painkiller—it is easy to find a coupon for $2 off any Aleve product.

You likely will have to register on the company's Web site and provide an e-mail address to access the coupons. Some Web sites let you print coupons as soon as you register...while others e-mail the coupons to you periodically. You might want to create one e-mail account specifically for this purpose.

You may need to download a coupon-printing program. Download these programs only from the Internet sites of well-known companies. Downloading programs from disreputable Internet sites can upload viruses onto your computer.

Among the companies that frequently feature appealing Internet coupons...

*The companies and Web sites listed in this article offer attractive coupons and rebates continually, but the specific offers mentioned are subject to change.

- **Betty Crocker/General Mills** (*www.bettycrocker.com*, click on "Coupons" at the top of the screen). The brands include Betty Crocker ...Cheerios...Chex...Pillsbury...Progresso...Yoplait...and Green Giant.

  Examples: $1.10 off two boxes of Cheerios...60 cents off one box of Nature Valley Granola Bars.

- **Colgate-Palmolive** (*www.colgate.com*, click on "Special Offers"). Brands include Colgate... Murphy Oil Soap...Palmolive...Speed Stick... and Softsoap.

  Examples: $1 off Colgate Sensitive toothpaste...50 cents off Murphy Oil Soap.

- **Del Monte** (go to *http://solutions.delmonte.com* and click on "Promotions").

- **Gorton's seafood** (go to *www.gortons.com*, click "Coupons & Promotions" at the top of the screen).

- **Iams pet foods** (at *www.iams.com*, click "Join").

  Example: $5 off Iams pet foods.

- **Procter & Gamble** (at *www.pgesaver.com*, register for the P&G Everyday Solutions free monthly newsletter). The brands can include Charmin...Olay...Crest...Metamucil...Tide... Downy...and Scope.

PHARMACY REBATE PROGRAMS

The major pharmacy chains frequently offer products at below cost to draw shoppers into their stores. The savings usually are provided through rebates, not coupons, however. Shoppers must sign up for the chain's rebate program, then log onto its Web site to enter code numbers from their receipts and request rebate checks to obtain their savings. (If you do not have Internet access, you usually can get rebate booklets in the stores, then mail in your receipts and rebate requests.)

These rebate programs are worth the trouble if you take advantage of numerous rebates each month. Pharmacy chain Web sites sometimes offer printable coupons as well.

- **CVS** (*www.cvs.com*). Sign up for the CVS "ExtraCare" rewards card, and get 2% back on most purchases and an extra $1 back for every two prescriptions filled. CVS also offers printable online coupons on its Web site.

Examples: $2 off any Centrum product… $1 off Listerine.

•***Rite Aid*** (at *www.riteaid.com,* click on "Single Check Rebates"). The Rite Aid Single Check Rebates program offers hundreds of dollars in savings each month. Also click "Online Shopping" for additional bargains.

MORE SAVINGS

Some retailers provide attractive rebates and coupons so frequently that it's worth checking out their Web sites…signing up for their newsletters…or enrolling in their loyalty programs before buying anything.

Also, you can pick up at your post office a "Mover's Guide" address-forwarding packet, which often contains store coupons.

•**Ace Hardware** (at *www.acehardware.com,* click on "Ace Rewards" at the bottom of the screen). The Ace Rewards program offers 10 points for each $1 you spend, with a $5 reward for each 2,500 points earned and 1,000 free bonus points for signing up.

•**Bed Bath & Beyond** (*www.bedbathandbeyond.com,* click on "Email Signup"). Sign up for the company's mailing list online, and receive a continual stream of coupons.

Example: 20% off any item.

•**Gap** (or Gap Inc. sister stores Old Navy and Banana Republic). Visit the Web site listed on your receipt. Fill out the quick survey for a discount off one regularly priced item.

•**The Home Depot** (*www.homedepotmoving. com*). Register a recent or upcoming move on the home center's Web site, and get low price alerts and special offers.

•**Lowe's** (at *www.lowes.com,* click on "Lowe's Moving Center" at the bottom of the screen, then "Offers & Services"). Get a 10% coupon on Lowe's purchases up to $5,000.

•**Walgreens** (*www.walgreens.com,* click on "Savings & Deals"). Walgreens' Web site features online promotions and printable coupons.

•**Staples** (*www.staples.com*). Staples often features office supplies priced below cost in its weekly circular or on its Web site.

•**True Value Hardware** (at *www.truevalue.com,* click on "Rewards"). The True Value Rewards program provides 10 points per dollar when you spend up to $150 over 12 months. If you spend between $150 and $400, you will earn 15 points per dollar. Points translate into monetary rewards certificates. Members receive other special offers as well.

The Best Deals Online

According to a yearlong Web survey, certain items tend to cost less on specific days of the week. *Take a look…*

Mondays: Men's and women's dress pants and sunglasses.

Tuesdays: Men's apparel.

Wednesdays: Shoes and kids' clothing.

Thursdays: Women's handbags.

Fridays: Accessories, such as jewelry, belts and scarves.

Saturdays: Intimates, jackets and outerwear.

Sundays: Swimsuits.

Study by ShopItToMe.com, which monitors sales at more than 100 online retailers.

Smarter Shopping

Do your research online even if you plan to buy at a store—you can find what you are looking for more easily using the Web, or at least reduce the choices that you inspect at the store. Use in-store pickup for online purchases—you save on shipping and may be able to pick up your purchase the same day. Get to know the salesclerks at favorite stores—they can tell you about upcoming sales.

Mike Gatti, senior vice president, member relations, Retail Advertising and Marketing Association, Washington, DC.

Eat Steak on a Hamburger Budget: Confessions of a Butcher

John Smith, a professional butcher for more than 30 years in retail and wholesale stores and meatpacking plants. He's the author of *Confessions of a Butcher: Eat Steak on a Hamburger Budget and Save $$$* (Ark Essentials). He lives in Idaho. For more information, go to *www.all-about-meat.com*

When families start to cut down on their household budgets, one of the first casualties often is meat. But if you know what to shop for, you can obtain delicious, high-quality beef, pork and chicken for a lot less money.

WHY MEAT COSTS SO MUCH

Beef and pork carcasses each have four or five sections, which are called primals. Butcher shops and supermarkets inflate prices by carving up these primal cuts into dozens of different shapes and sizes with fancy names, such as "rib eye" and "tenderloin."

Result: Those precut, prepackaged meats that most of us buy are grossly overpriced and have as much to do with marketing as how tasty and tender they are.

You can request much cheaper and equally delicious alternatives from the butcher working behind the meat counter where you shop. You just have to know what to ask for. It doesn't hurt to be on friendly terms with the butcher either. Often the cheaper version is virtually the same and from the same primal. *Here, a few examples of pricy cuts and their money-saving alternatives...*

RIB EYE STEAK

A cut from the tender muscle over the backbone and ribs of the beef (prime rib), this steak is beautifully marbled with fat, loaded with flavor and grills well.

Cost: About $12.99/lb.*

Alternative: Chuck eye is virtually the same muscle as the rib eye, but it is the section that extends into the chuck shoulder of the beef.

Best: Ask the butcher to cut about a four-inch roast off the front of the boneless chuck. Then ask him/her to peel out the chuck eye and cut it into steaks.

Cost: As low as $1.99/lb.

BEEF SHORT RIBS

This wonderful cut of beef for barbecuing or braising comes from the cross rib, a section extending from the shoulder to the ribs of the cattle. Unfortunately, about half of what you're paying for is bone and fat.

Cost: About $4.99/lb.

Alternative: Flatiron. This cut from the top of the shoulder blade probably is the most underrated cut of beef at the meat counter. It's delicious but unattractive, with what appears to be a thick seam of gristle going down its center. Actually, that's not gristle, just a gelatin-type substance that melts away when you cook it.

What to request: Wait until there is a sale on cross rib roasts, which happens frequently. Then ask your butcher to carve a flatiron roast for you out of the cross rib. Have him cut the flatiron into boneless country-style ribs. They barbecue just as well as short ribs, but you get more for your money because there's no bone.

Cost: As low as $1.99/lb.

LEAN GROUND BEEF

Regular ground beef is so fatty that many consumers are willing to pay for the leaner version with less than 10% fat even though it can cost two or three times as much.

Cost: As high as $6.99/lb.

Alternative: Bottom round, which is a very lean, meaty and inexpensive cut of beef.

What to request: Ask your butcher to grind up a bottom round roast.

Cost: About $1.99/lb.

BEEF STRIPS FOR STIR-FRY OR FAJITAS

Supermarkets often use whatever cheap cuts of beef they have available for these two cuts but sell them at gourmet prices.

Cost: About $8.99/lb.

*Prices in this article are typical of butcher shops in Idaho. Prices may vary at supermarkets and butcher shops across the country.

Alternative: Rump roast is the cut of meat that butchers often use to make prepackaged beef strips.

What to request: Ask your butcher to cut the rump roast into thin strips.

Cost: As low as $1.99/lb.

PORK TENDERLOIN

The "filet mignon" of the hog, tenderloin comes from the major muscle inside of the backbone between the shoulder blade and hip socket.

Cost: About $5.99/lb.

Alternative: Boneless loin roast is a very tender cut that comes from the muscle near the backbone.

What to request: Your butcher can carve you an entire roast or cut it into medallions for frying, chunks for barbecuing or thin slices for stir-fried dishes.

Cost: As low as $1.99/lb.

ROASTING CHICKENS

These really are just very large whole fryer chickens.

Cost: About $1.69/lb.

Alternative: Whole fryers. This is the best value in the entire meat section. It's fine to buy them prepackaged without the butcher's help.

Cost: About $0.69/lb. to $1.29/lb.

If you like dark meat, you can save even more money—there are frequent sales on prepackaged fryer hindquarters (the drumstick, thigh and part of the back).

Cost: As low as $0.59/lb.

VEAL

This meat from a male dairy calf has a lighter color and a more delicate taste than adult beef.

Cost: About $12.99/lb.

Alternative: Boneless pork sirloin. A tender cut of pork from the backbone of the hog near the upper hip, it's nearly the same color as veal and mild in flavor.

What to request: Ask your butcher to slice the pork sirloin very thin, and it will make a delicious substitute in such dishes as veal Parmesan and veal scallopini.

Cost: As little as $1.99/lb.

ITALIAN SAUSAGE

Supermarkets use the fatty pork trim from the day's cuttings or cheaper cuts of pork to grind into sausage.

Cost: About $3.99/lb., more if it's made into links.

Alternative: Pork shoulder butt, which is meat from the top portion of the front leg of the hog. It's a well-marbled cut that's tougher than other pork meat because it comes from active muscle.

What to request: Have your butcher grind it. Then you easily can mix it with Italian or breakfast sausage seasoning yourself. Without seasoning, it's a great substitute for ground beef.

Cost: About $0.99/lb.

Entertaining for Less at Restaurants

Barbara Pachter, president of Pachter & Associates, a communications training firm in Cherry Hill, New Jersey. She's the author of many books, including *When the Little Things Count...and They Always Count* and *The Power of Positive Confrontation* (both from Da Capo). Her Web site is *www.pachter.com*

Business and personal budgets are now cut to the bone by this recession—but we still may need to take clients out for a meal or treat out-of-town guests to dinner.

Solution: Limit the cost of eating out while still appearing as munificent as ever. *Here is how...*

- **Choose restaurants that seem pricier than they are.** You don't have to bring guests to the most expensive restaurant in town—just avoid eateries that look cheap. When we entertain, the visual impression offered by the dining room can be as important as the quality of the food. The waitstaff must be professionally dressed—no jeans or fast-food–type uniforms...the tables must have tablecloths... the room must seem clean and fresh...and there should not be a TV.

Be ready to explain why you chose this particular restaurant over the better-known alternatives. *Two options...*

•Eat at the restaurant before inviting important guests, then provide a personal endorsement. *Example:* "It's one of those great places that only locals know about."

•Cite a glowing review. Search the online archives of your local newspapers...or search the name of the restaurant and town on Google.com to find reviews. *Example:* "The Tribune gave this place a great review. I've been meaning to give it a try."

•**Recommend dishes from the midprice range.** You can't tell your guests what to order, but you can provide a rave review of an entrée that isn't too expensive.

Example: "I always come to this place for their chicken marsala. It's really the best thing on the menu."

•**Use a little wine research to trim a lot from the bill.** Restaurants usually offer some perfectly nice wines for less than $25 a bottle. Trouble is, selecting one of these less expensive wines could make you appear cheap.

Solution: Review the restaurant's wine list prior to your important dinner, and jot down a few of the more affordable bottles. (The wine list might be available on the restaurant's Web site. If not, visit the restaurant in person and ask to see it.) Look these up in a wine guide, such as *Parker's Wine Buyer's Guide* (Simon & Schuster) or *Hugh Johnson's Pocket Wine Book* (Mitchell Beazley). Note two or three wines of different varieties from the list that earn favorable reviews. At your dinner, use these ratings to validate your inexpensive choice in the eyes of your guests.

Example: "Robert Parker gave this wine 91 points. Let's give it a try."

•**Preorder dinner for large groups.** Ask to speak with the restaurant's manager when you call to make a reservation for a group of 10 or more. The manager might be willing to let you create a special menu for your group. To control your costs, omit the restaurant's priciest dishes from this menu.

The restaurant manager even might be willing to negotiate a special discount...or a fixed "per head" cost for your dinner, particularly if it is on a slow weeknight.

You will have to give the restaurant at least several days' notice to arrange a special menu. The larger your party, the greater the odds that the manager will agree.

Helpful: Let the manager know if you treat groups to meals frequently. Discounts and other special terms are most likely for customers who bring repeat business.

•**Don't order the specials.** Specials often are priced 10% to 40% higher than menu listings. Many restaurants do not even say how much specials cost unless customers ask—and you'll seem cheap if you ask.

You can't prevent your guests from ordering the specials...but avoid restaurants likely to feature ultraexpensive lobster, crab or steak entrées.

•**Clip coupons.** Even expensive restaurants sometimes issue coupons during difficult economic times. These coupons might be in regional "entertainment" coupon books...in your local newspapers...or mailed to those who sign up for the restaurant's mailing list on its Web site.

Do not let your guests see you use a coupon—doing so seems cheap. Excuse yourself from the table to pay the bill. If a coupon must be presented in advance, arrive at the restaurant before your guests and ask the manager to have the discount applied confidentially.

•**Remain sober.** A tipsy host might fail to notice that a guest has taken over the wine ordering and made a budget-busting selection. Besides, the more alcohol you drink, the more your guests are likely to drink, driving up the bill.

•**Host a lunch rather than a dinner.** Restaurants will often price the lunch entrées as much as 50% lower than dinner entrées...and your guests are likely to drink less alcohol at lunch.

•**Avoid paying a big bar tab.** If the group wants to go to a bar after your dinner, agree to this and pay for the first round—then come up with a polite reason why you can't stay any longer. Otherwise, you'll be expected to pick up the entire bar tab.

Example: "I'd love to stay longer, but I have an early meeting tomorrow."

How to Get a "Nice Guy Discount" on Appliances, Electronics, Furniture And More

Jeff Yeager, dubbed "The Ultimate Cheapskate" by NBC's *Today* show, honed his cheapskating skills during 25 years working with underfunded nonprofit agencies. He lives in Accokeek, Maryland, and is author of *The Ultimate Cheapskate's Road Map to True Riches* and *The Cheapskate Next Door* (both from Broadway). His Web site is *www.ultimatecheapskate.com*

With dollars stretched very tight these days, retail customers are scarce. And when customers are scarce, they gain bargaining muscle. Shoppers who are willing to negotiate even a little often get better deals.

A 2007 survey by the Consumer Reports National Research Center found that more than 90% of consumers who got up the nerve to negotiate on things such as electronics, appliances, furniture and even medical bills reported receiving a discount at least once during the survey period, with most saving $50 or more each time they were successful.

Being "The Ultimate Cheapskate," I routinely negotiate on a big range of purchases—during both good times and bad—frequently shaving 5% to 10% off the asking prices and sometimes 20% or more on big-ticket items. For this article, I tapped my bargain basement brain trust of more than 300 volunteer "miser advisers" for their best negotiating tips.

Our mantra: It never hurts to ask, but always be both friendly and polite. Also, first impressions are important, so it is best to dress nicely but casually—a slovenly appearance can promote suspicion, and overdressing suggests wealth and therefore an ability to pay more.

GENERAL STRATEGIES

The first step is to make sure that the person you're speaking with has the authority to negotiate. If not, ask to speak to someone who does. "Is there a manager or someone I can speak with about the possibility of getting a better price on this product?" often does the trick.

For all major purchases, such as appliances, computers and furniture, do your homework to find out how much an item sells for elsewhere. If you know that an item is cheaper elsewhere, it's usually best to let the salesperson know that you're wise to the fact that his/her price isn't the best around. Even if the retailer already has the best price, there is no downside in asking for an even sweeter deal. As one miser adviser told me, "I've never had anyone raise the price because I asked him to lower it."

It's usually best to state up front the amount that you're willing to pay, adjusted to allow for some haggling.

Example: If you're willing to pay $50 for an item that is marked $60, you might start off with a lowball offer of $40 or $45, with the hope of compromising somewhere around $50.

You don't have to name a price. You can just ask, "Can you do any better on this?" In keeping with the importance of being friendly, many times I ask for (and receive) a "nice guy discount," based solely on the fact that I'm a nice guy. It's as simple as asking, "Can you do any better on the price?" then adding, with a smile, "What about giving me a nice guy discount, because I'm a nice guy?" If nothing else, I bet you'll get a free smile out of the salesperson.

When asking for a discount based on poor service, damaged merchandise or the like, be honest. Don't fabricate or exaggerate, but politely speak your mind if you are dissatisfied in any way or think that the condition of an item warrants a price reduction. Just say to the person in charge something like, "I'm not trying to be difficult, but I feel I should let you know that the service I received today was disappointing," and provide one or two details. Let the person in charge respond. He/she often will offer some type of make-good concession, but if he doesn't, you can then ask, "Is there anything you can do to keep me as a future customer?"

WHEN THE ANSWER IS "NO"

Be prepared for rejection because the answer often is "no." Handle this gracefully, and don't be embarrassed or get nasty. On major purchases, when the initial response is "no," I generally say, "Is there anything I can do to change your mind?" followed by, "Is there anyone else I can speak with?"

If, in the end, the answer remains "no," I thank the salesperson or manager for his time and tell him that I'm going to shop around. Occasionally (but rarely) he will reconsider as you are headed for the door. You always can slip back later to buy the item if, in fact, you can't do better elsewhere.

FINE-TUNING YOUR STYLE

With these general strategies in mind, here are some of the finer points when it comes to cutting the best deal…

- **Flash the cash.** Offering to pay with cash instead of a credit card often can convince a retailer to knock a few dollars off of the price, because that's what you're saving him in credit card–processing fees. And actually showing the greenbacks when you make your best offer sometimes can close the deal.

- **"I can't afford it."** In times such as these, there's nothing wrong with telling a merchant the truth. Don't break out the violins—simply come clean and say something along the lines of, "I really like this product, but to be honest with you, my budget is pretty tight these days. Can you do any better on the price?"

- **Watch for sales before and after you buy.** Many retailers will give you the sale price even when an item is not on sale or match a competitor's sale price, sometimes even before or after the fact. Be prepared to go back to a merchant and suggest that you will return an item for a refund if he does not give you the lower sale price. Some retailers have a policy that if an item goes on sale within a certain time period—say, 10 days or two weeks—they will refund the difference.

- **Ask to cancel your service.** Particularly when it comes to dealing with service providers over the phone, politely stating that you would like to talk to someone about canceling your service (cable service, phone plans, credit cards, etc.) usually will get you connected—and pronto—to someone whose job it is to keep you as a customer. This is the person who is authorized to cut you the best deal possible.

- **Never on a Monday.** In my experience, the best bargains are made late in the week, particularly on Fridays and especially before holidays or three-day weekends. Everyone is in a good mood and wants to wrap things up, and salesmen often want to meet their weekly quotas. Avoid negotiating early in the week.

- **"Do any discounts apply?"** If you are still gun-shy about haggling, start with this simple baby step—always ask whether any "promotions" or "other discounts" might apply to you. Do this when you are in a store or making a catalog purchase over the phone. "Promotions" are special deals that salespeople (particularly at catalog companies) can mention only if the customer asks first. Many merchants also provide discounts to members of AARP, AAA, warehouse clubs, etc., and even if you're not a member, they sometimes will give you the same break if you ask.

Example: I stayed at a hotel recently and asked if an AARP discount would be accepted. The desk clerk said "no," but she immediately took 15% off the price of my room, explaining that if the hotel did offer an AARP discount, that's what it would be.

Going-Out-of-Business Sales: How to Get the Best Deals

Sue Goldstein, a bargain-shopping expert and diva of discounts for over 37 years. Goldstein has written more than 70 books on the topic, including *The Underground Shopper's Guide to Online Bargains.* She also hosts a radio program.

Retail bankruptcies and cutbacks are creating a flood of going-out-of-business sales.

What most people do not know: To get real bargains at liquidation sales, you need to be especially careful. That is because most of these sales are run by outside liquidation specialists that have zero incentive to retain you as a customer. They use merchandising tricks that could leave you with the illusion of a great deal that doesn't save you much money at all.

My favorite strategies for getting the most from going-out-of-business sales...

• **Skip the first few weeks of the sale.** Liquidators typically start with a 10% storewide discount.

But there's a catch: All the prices are first raised up to the full manufacturer's suggested retail prices (MSRPs) before the markdown is applied. That means many items start out at prices higher than what the store sold them for before bankruptcy.

Liquidators are hoping to attract a flood of customers and prey on consumer excitement and naïveté.

Better: Wait until week four. A liquidation sale generally runs six to 12 weeks, with prices dropping by about 10% a week. For shoppers, it's a cat-and-mouse game because as the discounts get deeper, the selection of products becomes more limited. I have found that week four is the sweet spot. That's when discounts are starting to get substantial, but there's still decent merchandise available.

• **Expect little help from salespeople or managers.** The liquidation sales staff is just a skeleton crew that cannot lower prices (if, say, you want to buy the floor model). They have little or no knowledge to answer your technical questions. They may not even know what merchandise will arrive at the store that week.

• **Confirm that a bargain really is a bargain.** This works best with brand-name items (especially electronics, toys and china), whose prices can be easily compared among various retailers. If you own an Internet-enabled phone, use it right in the store as a price checker. Key the product name and model number into a search engine, such as Google, or a shopping or price-comparison site to see what it is selling for elsewhere. If you cannot use your cell phone, write down the model number of the item you want, then go on the Internet at home.

Examples of sites where you can compare prices: *www.amazon.com...www.ebay.com...www.consumersearch.com...www.pricegrabber.com.*

Smart: Phone the store's nearest competitors. They are sometimes willing to match the liquidator's sale price. If you can get the same deal, go with the healthy store.

• **Check the price tag on an item to make sure that it looks like the others throughout the store.** Many liquidators supplement a store's existing stock with their own inferior merchandise or leftovers from previous liquidations. If the price tag has a different typeface, format or color, be wary.

Example: Electronics that may be brought in as part of excess inventory are sometimes reconditioned but sold as brand-new.

• **Inspect your merchandise thoroughly before purchasing.** Never purchase a product if you're not allowed to open the box first in the store. When you open the box, make sure that the product comes with the appropriate accessories, instruction booklet and manufacturer warranty and that the item is in good condition. Plug in all electronics to make sure they work. Most liquidators impose a "no-return, no-exchange" policy. If you get home and realize that there is a problem, you're out of luck."

A Man's Guide to Dressing Well for Less... From a Savile Row–Trained Tailor

Stephen Kempson, a Savile Row–trained tailor and founder of Stephen Kempson London, a custom tailor and clothier located just off Madison Avenue in Manhattan. Kempson has outfitted leaders in business, entertainment and the media. His Web site is *www.stephenkempson.com*

Many men have trimmed their clothing allowances these days because of the weak economy, but this is no time to look shabby. Wearing old or low-quality suits can create the impression that you are old or low quality. *Fortunately, you can get a great look without paying a lot...*

WHERE TO SHOP

High-end department stores' private label suits offer the best value for the money. These suits typically are comparable in quality to the designer suits sold at that store but at a fraction of the expense. Top department stores employ skilled salespeople and tailors, which greatly increases the odds that you will wind up in a suit appropriate for your body type.

Among the best department store private label suits...

• **Nordstrom's John W. Nordstrom and Broletto labels.** These suits in the $600 range can be just as handsome as Hickey Freeman suits costing $1,000 or more, and Nordstrom's sales staff is excellent. There is arguably no better value in men's suits.

• **Saks Fifth Avenue label.** Saks's private label suits also compare favorably to those costing much more. (Suits start at $695.) Saks, too, employs very qualified salespeople.

Clothing discounters offer attractive bargains as well, but they typically do not provide high-quality customer service. Shopping for suits at discounters is appropriate only if you already know which suits and sizes tend to look good on you...and you have a tailor you trust to do alterations.

SUIT SELECTION

If your budget is limited, it's better to purchase one or two high-quality suits than three or four less expensive suits.

Not only do well-made suits look a lot better, they last longer, making them a smart long-term investment. Cheap suits can start to show wear after just a few trips to the dry cleaner.

Choose timeless styles that won't look dated in a few years. That means dark gray or blue fabric...and subtle patterns, such as solids or barely visible stripes.

One- or two-button suits can be the right choice for short, stocky men who look boxy in three-button suits. Double-breasted suits are a good choice for very slender men.

Select suits made from medium-weight 8.5-ounce to 10-ounce fabric. Such material is appropriate year-round, eliminating the need to purchase different suits for each season. Air-conditioning and heating make very heavy or lightweight fabrics impractical for modern life anyway.

SHIRTS, SHOES AND ACCESSORIES

To finish off your look and wear with your suit...

• **Dress shirts.** Conservative white or light blue dress shirts are timeless and especially popular now. A subtle stripe or small check pattern on a dress shirt is acceptable as well, but avoid bold patterns.

Most men look best in dress shirts that have spread or semispread collars, instead of button-down collars. Classic French cuffs paired with a simple cuff link add a touch of elegance.

Example: Charles Tyrwhitt dress shirts with French cuffs are an excellent value. Most are $59, or four for $199 (866-797-2701, *www.ctshirts.co.uk*).

• **Ties.** Understated ties, featuring solid colors or subtle stripes, have replaced the bold stripes and complex designs of years past.

• **Pocket squares.** Pocket squares provide inexpensive elegance. White linen and white cotton pocket squares always are a perfect choice—they look fresh and classy with just about any suit and tie.

Avoid matched pocket-square-and-tie sets—these can seem too by-the-numbers.

• **Socks.** Men's fashion always becomes understated when the economy falters, but many men still are injecting fun and color into their office apparel through their socks. Diamond-patterned, polka dot and argyle socks are all quite popular.

• **Shoes.** It's worth spending a few extra dollars to buy good shoes. Many people will form a first impression of you based on the quality of the shoes that you wear.

Dark brown shoes now are considered more stylish and elegant than black, even if paired with blue or gray suits. (However, black suits still require black shoes.)

Favor lace-up shoes when wearing a suit, and avoid shoes with tassels, which look dated. And, of course, always keep your shoes well-shined.

Example: Allen Edmonds produces excellent shoes for men in a relatively affordable price range (877-817-7615, *www.allenedmonds.com*).

How *Not* to Ruin Your Flat-Panel TV: Advice From the Geek Squad

Stephen Rhoades, a master installer specializing in home theater products with Geek Squad, a 24-hour technical support service owned by consumer electronics retailer Best Buy, *www.geeksquad.com*. He is based in Saratoga Springs, New York.

Dust and fingerprints can detract from a flat-panel TV's picture quality—and improper cleaning can cause permanent damage.

Traditional "tube" televisions are simple to clean—just spray a little glass cleaner on the screen, then wipe it off with a paper towel. Don't try this with a panel-screen TV (plasma, LCD or projection). The chemicals in window cleaners can permanently fog or smudge your TV's screen or even remove its antiglare coating. Also, spray-on cleaners can get inside flat panels and cause serious damage—and because many flat panels are plastic, paper towels can scratch the screen's surface.

BETTER CLEANING

Buy a cleaner designed specifically for flat-panel televisions or just for laptop computer screens—these cleaners are virtually identical. They do not contain alcohol, ammonia or strong solvents that could damage the screen... nor do they contain soaps that could leave a residue. They are sold at electronics and computer stores.

Also, buy microfiber cloths, such as those marketed for cleaning laptop screens, eyeglasses or camera lenses. Microfiber cloths are extremely nonabrasive, minimizing the risk of scratches. They do a wonderful job of picking up both dust and the oils left by fingerprints.

Cotton rags, bath towels, paper towels, tissues and toilet paper feel soft on our skin, but they actually are somewhat abrasive and can leave tiny scratches on a flat-panel screen. Paper towels also sometimes carry a static charge that could, in theory, damage your television's electronics.

TO CLEAN YOUR FLAT-PANEL TV

• **Turn off your TV.** Dust and smudges will be easier to see against a black background.

Apply a small amount of cleaner to your microfiber cloth. Never spray cleaner directly onto the screen—excess fluid could run down the screen and pool in the gap between the screen and the lower portion of its frame. This fluid could short out the TV's circuits or distort the lower portion of the picture.

• **Gently wipe the screen.** Resist the urge to scrub harder if certain smudges prove difficult to remove. Pressing hard might permanently damage an LCD screen...or crack the plasma screen. Instead, continue to gently and patiently wipe the smudged area.

PROTECTING YOUR TV

Three more ways to avoid damage to your flat-panel TV...

• **Use a surge protector that includes a "video filter."** This not only protects your television from surges in your power line, it also protects it from surges in the cable line caused by lightning strikes.

• **Double-check that you have connected your TV properly before turning it on for the first time.** Crossed connections can cause significant damage.

Example: You could overload your TV's circuits if you accidentally plug an audio cable into your flat-screen TV's video input.

• **Read the section of your plasma television's manual that covers burn-in.** "Burn-in"—a permanent ghost image of something previously displayed on the screen—is much less likely with today's plasma TVs than with early models. It still is possible, however, particularly during the first few hundred hours that a plasma TV is in use.

Your plasma TV's manual explains how to enable the set's burn-in safeguards...and how to avoid major burn-in risks.

Say "No" to an Extended Warranty—What Is Better...

Jack Gillis, director of public affairs for the nonprofit Consumer Federation of America, one of the country's largest consumer advocacy organizations, Washington, DC, *www.consumerfed.org*. He is author of *The Car Book 2011* (Gillis).

Extended warranties are almost always a bad deal for consumers. Warranty providers analyze product breakdown histories and repair costs, then structure their coverage to limit the number of claims—often by strategically limiting what is covered and/or how long coverage lasts.

Those tempted by extended warranties despite their drawbacks should at least read all the fine print to understand what they're getting. For instance, you do not want to have to pay high shipping charges to get your item to the repair center, especially if it's a large item, and you don't want a warranty that allows the warranty provider many weeks to do repairs, especially if it is an item that you use every day, such as a refrigerator.

Computers, in particular, are likely to break down during their extended warranty periods, but the warranty is likely to cost up to one-half the price of the computer—more than most repairs. Also, many problems turn out to be software problems, which are not covered. And many laptop warranties do not cover damage sustained in falls.

SOME ALTERNATIVES

Instead of buying an extended warranty, consider the following...

- **Use a warranty-extending credit card,** such as American Express (800-225-3750 or *www.americanexpress.com*) or Visa Signature (800-882-8057 or *www.visa.com/signature*), which automatically doubles manufacturers' warranties up to an additional year.*

- **Self-insure.** Ask how much the extended warranty costs, then put that amount into an interest-bearing account. Use this account to pay for repairs if something breaks.

*Offers and rates subject to change.

AUTOMOBILES

Automotive extended warranties can easily cost more than $1,000—yet most modern vehicles do not experience expensive problems during their extended-warranty periods, which rarely go beyond seven years or 100,000 miles.

If an extended warranty is worthwhile to you because it helps you sleep at night, bypass the dealership and opt instead for the "mechanical breakdown insurance" now provided by many major vehicle insurers. This insurance serves a similar function but typically at a much lower price...and buyers can pay for their protection as they go, which gives increased flexibility.

Example: GEICO Mechanical Breakdown Insurance is available for vehicles less than 15 months old that have been driven less than 15,000 miles. It typically costs less than $100 per year—sometimes considerably less, depending on the vehicle. The coverage can be renewed for up to seven years or 100,000 miles, whichever comes first. There's a per-repair deductible of $250 (call 800-861-8380 or check *www.geico.com*).

When considering any auto extended warranty or breakdown insurance...

- **Make sure the coverage allows you to select your own repair shop.** Call your preferred shop to make sure it accepts the coverage before signing up.

- **Scan the contract for a list of parts that are not covered.** Good coverage should include everything except parts that regularly wear out, such as brake pads, batteries and tires.

- **Avoid extended warranties offered by third parties other than large insurers.** The terms might sound attractive, but these providers often hide important limitations in contract small print...try to deny valid claims...and/or go out of business, stranding customers with worthless warranties.

Cut Your Energy Bill by $1,500 This Summer

John Krigger, founder of Saturn Resource Management, an environmental consulting, training and publishing company located in Helena, Montana. He has served as a consultant to the US Department of Energy and is coauthor of *The Homeowner's Handbook to Energy Efficiency* (Saturn Resource Management, *www.homeownershandbook.biz*).

You can trim your energy bills by more than $1,500 this summer just by taking these simple steps...

• **Use window fans after sunset.** Outside temperatures can drop quickly once the sun sets, even in the middle of the summer. Turn off your air conditioner, and turn on a window fan. Fans use only a fraction of the electricity of air-conditioning and may make you just as comfortable when nighttime temperatures drop.

Savings: Two fans combined likely use just 5% of the electricity that it takes to air-condition a home. If you can turn off your air-conditioning for 10 hours each night on 100 nights each year, you easily could save $500.

• **Use fans to circulate the air when you do turn on your air-conditioning.** When you shut the windows to turn on air-conditioning, you rob yourself of the cooling power of the wind. Supplement your A/C with fans, and the air moving around the room will make you feel four degrees cooler. Your fans will use a lot less electricity to achieve this four-degree drop than your air conditioner would. Turn off fans whenever you leave a room—the electricity is wasted if no one feels the breeze.

Savings: As much as 6% of your air-conditioning costs, which for some households is $100 to $200 per year.

• **Draw your drapes or blinds to prevent direct sunlight from heating your home on hot summer days.** White or metallic venetian blinds or opaque roll-down shades can reflect much of the sun's heat back out, reducing or even eliminating the need for air-conditioning.

Savings: As much as 40% to 45% of your cooling bills if you currently have uncovered windows—that could be close to $1,000.

• **Use your pool pump and filter less often.** Pool owners often set their pumps and filters to run between 12 and 24 hours a day—but as little as four hours a day might be sufficient. Experiment with shorter run times until you find your pool's minimum acceptable filter usage.

Helpful: Set the pool's pump and filter to run in the morning and late evening, not between noon and 6:00 pm, when summer electricity demand peaks and rates may be higher.

Savings: Perhaps $20 to $30 per month, depending on how many days of the year your pool is in use.

5 Simple Ways to Make Your Car Last 300,000 Miles

Eric Peters, a Washington, DC–based automotive columnist and author of *Automotive Atrocities! The Cars We Love to Hate* (MBI). His Web site is *http://ericpetersautos.com*

When you drive your car regularly, some wear and tear is to be expected. But you can take important steps to reduce excessive wear—and in the process, save money on car maintenance and ensure that your vehicle runs for as long as possible.

Bonus: The resale value of a well-maintained car always is greater than that of an identical car that did not receive proper care.

KEEP YOUR CAR BATTERY FULLY CHARGED

Most people do not pay attention to a car battery unless it stops working, but keeping your battery at full charge extends its useful life. Repeated charging and discharging can weaken the battery's ability to hold a charge over time.

Your auto battery also becomes depleted when you don't use the vehicle for more than a few weeks. Even though the car is not running and all accessories are shut off, if the battery is connected, there is a gradual draw of current.

What to do: To avoid depleting your battery, don't use the radio, headlights, interior lights and any other accessory when the engine is off.

If your car is not used regularly, consider buying an automatic "trickle charger." This device is connected by cables to the car battery in the car and plugged into a household electrical outlet to provide a charge. I prefer the automatic models, which cannot overcharge your battery because they automatically shut down when the battery reaches full capacity. Trickle chargers are available at auto-parts stores for about $40.

FILL YOUR GAS TANK

A full or nearly full tank reduces the odds that you will need expensive fuel system service in the years ahead. Most gas tanks are made of metal, and a partially empty fuel tank is prone to rust. Rust particles flake off and can clog fuel filters, fuel lines and fuel injectors, leading to costly repairs. In addition, rust can eat through the tank, creating holes. That might take 10 to 15 years, but modern cars often last that long and longer. Replacing a gas tank (and fuel lines) is an expensive job.

What to do: Keep your gas tank as full as possible at all times. Never let it get lower than half a tank.

Bonus: You will not ever have to make an emergency almost-empty stop at a gas station that charges more than an average price for gas.

WATCH YOUR TIRES

Today's tires are much more reliable than tires in the past—so much so that people tend to not think about their tires or check their air pressure.

Result: Underinflated tires are more common today. Tires that are underinflated create more friction than those that have the right amount of pressure. This hurts gas mileage and can cause tires to wear out faster.

With today's high-quality tires, air leakage typically is very slow and might not be noticeable to the eye until the pressure has dropped to dangerously low levels.

What to do: Check your tire pressure. Almost all new cars now have built-in electronic tire-pressure monitors. For older cars, it's wise to check your pressure the old-fashioned way, using a handheld gauge, at least every two weeks. It is best to do this when the tires are "cold" (not warm from driving). Add air whenever tire pressure falls below the carmaker's recommended minimum level. This is listed in the owner's manual or on a sticker on the inside of the driver's door jamb.

OIL CHANGES

Oil's main job is to capture contaminants that would otherwise contribute to the wear and tear of the car's engine.

What to do: Keep the engine well-serviced by always changing the oil at the prescribed time. Don't go longer than one month or 200 to 300 miles past the mileage/date interval.

PROTECT YOUR CLUTCH

The clutch on a car with a manual transmission wears down during the course of normal use, mainly because of friction. Replacing the clutch can cost $1,000 or more, so the longer you can go between clutch jobs, the better.

What to do: Most wear and tear takes place when you start and stop the car and shift gears. To cut back on wear and tear on the clutch, try to minimize stop-and-go–type driving as well as gear changes.

Example: Try to maintain your vehicle's momentum by anticipating changing lights and the ebb and flow of traffic. It is much easier on the clutch to "roll out" in second or third gear than to start from a dead stop in first gear. When you change gears, do it smoothly, not abruptly.

Important: Avoid excessive use of the clutch or "riding" it (partially engaging the clutch, increases friction and can wear it out).

To Keep Your Car Running Smoothly: 6 Things You Should Never Skimp On

Eric Peters, a Washington, DC–based automotive columnist and author of *Automotive Atrocities! The Cars We Love to Hate* (MBI). His Web site is *http://ericpeters autos.com*

People are understandably worried about the economy today, and they are trying to avoid unnecessary expenses. When it comes to your vehicle, there are some aspects of car maintenance that you might think you can skimp on to save money, but don't. Cutting corners or postponing maintenance actually can cost you more money in the long run. *What you should never skimp on...*

• **Oil.** Buy the grade of oil that meets the vehicle manufacturer's recommended American Petroleum Institute (API) or Society of Automotive Engineers (SAE) service rating, which is indicated in the owner's manual.

Using lower-grade oil may damage your engine. It also could invalidate your warranty coverage if you have a contested oil-related engine problem and you can't prove that the vehicle was serviced according to the manufacturer's requirements.

In addition, be sure that the oil filter you use meets the vehicle manufacturer's requirements, as specified by the owner's manual or the dealer.

Helpful: Keep all receipts related to servicing your car, including those for oil and filter changes, so that you can prove your car was serviced according to all of the manufacturer's specifications.

If you know how to do it, changing the oil and filter yourself is the least expensive approach. But not everyone likes to do that—or wants to deal with the mess of disposing of the old oil and filter.

Mechanics and independent shops generally are less expensive than having the work done by the car dealer.

Regardless of who does the job, check the dipstick afterward to confirm that the oil level is between the low and high marks. Some places have been known to overfill or underfill the crankcase.

• **Oil changes.** It might seem that stretching out the time between the manufacturer's maximum recommended oil change interval is a good way to economize, but it's not. It can accelerate wear and tear on your engine. I recommend erring on the side of caution—and always trying to change the oil at the prescribed interval. You probably won't hurt the engine if you miss the mileage/date interval by a little bit—for example, up to a month or about 200 to 300 miles—but don't try to go longer than that.

• **Radiator service.** The key to a well-performing radiator is the quality of coolant, the liquid that runs through it. Old or contaminated coolant can ruin an engine by causing corrosion or rust, especially because many engines today are made of alloy, not cast iron. It also could lead to overheating, which in a modern engine with aluminum cylinder heads (which warp more easily than cast iron) risks serious damage.

Check the condition of the coolant in your radiator—or have a competent mechanic check it for you—at least every two years regardless of the advertised shelf life of the coolant.

This is easy: When the engine is cold, open the radiator cap and take a look. (Touching the cap when it is hot is dangerous—taking the cap off the pressurized system can result in a spray of coolant.)

Fresh coolant is bright green or orange-red (if it's the "long-life" type) and translucent, not cloudy. Coolant should never look dirty. If it does, there is a problem with the coolant or something else in the engine, and this should be checked immediately.

Wise: Periodically have a mechanic open the radiator cap when the engine is cold to check the fill level. Looking at the translucent coolant overflow tank is not as effective. These tanks often are discolored, and the level is hard to gauge accurately, especially if the car is more than a few years old.

Any loss of coolant is cause for further investigation. Catching problems both big (a failing head gasket) and small (a minor, pinhole-type leak) can help avert a major, and expensive, breakdown.

• **Wiper blades.** For the sake of visibility and safety, don't skimp on replacing your wiper blades. Blades should be replaced as soon as they no longer clear the glass without causing streaks. Wiper blades typically last about six months but sometimes wear out much sooner if subjected to harsh conditions. Brutal summer sun and rough, ice-encrusted winter windshields are especially hard on wiper blades.

• **Car washes.** It is false economy to not wash your car. Keeping your car clean helps prevent rust and maintains the paint's shine, which aids the resale value at trade-in time. If you have the time to wash your car yourself, you'll save money. But if you really don't have time, it's worth paying to have the car washed for you.

• **Regular unleaded vs. premium gas.** If your car requires premium gas (as indicated in your owner's manual), do not use regular (or even midgrade) gas. You probably won't hurt your car's engine, but your mileage will suffer and you will have lower horsepower output. To accommodate the lower-octane gas, the engine will perform in the midrange—meaning it will not run poorly, nor will it run at its absolute best.

How to save: If your owner's manual merely recommends premium gas, you can save money by using regular gas, which typically is at least 20 to 30 cents less per gallon. You might not get all the horsepower your engine is capable of delivering, but this is something you may not miss.

You might suffer a slight mileage drop that could eat away at the savings at the pump, so compare mileage when running on regular and premium gas to see whether using premium is worth it.

Simple Secrets of Living Debt-Free from Those Who Don't Owe a Penny

Jeff Yeager, dubbed "The Ultimate Cheapskate" by NBC's *Today* show, honed his cheapskating skills during 25 years working with underfunded nonprofit agencies. He lives in Accokeek, Maryland, and is author of *The Ultimate Cheapskate's Road Map to True Riches* and *The Cheapskate Next Door* (both from Broadway). His Web site is *www.ultimatecheapskate.com*

If you can't afford to pay for it now, you can't afford it. When my grandfather told me that 40 years ago, it didn't sound nearly as radical as it does today. Grandpa borrowed money only once in his life—to buy a house—and even then he paid it off long before the bank required.

Of course, times are different now. Everything costs so much more. There's no way you can live comfortably these days without borrowing money and going into debt.

Wait a minute! If you believe those last three sentences, then have we got an article for you. Those three sentences are as false as Grandpa's teeth.

I picked the brains of some leading personal finance experts and my own network of volunteer "Miser Advisers" to gather their thoughts on living comfortably without going into debt—or at least without borrowing to the extent that most Americans do today. *Here are their secrets...*

• **Be afraid, be very afraid, of credit cards.** To paraphrase Jack Nicholson's character in the movie *A Few Good Men*, "Credit cards? You can't handle the credit cards!" Roughly 60% of active credit card accounts are not paid off every month. Many people think that they can game the system—earn lots of bonus points or cash back by frequently using a credit card—and pay it off every month. In reality, most people just end up in debt.

• **Pay in cash, and you certainly will spend a lot less.** According to Bankrate.com, the average credit card purchase now ends up costing 112% more than the purchase price (that's right, more than twice as much) because we fail to pay it off right away.

To me, there are only a few wise uses of a credit card. These include establishing your credit history...actual emergencies...and transactions such as car rentals that require a card.

• **Practice the art of procrastination.** When it comes to living free of debt, procrastination can be a virtue, not a vice. We've all had buyer's remorse. That's the feeling of regret you get when you buy something that disappoints you. Buyer's remorse often is compounded by a sense of guilt when you buy something on credit. The purchase has disappointed you, and you haven't even paid for it yet.

Practice procrastination when it comes to all your discretionary purchases, especially if you plan on using a credit card. Wait at least one week between the time you see an item in a store or online and the time you go back to buy it. Chances are good that you will decide that you don't want it after all. And whenever you do buy, save your receipts so that you can return items you regret for a full refund.

• **Shine up that used car.** When it comes to buying an automobile, the smart money is almost always on buying a used (but not abused) vehicle, so you let the guy who buys the new car pay the 20% or more in value that most new cars lose in their first year of ownership.

Still have that urge-to-splurge on a new car? Anthony Manganiello, in his book *The Debt-Free Millionaire*, offers this simple advice that helps him resist the call—keep your car really clean. He says that a sparkling used car feels like a new car and helps him resist the unending barrage of car commercials.

• **Buy a home, not a castle.** Granted, few people can afford to buy a home without taking out a mortgage, but that does not mean that you need to live your entire life with a mortgage hanging over your head, as many Americans do. The secret is to choose a house costing no more than 75% of the maximum amount you can qualify to borrow and then aggressively paying off your mortgage early.

"The priority is to get into something you can afford and then work on trading up or improving the house you have," says personal finance columnist Gregory Karp in his book *Living Rich by Spending Smart.*

Once you're in that affordable home, begin making extra principal payments to pay off the loan early. If in the course of a year you make just one extra monthly payment, you can knock years and many thousands of dollars in interest off your mortgage.

• **Ask yourself, "When is Christmas next year?"** That sounds like a strange question, but as Heather Wagenhals of the *Unlock Your Wealth Foundation* points out, many people are financially blindsided every year by holidays, vacations and other "spending events" that can be planned for well in advance.

The same goes for "emergencies." Certainly it is possible to have a truly unanticipated financial emergency, but for many people, almost everything is a real emergency because they have failed to plan—and save—for even those things that can be anticipated. A car with 100,000 miles on it needing repairs shouldn't be an emergency. You know it's going to need repairs...you just don't know exactly when.

• **Figure out what Grandpa would do.** If you still aren't convinced that it's possible to live debt free, or nearly so, like previous generations of Americans did, keep track of everything you spend money on for a month. Then look at that list, and ask yourself one simple question, "Did my grandparents spend money on that?" A second or third automobile? Unlikely. More than one TV? Doubtful. Meals in restaurants, other than for very special occasions? Rarely. Pet-grooming services? Not a chance. Bottled water? Are you crazy? Tanning salons? Forget about it!

Digging Out of Debt: 6 Strategies That Work

Gerri Detweiler, personal finance expert for the credit education Web site Credit.com, San Francisco. She is a former executive director of Bankcard Holders of America, a nonprofit consumer education and advocacy group, and coauthor of several books, including the e-book *Reduce Debt, Reduce Stress* (Good Advice).

The average American adult now carries more than $16,000 in debt (excluding home mortgages)—and that figure is likely to climb.

The best paths out of debt, starting with those most appealing to the largest numbers of debtors...

CREDIT COUNSELING

A nonprofit credit-counseling agency might be able to help you set up a three-to-five-year debt-repayment plan. Anyone struggling with debts should give this a try. The agency will decrease with your creditors to try to decrease your interest rates and perhaps get some fees waived. Unfortunately, not all of your creditors are likely to agree to do this, but at least some will. Once this repayment plan is in place, you send a single debt-payment check to the agency each month, and it distributes the money to your creditors. Credit-counseling agencies also provide useful money-management advice.

How to get started: Choose a credit-counseling agency that has been in business for at least 10 years and has been approved by the US Trustee's office. (On the Department of Justice Web site, *www.justice.gov,* click on "A-Z Index" at the bottom of the page, then "Credit Counseling and Debtor Education," then "List of Approved Credit Counseling Agencies.") Expect to pay an initial fee of perhaps $50 and a monthly fee of $30 to $50.

Drawbacks: If your debts are so great that there is no feasible way for you to pay them back within three to five years...or you have lost your job and cannot pay off your debts at all in the near future, a credit-counseling organization will not be able to construct a debt-repayment plan that you can afford.

Helpful for home owners: The US Department of Housing and Urban Development (HUD) sponsors free counseling agencies that provide advice on credit issues, mortgage loan defaults and foreclosures. For agencies in your state, go to *www.hud.gov/offices/hsg* (click "Single Family," then "Housing counseling").

RETIREMENT ACCOUNT LOAN

If you have a 401(k) or 403(b) retirement account or a pension plan where you work, it's likely that you can borrow against the value of your account or plan so that you can pay off other debts. These retirement-account loans generally are capped at either $50,000 or 50% of the amount in the account, whichever is less, and must be repaid within five years. You might be allowed to borrow up to $10,000 even if this represents more than half of your account balance. (If you have a defined-benefit pension plan, the amount you can borrow may be determined by the number of years you have worked for your employer or some other formula.) Interest is charged—typically 6% to 8%—but this interest is paid to your own retirement account. Ask your employer's retirement-plan administrator whether you can borrow.

Retirement-account loans do not require a credit check, which makes them particularly attractive for people with low credit scores.

Drawbacks: Retirement-account loans that are not repaid within five years are treated as distributions, triggering income taxes and a 10% IRS penalty. If you change or lose your job—a concern in today's economy—your employer might require you to pay back the loan immediately. Money borrowed from your retirement account misses out on tax-deferred growth until it is repaid.

PERSONAL LOAN

Personal loans are unsecured loans with interest rates that can be well below typical credit card rates. Consolidating credit card debt into a personal loan can lower debt costs so that debts can be paid off sooner.

Many banks have stopped issuing personal loans in this credit crunch. Try a local credit union or a "social lending" company instead. Social lenders bring together borrowers with investors who desire to make loans to earn interest. One reputable social-lending company is Lending Club (866-754-4094, *www.lendingclub.com*).

Drawbacks: Only borrowers having credit scores above 660 to 680 are likely to qualify. Loans seldom exceed $5,000 to $15,000, not enough for many individuals who are mired in debt. Loans typically last just 36 months, so sizable monthly payments are required.

HOME-EQUITY LOAN

Home-equity loans and home-equity lines of credit (HELOCs) let home owners borrow against the equity that they have in their property—assuming that they have any equity left after the recent real estate declines. (A home-equity loan provides cash in a lump sum, while a HELOC provides revolving credit.) This money can be used to pay down high-rate debt. Falling property values and increasingly cautious lenders have made these loans difficult to obtain, but most home-equity loans typically carry interest rates of just 6% to 8%, and the interest paid on these loans usually is tax deductible.

Drawbacks: If you pay off credit card debt with a home-equity loan or HELOC, you are trading unsecured debt for secured debt (your home is the collateral)—and you could lose your home if you fall behind on debt payments. Adding to the amount that you owe on your home could make it harder to sell the home and move.

DEBT-SETTLEMENT FIRM

A debt-settlement company will attempt to convince your creditors to settle for less than you owe, perhaps 50 to 60 cents on the dollar. That's very different from a credit-counseling company, which will attempt to help you pay back the full amount that you owe but with lower fees and interest. Your creditors might accept these terms if they believe that you will otherwise default on your loans. To increase its leverage, the debt-settlement company often will instruct you to stop making debt payments while it negotiates.

Choosing your debt-settlement company: Reputable companies charge primarily based on the amount that they save you—not the amount you owe—with only modest up-front fees. That might be a set-up charge of a few hundred dollars and 15% to 25% of the amount you will save. Reputable companies also warn clients about the downsides of debt settlement (see below). The firm should propose a plan that will have you out of debt in less than 36 months—any longer and creditors are more likely to sue than accept the terms. It's a good sign if the debt-settlement company has been in business at least 10 years and belongs to the Association of Settlement Companies (*www.tascsite.org*).

Drawbacks: You are likely to be besieged by calls from collection agencies and might be sued by your lenders when you stop making the loan payments. There are any number of disreputable debt-settlement companies that charge high fees but do little for their clients. And, you should know that you may owe income taxes on any debt that is forgiven. Working with a debt-settlement company will harm your credit rating—sometimes severely. The size of the hit depends on the current status of your debts. If you already are behind on payments to multiple creditors, entering debt settlement might not make a huge difference. If you have not missed any payments yet, debt settlement is the equivalent of defaulting on all of your loans and your credit score could drop by more than 100 points.

Bottom line: Debt settlement is a viable option only if your debt problems are so substantial that you see no other way to pay off your debts and if you take extreme care to use an honest debt-settlement company.

BANKRUPTCY

It might be possible to cancel your debts though a Chapter 7 bankruptcy...or to reorganize your debts through a Chapter 13 bankruptcy despite the hurdles recently added to the bankruptcy process. Discuss your options with a bankruptcy attorney—bankruptcy laws are too complex to sort out on your own. Select an attorney who is a member of the National Association of Consumer Bankruptcy Attorneys (*www.nacba.org*). The initial consultation typically is free. Expect legal costs of around $900 to $2,000 if you do file. If you cannot afford this, contact your state's bar association and ask if there's a state legal aid society that can provide a lawyer for less or for free.

Drawbacks: Going bankrupt will devastate your credit rating and remain on your credit report for 10 years, compared with a maximum of seven years for other credit missteps. Certain debts—including child support, alimony and student loans—might not be discharged by bankruptcy. Recent changes to bankruptcy laws make it impossible for some debtors who have large amounts of disposable income to qualify for Chapter 7 bankruptcy at all. Many of your assets could be seized.

Best Credit Cards If Your Credit Score Isn't the Greatest

Emily Peters, personal finance expert most recently with Credit.com, a leading resource for credit information online founded in 1995, San Francisco. Previously, Peters was with the consumer division of the credit-tracking bureau TransUnion.

A good credit score is at least 700 (out of 850), and for the best bargains on credit cards, you need a score of 720 or above. About 15% of Americans score between 650 and 700, a range in which credit bureaus view you as a "fair" credit risk—not bad, but not ideal. If that's you, the current credit squeeze has limited your options, but you still can find attractive offers.

FOR PEOPLE WITH "FAIR" CREDIT SCORES

For a low annual percentage rate (APR) on balances, consider the Capital One Platinum card (800-695-5500 or *www.capitalone.com*). It charges a $19 annual fee (waived for the initial year), and the 19.8% APR, although it sounds high, is relatively low for a card available to people with scores of less than 700.*

For cash back on purchases, you have the option of Capital One Cash Rewards (800-695-5500, *www.capitalone.com*), with a $39 annual fee and APR that ranges from 17.9% to 22.9%. You get 1% back on all your purchases with no limits, plus 2% cash back on purchases at gas stations and major grocery stores. There is no transfer fee. In the long run, however, customers with less than perfect credit are better off not looking for rewards cards, which often have high interest rates and fees.

For students, here's a card that has few surprises. The Discover It for Students Credit Card (800-347-2683, *www.discovercard.com*), which offers a variable 12.99% to 18.99% APR with no annual fee and cash back bonuses to both full- and part-time students at universities and at trade schools, has a reputation for not raising rates or fees or otherwise changing terms.

*Offers and rates subject to change.

If you want a card that prevents the holder from exceeding preset spending limits, try the Mango Prepaid MasterCard (*www.mangomoney.com*). A prepaid card does not charge interest, because you are not borrowing money. Instead, you set up direct deposit to an account linked to the card. This alternative is appropriate for someone who doesn't want the temptation of credit or for a child or nanny. It also is useful for people who can't or don't want to open a bank account and who don't want to pay for expensive check-cashing services.

CHECK YOUR SCORE

To monitor your credit reports and credit scores, subscribe to Identity Guard for $17.99 a month, with the first two weeks free (800-452-2541, *www.identityguard.com*). You also could check on your credit reports (not credit scores) free every 12 months at AnnualCreditReport.com. (For help on improving credit scores, see *www.credit.com* or *www.myfico.com*).

Best Way to Dispose Of Credit Cards

Shred unwanted credit cards or cut them into many small pieces, and dispose of the bits in separate garbage bags. Cutting an old card in half is no longer enough.

Reason: Some cards give the entire credit card number on both the front and the back. A crook who finds only one half of the card might be able to figure out the complete number by combining the numbers on the back with those on the front.

Edgar Dworsky, founder of ConsumerWorld.org in Boston.

It's Harder Than Ever to Get a Great Credit Score: How to Do It in These Tricky Times

John Ulzheimer, a nationally recognized credit expert and former president of consumer education for Credit.com, a credit information Web site located in San Francisco. Ulzheimer previously worked at the credit-rating organizations Fair Isaac (FICO) and Equifax, and is author of *You're Nothing but a Number: Why Achieving Great Credit Scores Should Be on Your List of Wealth Building Strategies* (Credit.com).

A single misstep can damage your credit score for years, which could make it harder to obtain a new mortgage, car loan or credit card at an attractive interest rate, especially during the lingering credit crisis.

Fortunately, you can recover most of your lost credit score points in as little as three years—if you make some smart credit moves. *What to do to restore your credit rating...*

GET A SECURED CARD

One of the best ways to rebuild damaged credit is to use your credit card responsibly. If there's a recent bankruptcy or an unpaid bill on your credit report, however, you may no longer qualify for a traditional, mainstream credit card.

You will very likely qualify for a "secured" credit card. These are available to virtually everyone, regardless of his/her credit score.

The catch: You'll have to make a deposit with the card issuer in advance that is equal to the secured card's credit limit.

The card issuer—a bank or a credit union—might be willing to return your security deposit and convert your account to a standard unsecured card in a year or two, assuming that you have made all of your payments on time.

Credit card comparison Web sites, such as Credit.com, can help you identify attractive secured card options.

Examples: Platinum Zero Secured Visa or Applied Bank Secured Visa, *www.appliedbank.com* and Citi Secured MasterCard, *www.citicards.com.*

Caution: Secured cards from some issuers charge such steep annual fees and sign-up fees that virtually the entire credit limit is used up by these fees before you use the card. Avoid these.

To make sure that your credit rating gets the full benefit of your responsible secured card use...

- **Confirm that the card issuer reports to all three credit bureaus**—Equifax, Experian and TransUnion—before signing up.
- **Don't confuse your secured card security deposit with a payment.** Some secured card users assume that the card issuer deducts their charges from the money they already have on deposit, so they don't bother to pay their bills. In truth, if the issuer must dip into your deposit, it will report your bill as unpaid, adding another black mark to your credit report.

USE CARDS LESS

Pay off your secured card balance, and any other revolving credit balances, in total every month. This will save you steep interest payments, and it could dramatically improve your credit score.

About one-third of your credit score is determined not by your payment history, but rather by the percentage of your available credit that you currently use, and lower is better.

Ordinarily, carrying a small balance on a credit card would not have a dramatic effect on your credit score—but if you have recently made some big credit missteps, it could. Why? When your credit rating dropped, your credit issuers most likely reduced your credit limits, or they revoked your credit. Perhaps your only credit card now is a secured card with a credit limit of less than $1,000. If your total available credit is low, carrying any balance means that your credit-utilization percentage will be too high, taking a major bite out of your score.

Helpful: Stop using your credit cards during the two months before you plan to apply for an important loan. Any balance present on your previous month's statement will probably still show up as your current balance on your credit report. You have to give the credit bureaus time to cycle through any statements with balances. Two months should be sufficient time to have a zero balance reported to the credit bureaus.

BECOME AN AUTHORIZED USER

If a close family member names you an "authorized user" of one of his credit cards, that credit account will be included on your credit record and can help raise your credit score. Make sure the account has a low balance...a long history of on-time payments... and, ideally, a high credit limit. Becoming an authorized user of an account with a history of missed payments or a high credit-utilization percentage could lower your credit score.

Your relative does not have to give you access to the credit card itself. Just naming you an authorized user of a credit card will not affect the relative's credit score.

Update: Fair Isaac, the company that calculates the well-known FICO credit scores, has recently changed its scoring rules to prevent abuse of this "authorized user" strategy. Fair Isaac will not divulge the new rules, but it appears that the strategy still will work as long as the credit card account to which you are added belongs to any close relative, such as a spouse or parent. Fair Isaac is trying to prevent credit-repair companies from adding their clients to the accounts of total strangers in exchange for fees. The new rules have not been adopted by all three credit bureaus, so for the time being at least, there still may be some benefit to being added to the account of someone other than a spouse or parent, such as a close friend.

NEVER DO THIS

Some well-known credit-repair strategies are best avoided...

- **Do not take out a car loan—or any other loan—simply to boost your credit score.** Managing your loan responsibly could benefit your credit score, but this benefit is not worth the high cost of unnecessary loan payments.
- **Do not hire a credit-repair firm.** Some of these are scammers that charge you a monthly fee but do nothing for you. The rest just submit letters to credit-reporting agencies on your behalf challenging the validity of negative listings on your credit report. If there are inaccurate listings on your credit report, you can challenge them yourself for free. Go to Credit.com, and click on "Learn How to Manage Your Credit Scores."
- **Do not hire a "debt settlement" company.** It will try to convince your creditors to accept less than the full amounts that you owe. Even if your creditors agree to this, they will report your debts as "settled," which is not the same as "paid in full." Your credit score will suffer.

Better: If you have debts that you genuinely cannot pay, contact a nonprofit debt-management organization affiliated with the National Foundation for Credit Counseling (800-388-2227, *http://nfcc.org*). These organizations try to convince creditors to reduce interest rates and void late fees, but—unlike debt-settlement companies—they will not ask creditors to accept less than the full amounts borrowed. If your creditors agree and you make your payments on time, your credit report will not suffer lasting damage.

Why It Pays to Use Your Credit Card

Curtis Arnold, founder and CEO of US Citizens for Fair Credit Card Terms, Inc., based in Little Rock, Arkansas. The company educates consumers about credit cards, and its Web site, CardRatings.com, features consumer reviews of credit cards. Arnold is author of *How You Can Profit from Credit Cards* (FT Press).

It is not always best to pay in cash. Putting a purchase on a credit card may help you if a service dispute comes up, because the *Fair Credit Billing Act* lets consumers dispute card-billing problems. This includes items that arrive damaged...items that are never delivered ...overbilling...double billing...and phantom or fraudulent charges.

For the quickest, fairest resolution when you dispute a credit card charge...

GET DETAILS IN WRITING

- **Insist on getting documentation from the merchant** if an item is going to be delivered to you...or promises are made about an item's condition or quality. Ask for written confirmation at the time of purchase stating when the item will be delivered...when the services will be provided...what services will be provided (in detail)...and what condition any items purchased will be in.

• **Save all your receipts.** These could help resolve your claim. True, your card statement should document the transaction, but receipts often include additional details, such as the formal name and contact information for the company, that can make all the difference in a dispute.

COMPLAIN TO THE MERCHANT

Your credit card issuer will not investigate your disputed charge unless you can show that you already have made a "good faith effort" to work out the problem with the merchant.

If possible, make a face-to-face visit and take any defective merchandise back to the store from which you bought it. If you talk in person or on the telephone, keep a detailed record of each conversation that includes times, dates, names and any promises made to you... or explanations of why your request for a refund is being denied.

CONTACT THE CARD ISSUER NEXT

Call the customer service number on the back of your credit card, and tell the phone rep that you wish to dispute a charge. Explain that you already tried to get the merchant to resolve the problem and that you want payment withheld if it hasn't been made already.

By law, card issuers are required to investigate only disputes of $50 or more and only those that took place within the buyer's home state or 100 miles of his or her home—but in practice, especially in the instance of outright fraud, card issuers rarely invoke the distance requirement and sometimes issuers try to resolve disputes on charges that are below $50 as well.

If you buy online or by phone: That purchase is considered to have been made at home.

Card companies often let customers file disputes over the phone—particularly when the dispute involves unauthorized use of a credit card—but in some cases, you will be sent a form and asked to file your claim in writing. (Many card issuers also let customers file claims online. Ask the phone rep how to do this.) Disputes typically must be filed within 60 days of receiving the bill.

Exception: There is no time limit for filing disputes over unauthorized use of a credit card.

The issuer must respond to your claim within 90 days or two billing cycles, whichever comes first. Until the matter is resolved, you won't have to pay the amount in dispute—and you will not accrue any interest. However, if your claim ends up being denied, the issuer can charge you interest going back to the date you filed the claim.

If you are unhappy with the dispute's outcome, your best bet is to file a complaint with your state attorney general, the Better Business Bureau and/or the Federal Trade Commission.

8 Insurance Myths That Can Cost You Dearly: The Truth About Home And Auto Insurance

J.D. Howard, executive director of Insurance Consumer Advocate Network, an insurance consumer advocacy organization, *www.ican2000.com*, Springfield, Missouri. Howard has been in the insurance industry since 1965, mainly as an independent insurance adjuster.

We buy insurance to protect ourselves against financial risks—but sometimes the greatest risk is that we don't fully understand our coverage. Insurance contracts are complex, with potentially important details buried in small-print legal jargon. Consumers often assume that common sense dictates when their insurance will protect them, but frequently you don't get as much coverage as you think you are getting, and sometimes you don't know enough to take advantage of the coverage that you do have. *The insurance myths that can cost you...*

HOMEOWNER'S INSURANCE

Myth: The "replacement cost" provision in my homeowner's policy means that I would immediately be paid enough to go out and replace or repair my ruined possessions.

Reality: Generally, replacement-cost coverage initially pays only the depreciated value—reflecting the reduced value because of age or wear and tear—of your damaged possessions when you file your claim. In this case, you would have to come up with your own extra cash to buy new replacement items and do repairs. You then would have to file a supplemental claim, accompanied by a copy of the purchase receipt, to get reimbursed for your cash outlay. Also, many policies set deadlines for acquiring these replacements, often as little as six or 12 months after the date of the loss—which may not allow enough time to replace a houseful of items.

What to do: Check the time limit. For structural damage, ask contractors if they are willing to work with your insurer to eventually recover the full cost. For damaged contents, replace some quickly and file your claim, then use the insurance settlement money to help replace more.

Myth: The mold exclusion in my homeowner's policy means that I'm financially responsible for resolving any mold problem that develops.

Reality: Your insurer is responsible for the mold-remediation costs despite this mold-exclusion clause if the mold stems from a covered event.

Example: A storm blows out several windows, and the rainwater that gets in leads to mold. Because the storm damage was covered by your policy, the mold is covered, too. Insurance companies sometimes attempt to reject mold-remediation claims that ought to be covered by claiming that the mold is unrelated to the covered event.

What to do: If your insurance company tries this, pay a mold-remediation service a few hundred dollars to determine the age and source of your mold. If you can establish that the mold dates to the covered event, the insurance company should back down.

Myth: Replacement of only the damaged sections of my home is covered by my insurance company.

Reality: If replacing a damaged section of carpeting, siding, flooring or some other element of the home creates a visible difference between the replaced section and the old section, the insurer must replace undamaged areas as well. This rule applies when there is a spot from which the undamaged section and the replaced section can be seen at the same time.

Example: A storm damages the siding on the north and east sides of your home. If there's a visible difference between new siding and old, the siding on the south side must be replaced, too, because there are spots from which the east and south sides can be seen at the same time...and the siding on the west side must be replaced because there are spots where the north and west sides can be seen at the same time.

What to do: If your insurer tries to dodge its responsibility to replace undamaged sections, write the adjuster a letter stating, "It is my understanding that in accordance with the line-of-sight rule, I'm entitled to replacement of the siding on the south and west sides of my home as well. (Change the description of what should be covered, as is appropriate.) If you have any doubts about this, please refer to your Fire, Casualty and Surety (FC&S) Bulletins and get back to me." Adjusters usually back down when policyholders cite this trade publication known by few outside the insurance industry.

AUTO INSURANCE

Myth: I have to live with the work that the repair shop does if my auto insurance requires me to take my vehicle to a specific shop.

Reality: Work done by a repair shop mandated by your auto insurance company's "Direct Repair Program" is automatically covered by your insurer. If you can show that the repairs were subpar or incomplete, you have the legal right to insist that they be redone.

What to do: Immediately after your insurer's mandated repair facility finishes its work, take the vehicle to a dealership service department and request an evaluation of the damaged area. If the vehicle was in a serious collision, specifically ask to get a four-wheel alignment. (These alignments use laser-diagnostics that often discover lingering problems with vehicles that have been in collisions.) Share the dealership's findings with your insurer, then say, "You've warranted these repairs, so make arrangements to take my car back to redo the repairs properly."

Myth: When I lend my car to a friend, my coverage still applies.

Reality: It depends on the policy. Some insurers now provide coverage only to drivers specifically named on the policy, a practice called "named insured only."

What to do: Read the terms of your insurance contract carefully before handing over your keys. Consider the driving skills of the person you're lending the car to, even if your coverage does extend to this driver—your insurance rates could be increased, even though you were not directly involved in the accident.

HOME AND AUTO INSURANCE

Myth: There's no harm in calling my insurer about a minor incident to find out if it's worth filing a claim.

Reality: Your insurance company will open a claim file as soon as you call the claims department, even if you don't pursue payment. More claim files typically mean higher premiums when it comes time to renew auto insurance, and homeowner's insurance providers sometimes cancel coverage when policyholders have multiple claim files. This can occur even if no payment is ever made on any claim.

What to do: Do not contact your insurer unless it is likely that the cost of repairs will significantly exceed your deductible. Obtain a repair estimate first if you are not certain.

Myth: An "independent" insurance adjuster sent by my insurance company will give me a fair shake.

Reality: An adjuster's job is to look out for the insurance company's bottom line. He/she will pretend to be your ally but will steer you toward options that save the insurer money, such as repairing damaged furniture rather than replacing it...or taking your damaged vehicle to a body shop that works cheap. This is the case even if the adjuster is employed by an independent company—these independent agents know that they will lose the insurance company's business if they fail to keep claim costs down. (Adjusters for a small number of insurance companies, including Chubb, Amica and St. Paul Travelers, typically do look out for their customers' interests. These organizations strive to be viewed as customer-friendly insurance providers.)

What to do: If you believe an insurance adjuster is not being reasonable, consider hiring a public adjuster, an insurance claims specialist who represents policyholders in their negotiations with insurance companies. First, say to the insurance adjuster, "My neighbor suggested I hire a public adjuster to represent me. What do you think?" Insurance company adjusters often become more flexible when they have reason to believe that the alternative is facing off with a professional public adjuster working on the policyholder's behalf. If you still are not satisfied, go ahead and hire a public adjuster. They can be found in the Yellow Pages, typically under "Insurance Adjusters" or "Adjusters–Public"...or through the National Association of Public Insurance Adjusters (703-433-9217, *www.napia.com*)...or on my Internet site (*www.ican2000.com*). Public adjusters typically charge approximately 15% of the total claim settlement.

Myth: I can cancel my insurance simply by not paying my renewal bill.

Reality: The insurance companies typically provide a grace period of about 30 days before terminating coverage when a bill is not paid. Policyholders are legally responsible for premiums charged during this grace period, even if they have no intention of continuing their coverage and already have obtained coverage through a different insurer.

Not paying the resulting bill is likely to put a black mark on your credit report and trigger calls from bill collectors. It's better to call and cancel an insurance policy that you no longer need, even if the policy has reached the end of a coverage period.

The 5 Words Never to Say To an Insurance Agent

J.D. Howard, executive director of Insurance Consumer Advocate Network, an insurance consumer advocacy organization, *www.ican2000.com*, Springfield, Missouri. Howard has been in the insurance industry since 1965, mainly as an independent insurance adjuster.

Five everyday words can raise red flags when it comes to filing a car, home or health insurance claim, making the difference between a speedy payment of your claim and a nightmare of delays or even rejection. Don't let a slip of the tongue cost you money.

1. Sorry. An auto accident is an emotional event—be compassionate but stick to the facts. Saying you're "sorry" to other people involved in the accident or to a claims adjuster implies that you are at fault, and it can be used against you. If you do blurt out "I'm sorry," stop there and use a better phrase later, when you give your formal statement. Never give a statement to a claims adjuster at the scene, especially if that person is working for the other party's insurer. Just say, "Not now." Your own insurance company should take your statement after the dust settles, when hidden damage or latent injuries may become evident.

2. Think. Whether you come home to water damage or have a fender bender, stay composed and report to your insurer factually what you know, not what you think, regarding cause or speed or other matters on which your opinion may be very wrong. Photograph the scene with a camera or cell phone. Even if you don't think you are injured in an auto accident, say, "I am not sure." If you feel pain, describe it—don't self-diagnose. Never sign a release from the other party's adjuster at the scene.

3. Flood. This word is a red flag for insurers because the typical homeowner's policy does not cover flood damage from rising groundwater. What it typically does cover is described in words such as, "sudden and accidental discharges from plumbing, heating or air-conditioning systems." Instead of saying "flood," tell your insurer something along the lines of, "The plumbing burst, and there's water everywhere." If you think you need flood insurance, check details of how you qualify at the government Web site *www.floodsmart.gov*.

4. Experimental. Most health insurance plans, especially HMOs and PPOs, require prior approval before you receive medical treatments that aren't common practice—those that are experimental, investigational or a part of clinical trials. Typically these procedures are excluded from coverage. So don't use the term "experimental" with your provider when describing treatment you want to undergo. Rely on your doctor or his/her staff to explain to your insurer why you need the procedure.

5. Whiplash. This term can encompass a range of injuries to the neck caused by sudden impact. When an adjuster hears the term, his knee-jerk reaction is that someone is making up an injury or trying to jack up payments from a claim. Instead, describe your symptoms.

Example: "I can't move my neck."

Better: Wait until your doctor makes a diagnosis, and share that with the insurer.

What Never to Say on Facebook...MySpace... Or LinkedIn

Rob Douglas, an information security consultant located in Steamboat Springs, Colorado, and the editor of *www.IdentityTheft.info*. He served as a consultant to the Federal Trade Commission on Operation Detect Pretext, a sting designed to catch information thieves. He previously was a private detective in Washington, DC.

Many users of social-networking Web sites unknowingly put themselves at risk. The Web sites such as Facebook, MySpace, LinkedIn and Twitter promote the impression that we are chatting with only our trusted friends, family members or colleagues—but there could be identity thieves, burglars or stalkers taking note. *Here's what not to reveal on social-networking sites...*

• **Addresses and birth dates.** Disclosing your home address or your place or date of birth could make you a target of an identity thief. Your home address even could attract a burglar or stalker to your home. If you are throwing a party and need to provide directions to your home, do so through e-mails sent directly to invitees, not through these Web sites.

If a social-networking Web site requires that you include your address or birth date in your profile, supply slightly inaccurate information.

• **Year of graduation from high school or college.** Knowing graduation dates helps scammers pretend to be former classmates—one common way to win victims' trust. Also, potential employers could use your graduation date to estimate your age, then reject you if they consider you too old. While this violates age discrimination laws, it would be almost impossible to prove.

• **Business contacts.** Professional networking Web sites, such as LinkedIn, typically let people on your contact list see the names and IDs of everyone else on your list. An unscrupulous competitor, a dissatisfied customer or a former employee could send a damaging message about you to everyone on the list. Or a competitor could target your clients if they are among your contacts.

Helpful: LinkedIn allows users to block access to their contact lists. Click "Account & Settings," then "Connections Browse" and select "No, hide my connections list."

Also, review your list of contacts every six months, and remove anyone who you wouldn't want knowing the details of your personal or professional life…and anyone who you are not 100% certain is who he claims to be.

• **Mother's maiden name.** Web sites and financial companies often use your mother's maiden name to confirm your identity, so it's prudent to keep that name as confidential as possible.

Avoid discussing current or former pets by name on social-networking Web sites as well. Pet names are another security question.

• **Your plans for travel and schedules of groups you belong to.** If you mention the dates of an upcoming vacation on a social-networking Web site…or that you've joined a book group that meets every Wednesday at 7:00 pm, you might unwittingly have told a burglar when your home will be vacant…or made it easier for a stalker to follow you.

Helpful: If you post your travel plans on a social-networking site, at least add a sentence suggesting someone else will be in the home… or that the property is well-secured.

Example: "I found a great dog-sitter, and I'm showing him how to use our new alarm system this afternoon."

• **Your valuables.** Don't discuss your expensive art, antiques or jewelry. It could make you a target for a burglar.

• **The name of your doctor, dentist or other health-care providers.** If a scammer learns where you receive medical treatment, he might attempt to obtain your insurance information. This could be sold to someone who doesn't have health insurance, who would then try to pose as you to obtain treatment.

Crime Is Up: How to Be Your Own Bodyguard

Irene van der Zande, cofounder, executive director and instructor at Kidpower Teenpower Fullpower International, a nonprofit organization that has taught personal safety and self-defense techniques to children, adults and seniors since 1989, Santa Cruz, California. For more, go to *www.kidpower.org*

Face-to-face crimes, including muggings and assaults, are up an average of 33% nationally in this shaky economy. We all need to become our own bodyguards when we're out and about. Most of us know the basic safety advice, such as always being aware of our surroundings. *Here are more tactics to stay safe when you're out in public…*

• **Program your cell phone with the local police number on speed dial in case there's trouble.** Police have told me that this often yields a faster officer response than 911 because a 911 operator has to route the call to a police officer. Check with your local police department to find out which would be faster in your region.

• **Always lock your car.** This seems like a no-brainer, but you would be surprised at how many people forget to do it. Lock your car even if you're just sitting in it for a few moments in a parking lot before you drive off.

• **Carry mugger's money if you are in a high-risk location, such as a bad neighborhood or a tourist locale in a foreign country.** Keep a wallet with $20 to $50 in small bills that's easily accessed, separate from your other valuables.

• **Press the panic button on your car key to set off the car alarm if someone frightens you.** Many alarms can be triggered from at least 45 feet away, sometimes 100 feet or more. The loud noise can deter would-be attackers.

• **Place your valuables down and move away if you are asked to give up your wallet or purse.** This increases the distance between you and the assailant.

• **Yell orders if you feel your life is being threatened.** If you give up your valuables, but the person says, "You're coming with me," or starts to attack or pull you, yell clear messages, such as, "Stop," and "Leave me alone," to the attacker. Then, if there are others around, yell, "Call the police," or "Call 911." Don't yell, "Help." The word "help" makes people afraid for their own safety and unsure of what to do.

Example: Late one night, an elderly woman's car broke down in a bad neighborhood. While she was waiting for the tow service, five young men got out of their cars and started threatening her. She screamed to a woman she saw, "Call the police." She then yelled at her attackers, "Stop right there! Get back in your cars and leave. The police are on their way." The men took off.

• **Know two easy moves targeted at the most vulnerable spots on the body** in case you must physically defend yourself. *Yelling, "No!" while you perform these moves helps give you more power...*

• The Eye Strike. Squeeze your fingers together (like a bird's beak), and jab them hard into the attacker's eyes. You also can claw your fingers like a rake across the eyes.

• The Groin Strike. Stand with your feet apart, and lift up your knee so that your thigh strikes between the attacker's legs and your knee jabs into his groin.

These moves aren't meant to disarm or overpower an attacker, which is difficult to do. You just want to buy yourself enough time to break away from his grasp. If you can manage to get a few feet away from him—all the while screaming—chances are high that he will flee to avoid being caught rather than chase you.

Don't Get Skimmed

Karen Larson, editor, *Bottom Line Personal,* Boardroom Inc., 281 Tresser Blvd., Stamford, Connecticut 06901.

Patrons of a Citibank near me recently got "skimmed" using the ATMs in the bank's own lobby. Crooks installed hidden devices to capture information encoded on the magnetic strips of bank cards. They then used the information to steal funds from victims' accounts.

Few banks and gas stations are doing enough to protect their customers, says Robert Siciliano, CEO of Boston-based security company IDTheftSecurity.com. *His advice...*

• **Examine ATMs carefully.** If the card reader extends outward from the face of the ATM, give the external portion a quick yank or twist. Do the same with the panel containing the keypad. Don't use the ATM if either feels loose. Be wary if the color of the plastic around the card reader or the keypad doesn't match the plastic elsewhere.

• **Don't assume that an ATM is safe because it is in a well-monitored location.** Last year, there was a rash of skimmings at ATMs near the registers inside busy supermarkets.

• **Look for tiny hidden cameras aimed at the keypad.** Crooks sometimes use these to learn victims' PINs. A camera could be hidden inside a bank brochure holder near the ATM keypad or in a fake speaker mounted on the ATM. To be safe, use your free hand to cover your typing hand.

• **Confirm that your card slides in and out of the card reader smoothly.** Jamming suggests a skimmer.

• **Be wary of gas pumps**—you might be skimmed. Use a credit card (or select "credit" when using a debit card)—laws protect credit card users from substantial losses.

• **Check your bank account regularly.** Contact the bank immediately if you notice any unexplained declines.

6

Fabulous Health After 50

Lessons for Living Longer...from the People Who Live the Longest

The average life expectancy in the US is 78.1 years, an age that is far less than our potential maximum life spans. On the Japanese island of Okinawa, there are approximately 50 centenarians (those who reach 100 years or more) per 100,000 people. In the US, at most 20 per 100,000 people reach this impressive milestone.

A long life is not an accident. Author and longevity expert Dan Buettner, in conjunction with the National Institute on Aging and the nation's top gerontologists, has studied what he calls the world's Blue Zones, areas where people enjoy unexpectedly long and healthy lives. In addition to Okinawa, the Blue Zones include Sardinia, Italy...Loma Linda, California (home to many Seventh-day Adventists)...and the Nicoya Peninsula in Costa Rica.

Important finding: Only about 25% of longevity is determined by genetics. The other 75% is largely determined by the choices that we make every day. *The average American could live up to 14 more good years by putting the following habits to work...*

CHOOSE ACTIVITY, NOT "EXERCISE"

In Sardinia, where the rate of centenarians is 208 per 100,000, many men work as shepherds. They hike for miles every day. Similarly, people in Okinawa get hours of daily exercise in their gardens. California's Seventh-day Adventists, one of the longest-living groups in the US, take frequent nature walks.

What these groups have in common is regular, low-intensity physical exercise. No, they do not necessarily lift weights or run marathons.

Dan Buettner, founder of Blue Zones, an organization that studies the regions of the world where people commonly live active lives past the age of 100. Based in Minneapolis, he is a writer for *National Geographic* and author of *The Blue Zones: Lessons for Living Longer from the People Who've Lived the Longest* (National Geographic). For more information, go to *www.bluezones.com.*

They merely stay active—and they do it every day throughout their lives.

Daily physical activity improves balance and reduces the risk for falls, a common cause of death among seniors. It lowers blood pressure and improves cardiovascular health. It increases the odds that people will be functionally independent in their later years.

Recommended: 30 to 60 minutes of moderate physical activity daily. This could include riding a bicycle or walking instead of driving.

EAT LESS

Okinawan elders intone this adage before eating—*hara hachi bu*—a reminder to cease eating when their stomachs are 80% full.

People who quit eating when they're no longer hungry (rather than eating until they feel full) find it easy to maintain a healthy weight, which reduces the risk for heart disease. This approach is more natural than conventional diets. *Helpful...*

- **Serve yourself at the kitchen counter, then put the food away.** People who do this tend to eat about 14% less than those who do not.
- **Use smaller plates and bowls.** Doing so makes servings look larger, which helps you eat less. In one study, people who ate from a 34-ounce bowl took in 31% more than those who used a 17-ounce bowl. Similarly, people drink at least 25% more when they use short, wide glasses instead of tall, narrow ones.
- **Buy small.** Most people consume about 150 more calories when they take food from large packages than when they take it from smaller ones.

LIMIT MEAT

In every Blue Zone, meat is consumed, at most, a few times a month. People in these communities live mainly on beans, whole grains, vegetables and other plant foods. These foods are high in fiber, antioxidants and anticancer compounds. Traditional Sardinians, Nicoyans and Okinawans eat what is produced in their gardens supplemented with staples like durum wheat (Sardinia), sweet potato (Okinawa) and maize (Nicoya). Strict Adventists avoid meat entirely.

Studies of Seventh-day Adventists show that a relatively high proportion eat nuts (any kind). Those who eat about two ounces of nuts five or more times a week have heart disease rates that are only half those who rarely eat nuts.

CONSIDER WINE

Research on long-lived people suggests that drinking alcohol in moderation is a powerful factor in living longer. It is consumed in three of the Blue Zones (Okinawa, Sardinia and Costa Rica). In Sardinia, the shepherds drink about one-quarter bottle of red wine a day. Their wine has two to three times more flavonoids than other wines (because of the hot climate and the way the wine is made). Flavonoids decrease arterial inflammation. Inflammation has been linked to atherosclerosis, diabetes and Alzheimer's disease.

CULTIVATE A SENSE OF PURPOSE

A study funded by the National Institutes of Health (NIH) found that people who are excited by life and feel that they're making a difference tend to live longer (and healthier) lives than those who just "get by."

Okinawans call it *ikigai* and Nicoyans call it *plan de vida,* but in both cultures, the phrase essentially translates to why I wake up in the morning. Anything that gives you a sense of purpose—even something as simple as taking pleasure in watching your children or grandchildren grow up well—can add years to your life.

DE-STRESS

Many people don't recognize that the 24/7 American lifestyle is literally toxic. It produces a chronic increase in stress hormones that triggers inflammation throughout the body.

Most of the world's longest-lived people incorporate some form of meaningful downtime into their daily lives. Nicoyans take a time-out every afternoon to socialize with friends. For Adventists, the Saturday Sabbath is a time to rest.

EMBRACE YOUR SPIRITUAL SIDE

Faith is a key element that most centenarians have in common. The Sardinians and Nicoyans are mostly Catholic. Okinawans have a blended religion that stresses ancestor worship. The Adventists form a strong religious community.

People who attend religious services are about one-third less likely to die in a given period than those who do not. Even among people who do not go to church, those with spiritual beliefs have less depression, better immunity and lower rates of heart disease.

PUT FAMILY FIRST

In the Blue Zones, a great emphasis is placed on family—and people who live with or maintain close ties with their families get sick less often than those without these ties. They also are more likely to maintain better mental and social skills throughout their lives.

The Diabetes Miracle: Natural Ways to Prevent And Even Reverse This Chronic Disease

Stuart A. Seale, MD, chief medical officer of Lifestyle Center of America, a diabetes center with facilities in Sedona, Arizona and Sulphur, Oklahoma. He also is lifestyle educator and staff physician for the Stopping Diabetes Program, Sedona. Dr. Seale is coauthor, with Franklin House, MD, and Ian Blake Newman, of *The 30-Day Diabetes Miracle* (Perigee). See *www.diabetesmiracle.org* for more information.

Type 2 diabetes is one of the numerous chronic diseases that often can be managed entirely without medication, particularly when it is diagnosed at an early stage.

Among individuals with insulin resistance, a precursor to diabetes, nearly all can reverse it with the same changes. Even with longstanding diabetes, many patients can discontinue most of their insulin/oral drugs when they incorporate significant dietary and other lifestyle changes.

CATCH IT EARLY

About 24 million Americans have type 2 diabetes (once known as adult-onset diabetes), and at least 57 million have prediabetes, an intermediate condition in which levels of fasting glucose (blood sugar) are between 100 milligrams per deciliter (mg/dL) and 125 mg/dL. What they have in common is an inability to effectively utilize insulin, the hormone produced by the pancreas that allows glucose to move from the bloodstream into the body's cells.

Most people who have diabetes are first diagnosed via a fasting blood sugar test. But by the time glucose levels are high, the disease already has progressed—and the cells that produce insulin may have already suffered irreversible damage.

Better: The fasting serum insulin test.

Cost: About $50 (which may be covered by insurance). High levels of insulin indicate insulin resistance, a condition that precedes sharply elevated glucose.

Anyone with diabetes risk factors, including obesity, high blood pressure, elevated cholesterol or a waist circumference of more than 40 inches in men or 35 inches in women, should have the fasting serum insulin test.

Those who have diabetes or are at risk for diabetes should consider making the following lifestyle changes. People sometimes complain about the "restrictive" nature of the changes needed to control diabetes. It does take some effort, but far less than dealing with the complications of the disease—which may include blindness, nerve damage and amputation.

NEAR-VEGETARIAN DIET

One study found that 21 of 23 patients were able to discontinue oral diabetes drugs after switching to a mainly meatless diet—of those on insulin, 13 out of 17 were able to quit taking the insulin.

A plant-based diet is high in fiber, which slows digestion and the rate of glucose absorption into the blood. This causes the pancreas to secrete less insulin, and it makes cells more sensitive to insulin's effects. People who consume little or no meat also tend to have lower cholesterol and blood pressure—important for minimizing the cardiovascular complications of diabetes.

The Diabetes Prevention Program research found that people at risk for developing type 2 diabetes who exercised regularly and ate a Mediterranean-style diet—mainly fruits, vegetables, legumes (beans, lentils) and whole grains, with only small amounts of meat a few times per month—decreased their risk of developing diabetes by 58%. In contrast, trying to prevent diabetes by using the popular medication *metformin* lowered the risk for developing diabetes by 31%.

CARBOHYDRATE COUNTING

Carbohydrate counting is among the most effective ways to control diabetes. *Main steps...*

• **Calculate net carbohydrate.** This is the amount of carbohydrate in a food minus fiber content. One cup of Kashi GoLean cereal, for example, has 30 grams (g) of total carbohydrates, but because this includes 10 g of fiber, the net carbohydrate is actually 20 g. You can find all of this information on food labels.

• **Identify "carbohydrate choices."** One carb choice equals 15 g of net carbohydrates.

Example: A slice of whole-wheat bread is one carbohydrate choice (about 15 g of net carbs).

Eat 9 to 13 carbohydrate choices daily for optimal control. Most people are advised to have three to five carb choices for breakfast.

Sample breakfast: One cup of old-fashioned oatmeal with milk or milk alternative, such as soy milk (two carbohydrate choices)... one cup of berries (one carb choice)...egg or tofu scramble with vegetables, such as mushrooms, bell peppers and onions (one carb choice)...one slice of toast with nut butter (one carb choice).

Have three to five carbohydrate choices at lunch and zero to three at supper. Eating lighter at night helps stabilize overnight and morning blood sugar levels.

Carbohydrate counting is confusing initially, but people quickly memorize the carbohydrate contents of the foods that they tend to eat most often.

Helpful: I advise patients to eat meals at the same time every day...and to eat about the same portion sizes to keep blood sugar levels stable.

GLYCEMIC INDEX

Some carbohydrates elevate blood glucose almost instantly—others much more gradually. The Glycemic Index (GI) is a measure of how quickly carbohydrates elevate glucose. A lower number indicates a slower glucose rise—and better glucose control.

Example: White bread has a GI of 73. It is transformed very quickly into glucose, which causes blood sugar levels to surge. A serving of carrots, on the other hand, has a GI of 32. The glucose conversion happens slowly, which causes steadier levels of blood glucose.

Recommended: Primarily consume foods with GIs of less than 55. Foods that are minimally processed, such as legumes and whole grains, generally have lower GI numbers. (See *www.glycemicindex.com* for a complete guide to the glycemic index.)

Helpful: Above ground vegetables, such as grains and leafy greens, typically have lower GIs than below-ground vegetables, such as potatoes and radishes. Fruit from the temperate climates, such as apples, pears and peaches, offer lower GIs than tropical fruits, such as bananas.

Also, if you feel like eating a food with a high GI (such as white bread), combine it with a low-GI food, such as peanut butter, to reduce the glucose surge.

POSTMEAL EXERCISE

Exercise helps people to lose weight, which improves insulin sensitivity and reduces cardiovascular risk factors.

Even without weight loss, exercise is very effective for managing diabetes, in particular when you exercise after meals. Exercise after meals makes it easier for muscle cells to absorb glucose from the blood. Patients who check their blood sugar two hours after eating, then test it again after a brisk 20-minute walk, typically see a drop of at least 30 points.

Strength training also is helpful. People who lift weights or engage in other forms of resistance exercise (such as push-ups) two or three times a week have an increase in muscle tissue, which increases metabolism and insulin sensitivity.

LOWER STRESS

In an emergency, the body releases cortisol. This is a "fight-or-flight" hormone that increases blood glucose to produce a quick surge of energy. Unfortunately, the same thing happens in people with daily stress. Their cortisol—and glucose—remains at chronically high levels, making diabetes more difficult to control.

Stress management is critical if you have diabetes. Most people find that a daily walk keeps them calmer. In addition, hobbies are a good way to defuse tension and stress. Others learn to meditate or practice yoga. Whatever you find relaxing, make time for it at least a few times a day.

Pine Nuts and Other Tricks to Drop Pounds

Jodi Citrin Greebel, RD, CDN, registered dietitian and president of Citrition, LLC, a nutrition consulting company in New York City. She is coauthor of *The Little Black Apron: A Single Girl's Guide to Cooking with Style & Grace* (Polka Dot). Her Web site is *www.citrition.com.*

Most weight-loss diets are hard to stick to. That's because you have to eliminate 3,500 calories to lose just one pound a week and that comes to 500 calories per day. This degree of calorie restriction can make people feel hungry all of the time—and reluctant to stick with any diet for very long. That's also why it is hard for people to maintain the weight that they do lose. Roughly 95% of those who lose weight are unable to maintain the weight loss longer than a year or two.

Better: Eat foods that curtail appetite and increase feelings of fullness. People who do this naturally take in fewer calories overall and are more likely to maintain their weight loss.

WHAT TO EAT

• **Protein at every meal.** Protein is a natural appetite suppressant. People who often feel hungry probably aren't getting enough protein.

Self-test: Have a regular meal or snack. If you are hungry again within two hours, the meal probably didn't include enough protein.

Protein should make up about 25% of every meal—three ounces to six ounces of protein is ideal. Good protein sources include chicken, seafood, lean red meats, egg whites, beans and low- or nonfat dairy.

Trap: Many traditional breakfast foods, such as a bagel or a Danish, are high in calories but low in protein. People who start the day with these foods invariably want to eat more within a few hours, adding unnecessary calories.

Always include protein with your morning meal—by spreading peanut butter on whole-wheat toast, for example.

Also helpful: High-protein snacks, such as string cheese or yogurt. They're more satisfying than carbohydrate snacks, such as pretzels or chips.

• **More fat.** Until recently, weight-loss experts advised people to eat less fat. This made intuitive sense because fat has about twice the calories as an equal amount of protein or carbohydrate. But today, after about 15 years of low-fat dieting, Americans are heavier than ever.

Reason: People who don't feel satisfied on a low-fat diet often eat excessive carbohydrates to make up the difference.

Fat is a satisfying nutrient. You may feel full after eating a lot of carbohydrates, such as pasta or bread, but you'll still want more. Fat, on the other hand, makes you crave less food, so you'll be less likely to fill up on calories from other sources.

Have a little fat with every meal. If you're having a salad, for example, use full-fat dressing in moderation rather than fat-free. Add a tablespoon of olive oil when making a pasta sauce. A slice of cheese or a serving of cottage cheese also provides satisfying amounts of fat.

Easy does it: Use fats only in small amounts to avoid excess calories. One tablespoon of olive oil, for example, has about 120 calories. Small amounts curtail your appetite without adding too many calories.

• **A handful of pine nuts.** A hormone called *cholecystokinin* (CCK) has been found to increase feelings of fullness. About one ounce or a small handful of pine nuts (which actually are seeds, not nuts) stimulates the body to release CCK. This reduces appetite and helps you feel fuller even when you take in fewer calories overall.

• **Fiber, especially early in the day.** High-fiber diets increase feelings of fullness and aid in weight loss. High-fiber foods also may stimulate the release of appetite-suppressing hormones.

Virtually all foods that are high in fiber, such as fruits, vegetables, legumes and whole grains, are relatively low in calories. People who eat a lot of these foods tend to feel full even when they take in fewer calories during the day.

Try to get 25 to 30 grams of fiber daily. Beans are high in fiber, with about six grams in one-half cup. Blackberries have about eight grams of fiber per cup.

- **Spicy foods as often as possible.** Cayenne, jalapeños, curries and other spicy foods contain capsaicin and other compounds that may increase metabolism and cause the body to burn slightly more calories. More important, these foods appear to affect the "satiety center" in the brain, causing people to feel more satisfied and consume fewer calories.

- **Water before a meal.** Drink a full glass of water before you start eating, and keep sipping water throughout the meal. Water takes up space in the stomach. Or you can start your meal with a broth-based soup (not a cream soup, which is higher in calories). People who consume liquids before and during meals consume fewer calories than those who go straight to the main course.

Caution: Avoid high-calorie liquids. Americans consume about 20% more calories now than they did 20 years ago. Many of these calories come from soft drinks, sports drinks and coffee beverages that include sugar and cream. Some of these drinks contain 400 calories or more, which could result in almost one extra pound of weight a week if consumed daily.

Late-Night Alert

Late-night eating causes more weight gain than eating during the day.

Recent finding: Mice that ate when they would normally have been sleeping gained 2.5 times more weight than mice that ate during their usual waking hours.

Fred Turek, PhD, professor of biology and circadian biology at Northwestern University, Evanston, Illinois, and principal investigator of an animal study published in *Obesity*.

Breakthroughs in Stroke Prevention And Treatment: New Findings Can Save Lives

Ralph L. Sacco, MD, professor and chairman of the department of neurology at University of Miami Leonard M. Miller School of Medicine. He is an international expert on both the prevention and treatment of stroke and president of the American Heart Association (AHA). Dr. Sacco also is the Olemberg Family Chair in Neurological Diseases and the Miller Professor of Neurology, Epidemiology and Human Genetics at the Miller School and neurologist-in-chief at Jackson Memorial Hospital, Miami.

Nearly 800,000 times a year—every 40 seconds—someone in the US suffers a stroke.

Ischemic stroke occurs when a clot blocks the flow of blood to the brain. This accounts for 87% of strokes. A hemorrhagic stroke results when a blood vessel in the brain ruptures and accounts for 13% of strokes.

These "brain attacks" often are deadly or disabling. Stroke is the third-leading cause of death (after heart disease and cancer), killing more than 143,000 Americans yearly. It's the leading cause of disability, and it can result in paralysis, spasticity, pain, speech problems and memory loss.

Good news: Researchers are discovering more effective ways to prevent and treat stroke. In a recent 10-year span, the death rate from stroke has fallen by 30% and the actual number of stroke deaths has declined by 13.5%.

The latest findings...

DECREASE YOUR RISK

Scientists at Harvard School of Public Health identified five lifestyle factors that can cut the risk for ischemic stroke by 80% and all strokes by almost 50%—not smoking, maintaining a normal weight, eating a prudent diet, exercising regularly and moderate intake of alcohol. *Also...*

- **Consider statin medication.** A report in the May 2009 issue of *The Lancet Neurology* analyzed the results of using LDL cholesterol–lowering statin medications to prevent stroke in 165,792 people. For every decrease in LDL of 39 mg/dL, there was a 21.1% decrease in the risk for stroke. Ask your doctor about whether a statin is right for you.

• **Eat more fish.** A study published last August in *Neurology* showed that people who ate tuna and other fish high in omega-3 fatty acids three times or more per week had a nearly 26% lower risk of having brain imaging findings of stroke, compared with people who didn't eat the fish regularly.

• **Drink tea.** Researchers at UCLA analyzed studies involving nearly 195,000 people and found that, compared with people who didn't drink tea, those who drank six cups of green or black tea a day reduced their risk for stroke by 42%, while those who drank three cups had a 21% reduction.

KNOW THE SYMPTOMS

Researchers working in the Division for Heart Disease and Stroke Prevention at the Centers for Disease Control and Prevention surveyed 86,573 adults about the five warning signs of stroke (see the next page). They reported their findings at the American Stroke Association's 2009 International Stroke Conference.

New finding: People at the highest risk for stroke—the elderly and those who have had a previous stroke—were the least likely to know the five stroke warning signals. Overall, only 37% of those surveyed knew all five signs and knew to call 911 immediately.

If you suspect stroke...

• **Don't call the doctor's office.** Calling a primary care doctor at the first sign of stroke delays patients from reaching the emergency room (ER), note researchers at West Virginia University-Morgantown. In their study, the researchers called primary care physicians' offices looking for advice on hypothetical stroke or heart attack symptoms. Nearly one-third of receptionists recommended scheduling an appointment for later in the day if symptoms continued.

• **Don't call the hospital help line if you're having stroke-like symptoms.** The operator may tell you to call your doctor. A study in *Stroke* showed that nearly one-quarter of hospital help-line operators mistakenly routed a caller describing classic stroke symptoms to primary care doctors rather than to 911.

RUSH TO THE ER

If you're having a stroke, the faster you call 911 and get to the emergency room...and the sooner you are treated with *tissue plasminogen activator* (or tPA), the blood-thinning, clot-dissolving intravenous drug...the less amount of brain tissue is likely to die...and the better the likely outcome, in terms of preventing death and disability. But many people who are having a stroke don't get to the ER right away—mostly because they don't think they're having a stroke.

Mayo Clinic researchers published in the November 2008 issue of *Emergency Medicine Journal* that the average time of arrival at the ER was after the three hours from the onset of stroke during which tPA was considered to be effective.

New finding #1: Researchers have found significant benefits—and no increased risk for brain injury—in people with stroke who were treated with tPA up to four-and-a-half hours after the onset of symptoms. Consequently, at the end of May 2009, treatment guidelines expanded the time to four-and-a-half hours that some patients can get the clot-busting drug.

Caution: It still is important to get treatment as soon as possible.

New finding #2: Three out of five stroke deaths occur in women. Women are 30% less likely than men to receive tPA in the ER, reported researchers from Michigan State University at the 2009 International Stroke Conference.

Possible reason: Women may not have any of the five classic stroke symptoms. Instead, they may suffer a loss of consciousness or sudden body pain other than a headache. If you or a loved one experiences these symptoms, ask to be checked for stroke.

PREVENT A SECOND STOKE

Each year, of the 795,000 Americans who have a stroke, 185,000 will suffer a second stroke. *To reduce your risk...*

New finding: One study reported at the American Academy of Neurology's 61st Annual Meeting in April 2009 proved that stroke victims who achieve "optimal levels" of four risk factors—LDL cholesterol, HDL cholesterol, triglycerides (blood fats) and blood pressure—were 65% less likely to have another stroke, compared with people who did not reach an optimal level of any risk factor. Those who achieved optimal levels of three risk factors were 38% less likely to have another stroke... two risk factors, 22% less...and one risk factor, 2% less.

---

5 Warning Signs of Stroke

If you experience one or more of these signs, call 911 immediately...

- **Sudden numbness or weakness in the face, arm or leg,** particularly if on only one side of the body.
- **Sudden, severe headache** with no known cause.
- **Sudden visual disturbance** in just one or both eyes.
- **Sudden confusion or difficulty speaking.**
- **Sudden dizziness, loss of balance, loss of coordination or difficulty walking.**

The Amazing Power of Aspirin

Randall S. Stafford, MD, PhD, medical director of Stanford Prevention Research Center, director of the Program on Prevention and Outcomes Practices at the Stanford Prevention Research Center and associate professor of medicine at Stanford University. Dr. Stafford is author or coauthor of more than 110 scientific papers in leading medical journals. He is on the advisory panel of experts of "Aspirin Talks," an educational campaign from the American College of Preventive Medicine.

It costs just pennies a pill—but for heart disease and stroke, the number-one and number-three killers of Americans, aspirin can be just as powerfully preventive as more expensive medications, such as cholesterol-lowering statins.

Two-thirds of people at high risk for heart attack and stroke do not take aspirin daily—that leads to an estimated yearly death toll of 45,000 people who might have lived if they had taken a low-dose aspirin every day. *And recent evidence shows that aspirin also plays a role in fighting colon cancer and possibly other diseases...*

PROTECTING DISEASED ARTERIES

If you've had a heart attack, taking aspirin daily decreases your risk for a second attack by 23%. If you have angina—chest pain that signals serious heart disease—daily aspirin reduces heart attack risk by 51%. Type 2 diabetes—which damages arteries, increasing risk for heart attack and stroke—is another reason for daily aspirin. Taking aspirin if you have diagnosed heart disease or type 2 diabetes is called secondary prevention—it is too late to prevent the problem, but you're controlling it.

What to do: If you have heart disease or type 2 diabetes, talk to your doctor about aspirin therapy. The recommended dosage for secondary prevention is 81 milligrams (mg) daily, or one "baby aspirin." There continues to be debate about whether 162 mg daily may be more protective for some people with heart disease or diabetes—ask your doctor.

PREVENTING HEART ATTACK

In March 2009, the US Preventive Services Task Force (USPSTF) recommended the daily use of aspirin for primary prevention—preventing heart attack and stroke in people who don't have diagnosed cardiovascular disease.

Because older age is a risk factor for heart attacks and strokes, the recommendation included all men between the ages of 45 and 79 and all women between the ages of 55 and 79.

Among these groups, the USPSTF said to use aspirin for primary prevention only in cases in which the benefits are likely to outweigh the risks. When aspirin blocks the production of blood-clotting *thromboxane,* it increases the risk for internal bleeding.

The benefits of taking aspirin are likely to be greater than the risks in those with an elevated risk for heart attack and stroke. These risk factors include high total cholesterol, lower than normal HDL (good) cholesterol, high blood pressure, smoking and older age.

Factors that may indicate aspirin is too risky for you include…

- **Recent bleeding from a stomach ulcer or hemorrhagic stroke,** caused by a ruptured blood vessel.
- **History of gastrointestinal (GI) bleeding** caused by other nonsteroidal anti-inflammatory drugs (NSAIDs).
- **Taking an anti-inflammatory corticosteroid,** such as prednisone.
- **Rheumatoid arthritis.**

AGE 80 OR OLDER

The USPSTF didn't include a recommendation for people age 80 or older, because there's not enough scientific evidence to know whether aspirin protects this age group. However, your risk for heart attack and stroke increases with age, so those over 80 are likely to benefit from aspirin, but they also are more likely to have GI or brain bleeding.

What to do: If you're 80 or older, ask your physician about taking aspirin. You probably shouldn't take it if you have a history of GI bleeding or falls (a head injury is more likely to cause hemorrhagic stroke in someone taking aspirin).

COLON CANCER

A study by researchers at Harvard Medical School, published in the August 12, 2009, issue of *The Journal of the American Medical Association*, showed that people with colorectal cancer who began taking aspirin regularly after diagnosis had a 29% lower risk of dying from the disease than those who never used aspirin. Researchers also found that those who used aspirin regularly before their diagnosis had a 61% lower risk of dying from the disease. Aspirin reduces inflammation, which may play a role in the progress of colon cancer.

What to do: If you've been diagnosed with colorectal cancer, talk with your doctor about taking aspirin. There is not enough scientific evidence to justify taking aspirin to prevent colorectal cancer.

USING ASPIRIN WISELY

Don't worry about the formulation. In most cases, aspirin does not cause GI bleeding because it irritates your GI tract—the bleeding is triggered by a systemic effect on COX (see below). That means enteric-coated tablets do not decrease the risk for GI bleeding.

Be cautious of blood-thinning supplements. Fish oil and the herb ginkgo biloba also affect platelets, increasing the risk for internal bleeding. If you're taking aspirin, talk to your doctor about whether it is safe to take those supplements.

Do not take aspirin and another NSAID at the same time. Recent research indicates that the NSAIDs, such as *ibuprofen* and *naproxen* (Aleve, Naprosyn), interfere with aspirin's ability to affect COX. If you take another NSAID, take it four to six hours before or after taking aspirin.

Think twice about stopping aspirin before surgery. Surgeons often ask patients to stop taking aspirin about two weeks before surgery. But if you take aspirin for secondary prevention, the risk for a heart attack may outweigh the risk for additional bleeding during surgery. Ask your physician.

If you think you are having a heart attack, call 911 immediately and take aspirin. Chew on an uncoated full-strength (325-mg) aspirin right away. Taking aspirin once a day for the next month can reduce the risk for death by 23% and may significantly reduce damage to the heart.

HOW ASPIRIN WORKS

Aspirin is *acetylsalicylic acid*—a compound that obstructs the activity of *cyclooxygenases* (COX), enzymes that are found in every cell.

COX help manufacture *prostaglandins,* hormones that control pain, fever and inflammation. COX also help to produce thromboxane, which allows cells in the bloodstream called platelets to stick together, forming blood clots.

By impeding prostaglandins, aspirin lowers fever, relieves acute pain including headache, and eases the soreness that accompanies inflammation. By reducing thromboxane, aspirin helps stop the formation of blood clots, reducing the risk for a heart attack and stroke.

Green Tea Lowers Heart Attack Risk by 30%...and Fights Cancer, Diabetes And Stroke

Patrick M. Fratellone, MD, executive medical director of Fratellone Medical Associates in New York City... an attending physician at St. Luke's Hospital, Roosevelt Hospital and Beth Israel Hospital in New York City... former chief of medicine and director of cardiology at Atkins Center for Complementary Medicine...and coauthor of a comprehensive review article on the health benefits of green tea in *Explore.* His Web site is *www.fratellonemedical.com.*

Green tea offers remarkable powers to combat disease. I think we all should include green tea in our daily health regimen.

The leaves of the evergreen shrub *Camellia sinensis* are used to produce green, black and oolong tea—but green tea contains the most *epigallocatechin* (EGCG). EGCG (a type of plant compound called a *polyphenol, flavonoid* or *catechin*) is a powerful anti-inflammatory and antioxidant. Research shows that chronic low-grade inflammation (produced by an immune system in overdrive) and oxidation (a kind of internal rust that damages cells) are the two processes that trigger and advance most chronic diseases. *Evidence indicates that green tea can prevent and treat many of these diseases...*

HEART DISEASE AND STROKE

Researchers studied 14,000 people ages 65 to 84 for six years. They found that men who drank seven or more cups of green tea a day had a 30% lower risk of dying from heart disease or stroke, and women had an 18% lower risk, compared with people who drank less than one cup of green tea a day.

How it works: Green tea can...

- **Lower blood levels of "bad" LDL cholesterol and reduce the oxidation of LDL,** which generates the small, dense particles that can clog up arteries and cause a heart attack or stroke.
- **Reduce the activity of platelets,** blood components that clump and form artery-plugging clots.
- **Prevent ventricular arrhythmia,** a spasm of the heart muscle that can trigger or worsen a heart attack.
- **Reduce high blood pressure,** a risk factor for stroke.
- **Improve the flexibility of the endothelium (the lining of the arteries),** boosting blood flow to the heart and brain.

TYPE 2 DIABETES

Type 2 diabetes is a major risk factor for cardiovascular disease and can lead to many other serious health problems, including kidney failure, blindness and lower-limb amputation.

In a study of 60 people with diabetes, those who took a daily supplement of green tea extract for two months significantly reduced *hemoglobin A1C*—a biomarker of blood sugar levels.

How it works: People with diabetes who drank green tea for 12 weeks boosted their levels of insulin (the hormone that helps move sugar out of the blood and into muscle cells)—and decreased their levels of A1C.

OVERWEIGHT

More than 65% of Americans are overweight. Those extra pounds are a risk factor in dozens of health problems, including cardiovascular disease, cancer, osteoarthritis and diabetes.

Researchers from the Netherlands reviewed 49 studies on green tea and weight loss and analyzed the results of the 11 most scientifically rigorous. They found that drinking green tea "significantly decreased body weight" and "significantly maintained body weight after a period of weight loss."

Why it works: EGCG blocks the action of an enzyme that breaks down *noradrenaline* (NA). This hormone and neurotransmitter stimulates the sympathetic nervous system, which controls heart rate, muscle tension and the release of energy from fat. By preserving NA, EGCG triggers your metabolism to stay more active and burn more calories.

CANCER

Researchers have conducted more than 1,000 scientific studies on the ability of green tea and EGCG to prevent and reverse cancer, including...

- **Breast cancer.** Researchers from Harvard School of Public Health found a 19% reduction in risk among women who drink more than three cups of green tea a day and a 27% reduction in risk for breast cancer recurrence.

- **Colon cancer.** Japanese researchers studied 136 people with colorectal *adenomas* (benign tumors that often precede colon cancer). Half of the participants were given a green tea extract. A year later, only 15% of those receiving the extract had developed new adenomas, compared with 31% of those who did not receive the extract.

- **Prostate cancer.** In a study published in *American Journal of Epidemiology*, Japanese researchers found that men with prostate cancer who drank five or more cups of green tea a day had a 48% lower risk of developing advanced prostate cancer, compared with men who drank less than one cup a day.

- **Lung cancer.** Chinese researchers found a 22% lower risk among those with the highest consumption of green tea, compared with those who did not consume green tea.

Why it works: EGCG interferes with cancer through various mechanisms, including stopping the production of factors that stimulate growth of tumors and inhibiting movement of cancer cells.

GUM DISEASE

Research links the chronic bacterial infection of gum (periodontal) disease to many health problems, including heart disease and diabetes. Japanese researchers studied nearly 1,000 men ages 49 to 59 and found that those who regularly drank green tea had fewer cases of, or less severe, periodontal disease. For every additional daily cup of tea these men drank, there was a significant decrease in the depth of periodontal pockets (the grooves around the teeth that deepen as gum disease advances), a decrease in the loss of attachment of the gum to the tooth and a decrease in bleeding.

How it works: The polyphenols in green tea may decrease the inflammatory response to oral bacteria.

THE RIGHT AMOUNT

To guarantee a sufficient intake of EGCG, I advise one or more of the following...

- **Drink green tea.** Five to 10 eight-ounce cups a day of regular or decaf.

Best: For maximum intake of EGCG, use whole-leaf loose tea rather than a teabag, using one teaspoon per cup. Steep the tea for at least five minutes.

- **Take a supplement of green tea extract.**

Minimum: 400 milligrams (mg) a day of a supplement standardized to 90% EGCG.

- **Add a drop of green tea liquid extract to green tea or another beverage.** Look for a product that is standardized to a high level (at least 50%) of EGCG, and follow the dosage recommendation on the label.

Example: HerbaGreen from HerbaSway, at 90% polyphenols, 50% from EGCG.

SAFE USE

Talk to your doctor if you use...

- **An antiplatelet medicine** (blood thinner), because green tea also thins the blood.
- **A bronchodilator,** because green tea can increase its potency.
- **An antacid,** because green tea can decrease the effect.

You Can Cure Heart Disease: A Doctor's Groundbreaking Program

Caldwell B. Esselstyn, Jr., MD, a surgeon, clinician and researcher at The Cleveland Clinic for more than 35 years. He has authored more than 150 scientific publications, including a 12-year landmark study showing that a plant-based diet can stop and reverse heart disease in severely sick patients. Dr. Esselstyn is an Olympic gold medalist in rowing and was awarded the Bronze Star as an army surgeon in Vietnam. He is author of *Prevent and Reverse Heart Disease: The Revolutionary, Scientifically Proven, Nutrition-Based Cure* (Avery). His Web site is *www.heartattackproof.com.*

In the mid-1980s, 17 people who had severe heart disease had just about given up hope. They had undergone every available treatment, including drugs and surgery—but all had failed. The group had experienced 49 cardiovascular episodes, including four heart attacks, three strokes, 15 cases of increased angina and seven bypass surgeries. Five of the patients were expected to die within a year.

Twelve years later, every one of the 17 was alive. They had had no cardiovascular events. The progression of their heart disease had been stopped—and, in many cases, reversed. Their angina went away—for some, within three weeks. In fact, they became practically "heart attack–proof." And there are hundreds of other patients with heart disease who have achieved the same remarkable results. *What you need to know...*

HOW THE DAMAGE IS DONE

Every year, more than half a million Americans die of coronary artery disease (or CAD). Three times that number suffer heart attacks. In total, half of American men and one-third of women will have some form of heart disease during their lifetimes.

Heart disease develops in the *endothelium*, the lining of the arteries. *There, endothelial cells manufacture a compound called nitric oxide that accomplishes four tasks crucial for healthy circulation...*

- **Keeps blood smoothly flowing,** rather than becoming sticky and clotted.
- **Allows arteries to widen when the heart needs more blood,** such as when you run up a flight of stairs.
- **Stops muscle cells in arteries from growing into plaque**—the fatty gunk that blocks blood vessels.
- **Decreases inflammation in the plaque**—the process that can trigger a rupture in the "cap" or surface of a plaque, starting the clot-forming, artery-clogging cascade that causes a heart attack.

The type and the amount of fat in the typical Western diet—from animal products, dairy foods and concentrated oils—will attack endothelial cells, cutting their production of nitric oxide.

Study: A researcher at University of Maryland School of Medicine gave a 900-calorie fast-food breakfast containing 50 grams of fat (mostly from sausages and hash browns) to a group of students and then measured their endothelial function. For six hours, the students had severely compromised endothelial function and decreased nitric oxide production. Another group of students ate a 900-calorie, no-fat breakfast—and had no significant change in endothelial function.

If a single meal can do that kind of damage, imagine the damage done by three fatty meals a day, seven days a week, 52 weeks a year.

PLANT-BASED NUTRITION

You can prevent, stop or reverse heart disease with a plant-based diet. *Here's what you can't eat—and what you can...*

- **What you cannot eat.** Do not have meat, poultry, fish or eggs. You will get plenty of protein from plant-based sources.

Also, no dairy products. That means no butter, cheese, cream, ice cream, yogurt or milk—even skim milk, which, though lower in fat, still contains animal protein.

Have no oil of any kind—not a drop. That includes all oils, even virgin olive oil and canola.

What you may not know: At least 14% of olive oil is saturated fat—every bit as aggressive in promoting heart disease as the saturated fat in roast beef. A diet that includes oils—including monounsaturated oils from olive oil and canola oil—may slow the progression of heart disease, but it will not stop or reverse the disease.

Generally, no nuts or avocados. If you are eating a plant-based diet to prevent heart disease, you can have moderate amounts of nuts and avocados as long as your total cholesterol remains under 150 milligrams per deciliter (mg/dL). If you have heart disease and want to stop or reverse it, you should not eat these foods.

- **What you can eat.** You can eat all vegetables, and legumes—beans, peas, lentils.

Whole grains and products that are made from them, such as bread and pasta can be eaten—as long as they do not contain added fats. Do not eat refined grains, which have been stripped of much of their fiber and nutrients. Avoid white rice and "enriched" flour products, which are found in many pastas, breads, bagels and baked goods.

Fruits are okay—but heart patients should restrict consumption to three pieces a day and avoid drinking the pure fruit juices. Too much fruit rapidly increases blood sugar, triggering a surge of insulin from the pancreas, which can stimulate the liver to manufacture additional cholesterol.

Drink certain beverages, including water, seltzer water, oat milk, hazelnut milk, almond milk, no-fat soy milk, coffee and tea. Alcohol is fine in moderation (no more than two servings a day for men and one for women).

SUPPLEMENTS

For maximum health, take five supplements daily...

- **Multivitamin/mineral supplement.**
- **Vitamin B-12**—1,000 micrograms (mcg).
- **Calcium**—1,000 milligrams (mg) (1,200 mg if you're over 60).
- **Vitamin D-3**—1,000 international units (IU).
- **Flaxseed meal** (ground up flaxseed)—one tablespoon for the omega-3 fatty acids it provides. Sprinkle it on cereal.

THE CHOLESTEROL CONNECTION

If you eat the typical, high-fat Western diet, even if you also take a cholesterol-lowering statin drug, you will not protect yourself from heart disease—because the fat in the diet will damage the endothelium cells that produce nitric oxide.

In a study in *The New England Journal of Medicine*, patients took huge doses of statin medicine to lower total cholesterol below 150 but didn't change their diets—and 25% experienced a new cardiovascular event or passed away within the next 30 months.

Recommended: Eat a plant-based diet, and ask your physician if you should also take a cholesterol-lowering medication. Strive to maintain a total cholesterol of less than 150 and LDL ("bad" cholesterol) below 85.

MODERATION DOESN'T WORK

The most common objection physicians have to this diet is that their patients will not follow it. But many patients with heart disease who find out that they do have a choice—between invasive surgery and nutritional changes that will stop and reverse the disease—willingly adopt the diet.

Why not eat a less demanding diet, such as the low-fat diet recommended by the American Heart Association or even the Mediterranean Diet?

Surprising: Research shows that people who maintain a so-called "low-fat" diet of 29% of calories from fat have the same rate of heart attacks and strokes as people who don't.

Plant-based nutrition is the only diet that can effectively prevent, stop and reverse heart disease. It also offers protection against stroke... high blood pressure...osteoporosis...diabetes... senile mental impairment...erectile dysfunction...and cancers of the breast, prostate, colon, rectum, uterus and ovaries.

Heart Attack Alert: How Daylight Saving Time Can Be Dangerous To Your Health

Michael Terman, PhD, professor of clinical psychology at Columbia University, director of the Center for Light Treatment and Biological Rhythms at New York–Presbyterian Hospital/Columbia University Medical Center, director of clinical chronobiology at New York State Psychiatric Institute and president of the Center for Environmental Therapeutics, *www.cet.org*, all in New York City. He is author or coauthor of more than 75 scientific papers appearing in leading medical journals.

In November, the US officially switches from Daylight Saving Time (DST) over to Standard Time (ST)—you "fall back" one hour. And in March, the US switches from ST to DST—you "spring forward" one hour.

Warning: These time changes can be dangerous to your health. Researchers looked at the incidence of heart attacks around the time switches—comparing the seven days right after the switches with the seven days two weeks before and two weeks after the switches...

In spring there was a 5% to 10% increase in heart attacks during the three days after the switch to DST.

In fall there was a significant spike in heart attacks on the Monday after the switch to ST.

The researchers theorized that sleep disruption from switching the clock may hurt the heart by increasing the activity of the *sympathetic nervous system,* which speeds heart rate, and by increasing the level of *cytokines,* immune cells that spark inflammation and damage arteries.

Research also shows that the sleep-disturbing switches can cause additional health-related problems, including insomnia, daytime fatigue, a decrease in daytime alertness and negative mood states, such as depression and anxiety.

We asked Michael Terman, PhD, one of the world's leading experts in this field, how to protect your health...

WHO IS MOST VULNERABLE?

Every person has an internal clock that matches wakefulness and sleepiness with the day-night cycle—a phenomenon called *circadian rhythm.* The science of how circadian rhythm affects health is known as *chronobiology*—and it has shown that each person has a genetically determined *chronotype.*

"Owls" are chronotypes that usually go to sleep very late and have difficulty waking up in the morning for a normal workday.

"Larks" feel sleepy at a so-called normal hour of the night (such as 10:00 pm) and wake up easily in the morning.

The vast majority of the population is somewhere in between the owl and the lark. But about 10% of the population are owls—and they have far more difficulty adjusting to time switches than larks. Owls are more likely to suffer from switch-caused health problems in the days and even weeks afterward.

If you're not sure whether you're an owl or a lark—or somewhere in between—go to the Web site of the Center for Environmental Therapeutics, *www.cet.org.* Click on "Therapeutic Resources & Tools," then on "Self-Assessment Tools" and finally on "Your Circadian Rhythm Type," which will open the "Automated Morningness-Eveningness Questionnaire." The 19 questions take about five to 10 minutes to answer, after which you will receive detailed feedback about your likely chronotype.

PROTECT YOURSELF

If you're an owl, there are many ways to modulate your internal clock so that you are less vulnerable to health problems from the sudden time switches...

- **Gradually set the alarm later.** During the fall switch from DST to ST, your goal is to allow your circadian clock to drift one hour later during the week or so after the switch.

If you typically wake up to an alarm clock at 7:00 am, set the alarm for 6:00 am ST on the Sunday morning of the switch, which is when you will be inclined to wake up anyway. Over the next six days, set your clock 10 minutes later each day until you arrive at 7:00 am ST.

Reverse this process in the spring, starting six days before the ST to DST switch. Set the alarm 10 minutes earlier each day so that you arrive smoothly at 7:00 am DST on Sunday morning.

- **Exercise every day.** Daily aerobic exercise helps stabilize the circadian system, preventing an owl's tendency to go to sleep later and later. It will help manage both time switches. But avoid aerobic exercise in the hours right before sleep, which can cause insomnia.

To help with the spring transition: As soon as the sun starts to rise after 7:00 am, take a brisk 20-minute walk outside right after you wake up, to jump-start your day. This is the best measure owls can take to prevent health problems caused by the March transition from ST to DST.

- **Eat regular meals.** Owls rarely feel hungry when they first wake up, so they skip breakfast. They then eat a big meal around 1:00 pm and tend to eat again late at night.

Best: Have breakfast within a half-hour of waking, eat lunch around noon and finish dinner before 8 pm. This helps normalize your circadian rhythm.

- **Take melatonin—the right way.** Melatonin, a hormone produced by the pineal gland in the brain, helps control wakefulness and sleepiness. It's usually not detectable in the blood at midday but begins to rise in the evening, about two to three hours before you feel sleepy.

In the general population, there is a six-hour spread between the average times that melatonin rises. If you're an owl, you tend to have a late onset—in some cases, as late as 1:00 am, so you don't feel sleepy until about 3:00 am. To decrease vulnerability to the time shift, an owl needs to feel sleepy earlier and can do that by taking a melatonin supplement.

Most people who take melatonin mismanage it, taking it like a sleeping pill, 30 to 45 minutes before bedtime. But by that hour, the brain has already started to produce the hormone, and the additional supplement has little effect.

Better: Take a very small amount of melatonin—0.25 milligrams (mg)—five hours before your desired bedtime, starting a week before the springtime switch to DST. Your circadian clock will sense that nighttime has begun and will adjust itself toward earlier sleep onset. Move the melatonin earlier as your sleep adjusts earlier, then stop it when you reach your goal.

After taking melatonin, remain in dim, indoor light because bright, fluorescent light or outdoor light reverses the effect. Also, refrain from intense physical exercise.

Resource: Microtonin, a 0.5-mg melatonin supplement (which can be cut in half), is available from The Vitamin Shoppe (866-293-3367, *www.vitaminshoppe.com*, $8 for 60 capsules).

- **Order a "dawn simulator."** You can adjust your circadian rhythm using a sophisticated device that plugs into your light fixture and "simulates" the outdoor transition from a starlight level of light to a sunrise level of light. The device permits you to gradually move "dawn" later in the day during the week or so after the "fall backward" switch to ST, and later in the day during the week or so before the switch to DST.

The subtly intensifying light passes through your eyelids, entraining your internal clock to the time you want to start your day—no matter what is happening outdoors.

Resource: You can buy a Dawn Simulator Sunrise System at *www.cet.org*.

Cost: $115.

How a Psychologist Survived "Terminal" Cancer

Neil A. Fiore, PhD, psychologist and founding member of the National Coalition for Cancer Survivorship. He maintains a private practice in Berkeley, California, and is former president of The Northern California Society of Clinical Hypnosis. He's author of *Coping with the Emotional Impact of Cancer* (Bay Tree). His Web site is *www.neilfiore.com*.

There have been tremendous improvements in cancer diagnosis and treatment in the last half-century. Unfortunately, the treatment of patients has lagged behind the treatment of disease. All cancer patients must cope with both fear and uncertainty—emotional challenges that the medical system overlooks, even though they play a necessary role in recovery.

MY STORY

I was diagnosed with testicular cancer 35 years ago—but the doctor didn't tell me directly. He called over a resident and told him, "Feel this calcification. That is cancer." I fired this doctor and chose to work with the head of the department, who was very good about informing me of the specific research on which he was basing his treatment decisions. Armed with the names of the medical journals, I read the studies at a medical library and came back with lots of questions. Then I asked my oncologist what my chances of survival were. He told me that since my cancer had spread to my left lung—and there was no known effective chemotherapy at that time—I had a 10% chance of surviving one year.

I decided then that I would do everything possible to fully participate in my own care. *What I discovered...*

TAKE CONTROL

My doctor wanted to do an eight-hour operation to remove my lymph nodes, even though the lymph nodes appeared cancer-free in tests. He believed that it would still increase my odds of survival. Luckily, I had done my homework. I argued that the cancer in my lungs was evidence that my lungs were doing their job of filtering the bloodstream and holding on to cancer cells. I needed a treatment that cleared my bloodstream of cancer. I wanted chemotherapy, even though it was experimental. After consulting a second oncologist, I got the chemotherapy—and I believe that it saved my life.

I am not suggesting that you become your own doctor. But I do suggest that you maintain some control over your medical decisions, ask questions of your doctor and seek second and third opinions if necessary.

LET IT OUT

With specific cancers, such as melanomas, the research shows that patients who express their emotions—especially anger and depression—have significantly more immune cells at the tumor site than those who keep their emotions bottled up. They also tend to have smaller tumors.

Helpful: If you are not comfortable talking about emotions, write about them. Every day, take 10 minutes to write down whatever you're feeling—the fear of death, concerns about pain, worries about loved ones, etc.

When I decided to stop chemotherapy (after 18 months of treatment), I wrote down every possible concern, risk, benefit and criticism I would face if my decision to stop proved to be a mistake. Answering all those "what if" voices helped me feel confident about my decision.

PUSH ASIDE STRESS

Deep, controlled breathing is one of the most effective ways to reduce the stress of cancer.

How to do it: Inhale deeply, hold your breath for a moment, then exhale slowly. Do this three times. Then close your eyes, and imagine that muscle tension is leaving your body. Imagine that you are surrounded by a giant protective bubble that will give you all the time that you need to push aside unwanted stress.

Allow yourself to try to stay in this meditative state for 15 to 30 minutes, and repeat it once or twice each day. Cancer patients who have used this technique consistently report that they recovered more quickly from surgery and treatments and experienced less pain. I did this despite the fact that one doctor told me that meditation would not help, when, of course, it did help.

FIGHT DOCTOR NEGATIVITY

Physicians tend to say things such as, "You have only a 10% chance of living one year," or "This is a highly toxic chemotherapy that you'll be taking."

Doctors are obligated to tell patients the odds and side effects. This doesn't mean that they should bombard you with negatives. A more compassionate doctor might say, "You're a fighter...give this your best shot," or "Most of my patients recover quickly from this treatment."

If you feel overwhelmed by negative information, tell your doctor. Explain that you're struggling to stay confident and would appreciate more positive reinforcement.

My doctor did not want to offer me "false hope." To stop his negative predictions, I told him that I promised I wouldn't haunt him if I died of cancer after he gave me hope that I might survive it. This helped him relax. He knew he had a patient who was taking responsibility for his life.

Don't Stand in Front of The Microwave and Other Radiation Dangers in Your Home

Magda Havas, PhD, associate professor, environmental and resource studies at Trent University located in Peterborough, Ontario, Canada. Dr. Havas is also a leading authority on radio-frequency radiation, electromagnetic fields, dirty electricity and ground current. She is coauthor, with Camilla Rees, of *Public Health SOS: The Shadow Side of the Wireless Revolution* (CreateSpace).

Virtually everything with a cord or battery emits electromagnetic radiation—but some devices will emit much more than others do. The official exposure limit for electromagnetic radiation, set by the Federal Communications Commission (FCC), is based on old research that considered tissue heating to be the danger threshold.

New research: Radiation levels up to 1,000 times lower than the FCC's guidelines have been shown to affect our health.

We interviewed Magda Havas, PhD, one of the leading experts in this field, about what to do...

CELL PHONES

In 2007, a study published in *The American Journal of Epidemiology* reported that cell-phone users who spent more than 22 hours a month on their cell phones were 58% more likely to develop tumors of the *parotid* (salivary) gland than those who did not use cell phones as often. Another study reported that the risk for *gliomas* (a type of brain tumor) and *acoustic* tumors (where the ear meets the brain) doubled on the same side of the head after a decade of cell-phone use.

Studies funded by the telecommunications industry consistently have indicated that cell phones are safe.

Main flaws: These studies typically lasted six years or less, not long enough for tumors to develop. In addition, most of the studies defined "heavy use" as using a cell phone just a few times a week—far less than the hours that many people spend on their cell phones every day.

Self-defense: Use your cell phone only for emergencies or to retrieve messages. Return calls on a regular phone. *When you do use a cell phone...*

- **Regularly switch the phone from one side of your head to the other** to minimize one-side radiation exposure.
- **Turn off your cell phone when you're not expecting a call.** Even when you're not talking, cell phones send and receive signals to communicate with towers and satellites.
- **Never let the cell phone touch your ear or other body parts.** When talking, hold it at least one inch away from your head. Text-messaging is better than talking because the phone is farther away from your head. Bluetooth (wireless technology) uses radiation, but generally, levels are lower than those from your cell phone. Turn off cell phones in shirt or pants pockets.
- **Use a pneumatic (plastic air-tube) earpiece to decrease the brain's exposure to radiation.** Mercola (877-985-2695, *http://products.mercola.com*) sells these headsets, which have a hollow tube near the head rather than a wire running to the ear.
- **Don't use a phone in the car.** Using a cell phone or any wireless device while driving (or while in a train, bus or plane) uses more power because the phone must continually be reconnecting with antennas. Also, the signal is reflected by the metal around you, so your exposure inside is higher than it is outside.

CORDLESS PHONES

Cordless phones, the kind with a base station and remote handsets that you can use anywhere in your house, use very similar frequencies to those used by cell phones. They pose the same risks.

Cordless phones with the designation Digitally Enhanced Cordless Telecommunications (or DECT) technology are the worst, because they constantly emit radiation whether you're using the phone or not. They're more dangerous than having a cell-phone antenna inside your home.

Self-defense: Replace all cordless phones with corded phones.

WIFI

The lion's share of new computers, printers and similar devices now come equipped with WiFi (or wireless) capabilities. Wireless signals are a strong source of electromagnetic radiation. As long as you are using a device that is receiving and sending information to and from the Internet without wires (this includes BlackBerries and iPhones), then you are being exposed to radiation.

Self-defense: Use cables to connect your Internet service to computers. Do not use a wireless router. Similarly, it is safer to hardwire your printer to the computer than to use a WiFi connection. Hardwiring means that you won't be able to easily use a single computer throughout the house or to "beam" a signal to your printer from another room. Some people find this inconvenient, but the added safety is worth it. You can have additional Internet cables installed in multiple rooms.

If you do use a wireless router: Place it as close as possible to the devices that it controls. At greater distances, the router is forced to amplify its signal. Turn off the router when you're not using the computer.

If you don't use a wireless router: Find out how to disable the WiFi settings in your computer and printer. In the "on" position, these settings prompt the devices to put out electromagnetic energy in order to find the nearest available router.

MICROWAVE OVENS

Medical technicians leave the room when X-rays are taken. People should be just as cautious with microwave ovens.

Reason: Just about every microwave oven that I have tested, including the newest models, leaks radiation. In my home, I could detect electromagnetic radiation from the microwave 20 feet away.

Self-test: Put your cell phone inside of the oven, and close the door (do not turn on the microwave). Dial your cell-phone number. If you hear the phone ring, the cell-phone signal was able to pass through the walls of the oven—meaning that microwaves are able to pass out.

Self-defense: Leave the kitchen when the microwave is on.

DIRTY ELECTRICITY

Household electricity normally is delivered at 60 cycles per second. Along with this stable current, however, come higher frequencies—spikes in power that cause surges of radiation from appliances and even unused electrical outlets.

This so-called "dirty electricity" has been linked to fatigue, headaches, difficulty concentrating and cardiac symptoms in people who are sensitive (known as electrohypersensitivity).

Self-defense: Surge protectors, commonly used to protect computers and other electronic equipment, will "clean" household current to some extent.

Better: Graham-Stetzer Filters. These devices filter electrical "noise." You just plug them into wall outlets. They're designed to clean up entire circuits in the house. The average North American home needs about 20 filters. When you plug the filters in, you can use a microsurge meter to measure the levels of dirty electricity and try to get the levels below 40 GS units. The filters and meters are available at some hardware stores and online at *www.stetzerelectric.com* and *www.lessemf.com.*

Cost: About $35 for a filter, $125 for a meter.

PLASMA TELEVISIONS

Plasma TVs generate high amounts of dirty electricity. Using one filter will not solve the problem—people with plasma TVs might have to use three or more filters to clean up the power, compared with just one filter for an LCD TV.

Self-defense: LCDs produce nearly as good a picture and produce less dirty electricity than plasma TVs.

How to Reduce Breast Cancer Risk by 43%: Prevention Tips

Shannon Puhalla, MD, assistant professor of medicine at the Magee-Womens Hospital of The University of Pittsburgh School of Medicine and a breast cancer specialist in the division of hematology/oncology at UPMC Cancer Centers. Her scientific articles on breast cancer and other cancers have appeared in several medical journals, including *Journal of Clinical Oncology* and *The American Journal of Hematology/Oncology.*

During 2010, about 207,000 American women were diagnosed with invasive breast cancer and about 39,000 died from the disease. Breast cancer is the second-leading cause of cancer-related fatalities for women, after lung cancer.

Good news: Scientific breakthroughs offer women new hope for prevention...

PREVENTION BREAKTHROUGHS

- **HRT update.** In 2002, the Women's Health Initiative (WHI)—a scientific study designed to demonstrate the many benefits of hormone replacement therapy (HRT) for postmenopausal women—found that those taking a combination of the drugs estrogen and progestin increased their risk of developing breast cancer by 26% (and increased their risk for heart attack by 29% and stroke by 41%). This unexpected result changed the opinion of doctors and their patients about HRT. Prescriptions for the therapy declined from 60 million in 2001 to 20 million in 2005—and breast cancer rates also declined. But some experts questioned the connection, saying that the drop in cancer rates was too rapid to have been caused by women stopping HRT.

New study: Researchers at Stanford School of Medicine looked at data from more than 56,000 women—15,000 in the original WHI study and 41,449 others. *They found that...*

- A 50% decrease in hormone use between 2000 and 2003 was correlated with a 43% reduction in breast cancer rates in 2002 and 2003.
- Among women who stopped taking HRT, rates of breast cancer declined by 28%—within one year.
- Women who stayed on HRT for five years doubled their annual risk for breast cancer.

All these results appeared in the February 5, 2009, issue of *The New England Journal of Medicine.*

What to do: Women at high risk for breast cancer and those who have been diagnosed with breast cancer should avoid HRT. Women at low risk for breast cancer can use HRT to control menopausal symptoms but only as a last resort and for the shortest possible duration and at the lowest possible dose (which varies per individual).

Your risk for breast cancer depends on many factors, such as your age and the number of your first-degree relatives (mother, sister, daughter) with a history of breast cancer.

Helpful: Use the National Cancer Institute's Breast Cancer Risk Assessment Tool at *www.cancer.gov/bcrisktool.*

- **The power of exercise.** Scientists in England analyzed 62 studies on physical activity and the risk for breast cancer—and found that the most active women had a 25% lower risk than the least active. *They also found...*
- Regular recreational activity, such as brisk walking, lowered risk more than doing household chores.
- Physical activity throughout life was the most protective, but exercising after menopause was more protective than exercising only earlier in life. The study appeared in 2008 in *British Journal of Sports Medicine.*

What to do: Researchers are now determining the exact type and amount of exercise that may help protect against breast cancer. In the meantime, a sensible recommendation is to exercise for at least 20 minutes five days a week. Most people find brisk walking is the easiest way to exercise regularly.

- **Weight control.** Losing weight may help you decrease risk for breast cancer—and stay alive after a diagnosis.

New study: Researchers from the National Cancer Institute analyzed five years of health data from more than 99,000 postmenopausal women. They reported that women who were not overweight at age 18 but who were overweight at ages 35 and 50 increased their risk of developing breast cancer by 40%, compared with women who maintained a normal weight or lost weight.

Theory: An estrogen buildup in fat tissue may trigger the growth of cancer cells in the breast.

Other recent studies show that overweight women diagnosed with breast cancer have faster-growing tumors, are more likely to have a recurrence and have lower survival rates.

What to do: If you have weight to lose, talk to a dietician about eating a low-fat diet similar to that used in the Women's Intervention Nutrition Study (WINS), which showed that a diet limited to 33 grams of fat a day or less lowered the recurrence rates of breast cancer. You can achieve that fat level by emphasizing fruits and vegetables, whole grains, legumes (beans, lentils) and lean meats...and avoiding red meat and full-fat dairy products.

Easy Way to Cut Breast Cancer Risk 40%!

Women who used calcium supplements daily for five years had 40% lower risk for breast cancer than those women who did not take calcium...women who took a multivitamin daily had 30% lower risk.

Jaime Matta, PhD, professor of pharmacology at Ponce School of Medicine, Puerto Rico and coauthor of a study of 725 women, presented at the American Association for Cancer Research's 2010 annual meeting.

Cancer-Fighting Superfoods: What to Eat Before, During and After Chemotherapy

Rebecca Katz, MS, visiting chef and nutrition educator at Commonweal Cancer Help Program in Bolinas, California. She is founder of Inner Cook, a Bay Area culinary practice that works with cancer patients, and executive chef for The Center for Mind-Body Medicine's Food as Medicine and CancerGuides Professional Training Programs. She is author, with Mat Edelson, of *The Cancer-Fighting Kitchen: Nourishing, Big-Flavor Recipes for Cancer Treatment and Recovery* (Celestial Arts). Her Web site is *www.rebeccakatz.com.*

Some people experience virtually no side effects from cancer chemotherapy, but this is rare. Most patients report at least some problems, including nausea, fatigue and diarrhea during the treatment.

Reason: The drugs that are used in chemotherapy are designed to kill fast-growing cancer cells. But they also damage fast-growing healthy cells, particularly in the mouth, digestive tract and hair follicles.

Good nutrition is critical if you're undergoing chemotherapy. It's estimated that up to 80% of cancer patients are malnourished. People who eat well before and during chemotherapy tend to have fewer side effects. They also are more likely to complete the full course of therapy than those who are poorly nourished and may feel too sick to continue. *What to do...*

• **Load up on nutrient-rich foods.** In the weeks before chemotherapy, patients should emphasize nutrient-dense foods, such as whole grains, vegetables and legumes. The high nutrient load of a healthy diet helps strengthen healthy cells so that they're better able to withstand—and then recover from—the effects of chemotherapy. *Good choices...*

• Dark leafy greens, such as spinach, kale and Swiss chard. They are high in antioxidants, such as beta-carotene, lutein and other phytonutrients. These compounds help minimize the damaging effects of *free radicals,* the tissue-damaging molecules that are produced in large amounts during chemotherapy. Kale is particularly good because it provides *indole-3-carbinol,* a compound that has anticancer properties.

• Olive oil, like green vegetables, is high in antioxidants. It's one of the best sources of *oleic acid,* an omega-9 fatty acid that strengthens cell membranes and improves the ability of the immune system to fight cancer cells. I like extra-virgin olive oil because it has been exposed to the least heat.

• Garlic. The National Cancer Institute reports that people who eat garlic regularly seem to have a lower risk for intestinal and other cancers, including breast cancer. The strong-tasting sulfur compounds in garlic, such as *allicin,* have strong antiviral and antibacterial effects—important for chemotherapy patients because they're susceptible to infection. With my recipes, I use fresh garlic. I smash it and let it sit for 10 minutes to allow the antiviral properties to become more accessible—then chop and cook. (To smash garlic, set the side of a chef's knife on the clove, place the heel of your hand on the flat side of the knife and apply pressure.)

• **Increase protein.** It's the main structural component of muscle and other tissues. People who undergo chemotherapy need a lot of protein to repair tissue damage that occurs during the treatments.

Recommended: About 80 grams of protein daily. That is nearly double the amount that healthy adults need. Cancer patients who increase their protein about a week before chemotherapy, and continue to get extra protein afterward, recover more quickly. They also exhibit more energy and less fatigue.

Try this: Two or more smoothies per day (made in a blender with juice or milk, a variety of fresh fruits and ice, if you like) that are supplemented with a scoop of whey powder. The protein in whey is easily absorbed by the intestine. And most people can enjoy a nutrient-rich smoothie even when they have nausea or digestive problems that are related to chemotherapy.

• **Drink to reduce your discomfort.** Stay hydrated both before and after chemotherapy sessions to reduce nausea. Drink liquids until your urine runs clear—if it has more than a hint of yellow, you need to drink more.

Helpful: Soups and broths provide water, as well as protein, minerals and vitamins.

• **Avoid your favorite foods two days before treatments.** It's common for chemotherapy patients to develop food aversions when they get nauseated from treatments and then to associate the nausea with certain foods. It's sad when people develop aversions and can never again enjoy their favorite foods.

• **Eat lightly and frequently.** People tend to experience more nausea when the stomach is empty. During and after "chemo days," keep something in your stomach all the time—but not too much. Patients do better when they have a light snack, such as sautéed vegetables or a bowl of broth, than when they go hungry or eat a lot at one sitting.

• **Treat with ginger.** When your stomach is upset, steep three slices of fresh ginger in a cup of simmering water for 10 minutes, then drink the tea. Or grate fresh ginger with a very fine grater, such as a Microplane, and put the shavings under your tongue. Ginger alleviates nausea almost instantly.

• **Overcome "metal mouth."** The medicines used in chemotherapy can damage the nerves that control the taste buds. Some people complain about a metallic taste in their mouths after treatments. Others notice that foods taste "flat" or that their mouths are extremely sensitive to hot or cold.

These side effects, known as *transient taste changes,* generally disappear a few weeks (or, in some cases, months) after treatments, but they can make it difficult for people to eat in the meantime.

Helpful: The FASS method. It stands for Fat, Acid, Salt and Sweet. Most people will find that it's easier to enjoy their meals, and therefore ingest enough nutrients, when they combine one or more of these elements in every meal.

For fat, add more olive oil than normal to meals...lemons are a good source of acid...sea salt has less of a chemical aftertaste than regular salt...and maple syrup offers sweetness with more nutrients (including immune-building manganese and zinc) than table sugar.

• **Try kudzu root.** Used in a powder form to thicken sauces, puddings and other foods, it soothes the intestine and can help prevent diarrhea. You also can dissolve one teaspoon of kudzu root in one teaspoon of cold liquid and drink that. Drink after meals, as needed. Kudzu root is available in most health-food stores.

• **Soothe mouth sores** with soft, easy-to-eat foods, such as *granitas* (similar to "Italian ices") or smoothies. The sores can be intensely painful, which makes it difficult to eat.

Recommended: Watermelon ice cubes. Purée watermelon, and put it in a tray to freeze. Then suck on the cubes. The cold acts like a topical anesthetic—you can numb the mouth before eating a regular meal. And the juice from the melon is just as hydrating as water but provides extra nutrients, including the antioxidant lycopene.

Natural Ways to Power Up Your Brain

Daniel G. Amen, MD, a Distinguished Fellow of the American Psychiatric Association and CEO and medical director of Amen Clinics, Inc., headquartered in Newport Beach, California, *www.amenclinics.com.* He is assistant clinical professor of psychiatry and human behavior at University of California, Irvine, School of Medicine, and his work has been the basis of several PBS specials. Dr. Amen is author of many books, including *Change Your Brain, Change Your Body* (Harmony).

You can improve your memory, energy, productivity and general well-being throughout your entire life by developing everyday habits that are good for your brain...

• **Get exercise that requires quick movements.** Exercise increases blood flow to the brain, ensuring a sufficient supply of oxygen and the nutrients on which the brain depends. Insufficient blood flow can lead to poor coordination and difficulty processing complex thoughts.

Exercise also increases the supply of *brain-derived neurotrophic factor* (BDNF), a protein that helps with the creation of new cells.

A recent study of people in their 70s found that those who exercised moderately or vigorously at least once a week were 30% more likely to maintain their cognitive skills than people who exercised less often.

Any type of exercise is good, but the ideal exercise for a healthy brain combines an aerobic workout with complex movements requiring quick reactions.

Examples: Dancing, tennis, table tennis, racquetball and juggling.

- **Eat berries, beans and salmon.** *Be sure that your diet includes...*
  - Lots of fruits and vegetables. Antioxidants in fruits and vegetables fight damage from free radicals—unstable molecules that damage cells, contribute to aging and promote inflammation, which is a factor in Alzheimer's disease. Berries are particularly rich in antioxidants.
  - Complex carbohydrates—such as cooked dried beans and whole grains. The brain uses sugar as its main energy source. Complex carbohydrates release sugar slowly. In contrast, white bread and other refined starches and sugars cause dramatic spikes and drops in blood sugar, leading to concentration problems and fatigue.
  - Cold-water fish. Any lean protein, including chicken and lean pork, helps build neurons. Salmon, cod and other cold-water fish have the added benefit of providing omega-3 fatty acids, which play an important role in maintaining nerve cell membranes. Other sources of these healthy fats are avocados, nuts and olive oil.
- **Boost vitamin D.** Vitamin D is believed to play a role in mood and memory. A recent study published in *Journal of Geriatric Psychiatry and Neurology* found a possible association between dementia and low levels of vitamin D.

The best source of vitamin D is sunlight—at least 15 minutes a day without sunscreen. If you spend most of the day indoors or live in a northern latitude, take a supplement with 400 international units (IU) of vitamin D daily.

- **Avoid food additives, such as monosodium glutamate, and artificial sweeteners, such as aspartame.** Though studies are inconclusive, anecdotal evidence suggests that these additives may have a hyperstimulating effect, causing confusion and/or mood swings.
- **Limit caffeine and alcohol.** Caffeine and alcohol reduce blood flow to the brain, depriving cells of nutrients and energy. Both can interfere with sleep, which is essential to healthy brain activity.

Both also can be dehydrating—the brain is 80% water, so anything that dehydrates has the potential to cause problems in thinking.

One or two cups of coffee or tea each day are harmless and enhance alertness, but heavy caffeine consumption—more than 500 milligrams (mg) to 600 mg a day, or about four to seven cups of coffee—should be avoided.

Alcohol poses additional dangers—it blocks oxygen from reaching cells' energy centers and reduces the effectiveness of neurotransmitters involved in both learning and memory. Heavy drinkers—people who consume four or more alcoholic drinks a day—have a higher risk for dementia.

Some people now drink wine daily because of evidence that it may be good for the heart. However, there are other ways to build up the heart—such as exercise and diet—that do not put the brain at risk. If you are accustomed to having a drink every day, consider cutting back to one or two drinks a week.

- **Avoid airborne toxins.** Fumes from paint, pesticides and other chemicals have been associated with brain damage. If you are exposed to strong fumes—for example, while painting the interior of your house or having your nails done—be sure that the area is well-ventilated.
- **Don't smoke, and avoid being in rooms where others are smoking.** Oddly, smoking can make you feel smarter by stimulating the release of neurotransmitters that improve reaction time, but nicotine constricts blood vessels, reducing blood flow and depriving the brain of nutrients.
- **Don't overdo electronic interaction.** Computers, mobile devices and other electronic devices can interfere with optimal brain function in several ways. They have an addictive quality, stimulating release of the neurotransmitter *dopamine,* which acts on the brain's pleasure centers. Over time, greater amounts of dopamine are required to get the same pleasurable feeling.

E-mail and text-messaging can interfere with concentration and encourage a state of mind that is alert to the next distraction, rather than focused on the task at hand. One study at London University found a temporary IQ loss of 10 points in people who constantly checked for messages during the day.

Best: Process e-mail and text messages at set times of day, not as each message comes in. Take frequent breaks away from the computer.

- **Protect your skull.** The brain is very soft. The hard skull that covers it has many ridges that can damage the brain during trauma. Yet people are careless with this precious organ.

Take all precautions to protect yourself from head injuries. Stabilize ladders carefully. Use nonslip mats in the bathtub and shower. Keep the floor in your house and the pathways outside it clear of debris that could cause you to trip and fall. If you bicycle or ski, be sure to wear a helmet.

- **Minimize stress.** Long-term exposure to high levels of the stress hormone *cortisol* is associated with a smaller-sized *hippocampus*—the brain area associated with memory—and with poor performance on memory tests.

Cope with stress by finding daily activities that calm you, such as exercise, meditation, prayer or yoga. During difficult times, focus on what you are grateful for and talk things out with someone who can help you keep an optimistic perspective.

This Brain Disorder Is Curable...but It's Often Misdiagnosed as Alzheimer's

Mark G. Luciano, MD, PhD, a neurosurgeon who is internationally known for his work in hydrocephalus. He is director of the Aging Brain Clinic and the CSF Laboratory, and head of Congenital and Pediatric Neurosurgery at the Cleveland Clinic, *www.clevelandclinic.org.*

The future can be bleak for patients with Alzheimer's disease or with other forms of dementia because these conditions rarely can be reversed. Yet there is evidence that about 5% of patients diagnosed with dementia actually have an unrecognized—and treatable—condition.

It's believed that at least 200,000 people in the US have excessive fluid in the brain, a condition called *normal pressure hydrocephalus* (or NPH). The fluid presses against the brain, causing poor balance, memory loss and other symptoms similar to dementia.

NPH occurs almost exclusively in adults 55 years old or older. It's called "normal pressure" because fluid accumulates so gradually that there isn't the sharp spike in pressure that occurs with acute hydrocephalus.

PROBLEM WITH BRAIN PLUMBING

Cavities within the brain called ventricles produce about a pint of *cerebrospinal* fluid a day. This fluid, which cushions the brain and spinal cord, is normally reabsorbed by tissues at about the same rate as it is produced.

In patients with NPH, the fluid is reabsorbed more slowly. This usually happens because of scar tissue within brain membranes. The scarring, caused by factors such as inflammation, previous hemorrhages (strokes) or a traumatic head injury, impedes normal drainage. Excess fluid enlarges the ventricles.

Pressure from accumulated fluid presses on nerves and other brain tissues. It also can compromise blood vessels, decreasing blood flow to the brain.

Result: Dementia-like symptoms.

EASY TO MISS

Most patients with NPH exhibit three key symptoms...

- **An unsteady gait** (they often walk with their feet far apart).
- **Urinary incontinence.**
- **Cognitive impairments,** including memory loss.

Why it's missed: The same symptoms can be caused by many different conditions, including a stroke, Alzheimer's disease or other forms of dementia. Urinary incontinence could be due to a prostate problem. Balance problems often are due to spine diseases, diabetes or inner-ear problems.

A CT or MRI scan will show if a patient has enlarged ventricles, but this isn't always caused by NPH. It's normal, for example, for the ventricles to enlarge with age. It can be difficult to distinguish normal enlargement from ventricle changes due to fluid pressure.

IMPORTANT CLUES

Problems with gait and balance typically are the first symptom of NPH—memory loss usually comes later. This is the opposite of what happens with Alzheimer's, in which cognitive symptoms usually occur first.

If a neurologist suspects that a patient has NPH, an imaging test will reveal, to some degree, whether ventricular enlargement is caused by excess fluid.

Next step: The removal of excess fluid. If a patient has NPH, removing as little as 50 cubic centimeters (cc's), about 10 teaspoons, of fluid through a lumbar puncture (spinal tap) often will improve symptoms within a day.

Sometimes, a more complicated procedure, *lumbar catheter insertion,* is necessary to diagnose NPH. A catheter is inserted into the area around the spinal cord. This permits continuous fluid removal (about a pint altogether) over 36 hours. The patient usually spends two nights in the hospital while fluid is removed from the brain. Then the catheter is removed, and he or she goes home for a few days. Then, at a follow-up appointment, the neurologist retests the patient's balance, cognitive abilities, etc. The doctor also will ask friends or family members if they have noticed an improvement in the patient's symptoms.

If the patient improved significantly, then a diagnosis of NPH is virtually certain—particularly if the symptoms return when fluid levels in the brain gradually rise to pretreatment levels (within three to five days).

SURGICAL DRAINAGE

The only treatment for NPH is to insert a shunt, a silicone tube, in the brain that continuously drains excess fluid. These shunts are extremely durable and potentially can last for decades.

Best choice: A programmable shunt that allows the neurologist to fine-tune the settings and increase or decrease the rate at which fluid is removed from the brain. A doctor can make adjustments to the valve with an external device without additional surgery. The programmable shunt is more expensive but often is covered by insurance. Check with your provider.

The procedure to implant a shunt usually takes less than an hour. The device is inserted into the brain, and a drainage tube is implanted under the skin. This tube carries drained brain fluid into the abdominal cavity, where it's absorbed into the bloodstream. Both the shunt and tube are invisible to others, although patients might notice a small bump on the head where the valve's implanted and a bump where the tube passes over the collarbone.

About 80% of patients who undergo the procedure experience significant improvements in memory, gait, etc. The improvements tend to be most dramatic in those who are diagnosed and treated early, before fluid buildup permanently damages brain tissue.

Although any brain procedure carries risk, shunt insertion is relatively safe. About 25% to 50% of patients undergo additional procedures to remove blockages from the shunt or drainage tube over the next two years.

Back Attack: A Top Doc's Simple Method To Relieve the Pain

Lee Hunter Riley III, MD, director of the orthopaedic spine division and associate professor of orthopaedic surgery and neurosurgery at Johns Hopkins University in Baltimore. He is coauthor of *The Back Book* (Johns Hopkins).

Back pain accounts for almost as many doctor visits as the common cold. In spite of its prevalence, misconceptions about back pain abound. *Common misleading beliefs...*

Myth: If you throw out your back, you should stay in bed until the pain is gone.

Fact: Although a day or two of rest may be necessary, one of the keys to healing is getting out of bed and moving around as soon as possible.

Myth: When your back hurts so much, it means something is seriously wrong.

Fact: People are shocked to find that getting out of bed or any kind of movement is excruciatingly painful. They worry that something may be terribly wrong. But these are common symptoms and usually not cause for worry.

Myth: For recurrent or chronic back pain, surgery is the best solution.

Fact: Only a few varieties of back pain respond well to surgery. In many cases, surgery can worsen chronic back pain.

Back problems are a normal part of aging, as is gray hair. Sitting and walking put a great deal of stress on the back over time. Joints enlarge and stiffen with age, but this does not mean you are doomed to suffer or have to restrict activities.

Good news: In the vast majority of cases, back pain can be treated with very simple measures. Approximately 95% of the time, acute back pain gets better within two months.

WHEN TO SEE A DOCTOR

Although most cases of routine back pain do not require a doctor's care, back problems can signal a serious condition, such as a fracture, infection or tumor...or a condition that may be helped by surgery, such as *spinal stenosis.*

See a doctor right away for back pain if you have a history of cancer...if you had a recent infection or are running a fever...if the pain is unremitting...if you also have pain or weakness in your legs...if your bowel or bladder habits or sensations have changed.

You also should see a doctor if incapacitating pain lasts more than one to two days or if milder pain lasts longer than two months.

SIMPLE TREATMENT

Most garden-variety episodes of acute back pain respond to simple, at-home steps...

- **Immediately begin taking an over-the-counter anti-inflammatory medication,** such as *ibuprofen* (Motrin), *naproxen* (Aleve) or aspirin. Choose whatever medication you usually take for minor pain, such as headache, as long as it is an anti-inflammatory and not merely a pain reliever (such as Tylenol)—follow instructions on the label.

Important: Take the anti-inflammatory for a full 12 to 14 days, even if you begin to feel better before that. Most people with back pain mistakenly stop taking medication after a day or two, the way they would for minor aches and pains. However, for back pain, the anti-inflammatory activity is cumulative and takes as long as two weeks to have its full effect. Do not increase the dose or take the drug more often than recommended without a doctor's okay.

If you don't notice any improvement within a few days, ask your doctor for a prescription-strength anti-inflammatory.

Avoid narcotic pain relievers, such as Vicodin. The pain relief is temporary, not cumulative. Also, these drugs make you lethargic, which could discourage you from moving.

- **Gradually increase your activity.** You can rest for a day or two, but studies show that when people with back pain get up and move around as soon as they can, they feel better more quickly.

This does not mean that you should immediately jump back into your everyday lifestyle and force yourself to endure extreme pain. Strike a balance—do not be afraid of a little pain, push yourself a bit, but don't overdo it.

- **Reduce stress and tension.** Stress magnifies pain signals and can overwhelm your ability to cope emotionally. Employ whatever stress relievers you previously have found to be helpful—such as gentle massage, a heating pad, warm baths, walking, deep breathing or spending time with close friends or family.

PREVENTING FURTHER PAIN

Once the acute phase has passed, take the following steps to avoid future problems. If you have not yet experienced severe back pain, these measures can help you prevent it—and to recover more quickly if it does occur.

- **Don't smoke.** Nicotine compromises blood supply and nutrition to the spinal discs.
- **Get plenty of calcium and vitamin D.** To keep the bones of the spine strong and guard against fractures related to osteoporosis, consume 1,200 grams (g) to 1,500 g of calcium a day, from food and supplements combined... and 400 international units (IU) to 800 IU of vitamin D from supplements.

• **Get and stay physically fit.** Talk to your doctor before starting an exercise program, but the following helps...

Aerobic exercise, such as walking or swimming, maintains joint flexibility and improves overall conditioning so that you can continue to move easily.

Strengthening and stabilizing exercises tone the muscles of the back, as well as the supporting muscles, such as the abdominals.

Your doctor or physical therapist can recommend exercises tailored to your ability level. *Or consider one of the specialized exercise programs, such as...*

• Pilates, which uses controlled movements on spring-operated machinery to increase abdominal strength and improve alignment and flexibility. For additional information, go to *www.pilatesmethodalliance.org*.

• The McKenzie Method, which takes a comprehensive approach to spinal health based on individualized extension and flexion exercises. For information, go to *www.mckenziemdt.org*.

• **Manage all your activities.** You probably won't have to—and shouldn't—give up your favorite activities, but you may need to practice new ways of sitting and moving that reduce strain on your back, including...

• When sitting, use a lumbar support and keep your ears, shoulders and hips aligned. Place feet flat on the floor—don't cross your legs.

• When you lift, hold whatever you are picking up as close to your body as possible. Bend your knees, and keep your back straight. Slowly straighten your knees using your leg muscles rather than your back to bear the weight of the object.

• When lifting something out of your car trunk, put your foot on the bumper for support.

• If you know that certain activities—such as gardening, raking or painting—make your back sore, plan ahead. Take an over-the-counter anti-inflammatory an hour or two before you start the activity, and keep taking the drug for a day or two afterward. Also, take a break from the activity every 20 minutes. Brainstorm modifications that minimize strain on your back. *Example:* If you are clearing the garage, don't move boxes by hand—use a dolly.

The Problem with Fosamax You May Not Know About

Susan E. Brown, PhD, director of the Better Bones Foundation and author of *Better Bones, Better Body* (McGraw-Hill) and Susan Ott, MD, who specializes in metabolic bone disease at University of Washington, Seattle.

The common misconception that bone loss is "forever" has led many people to turn to *biphosphonate* medicine such as *alendronate* (Fosamax). "Fosamax, for osteoporosis, is one of the 'anti-resorptive' drugs," says Dr. Susan Brown, director of The Osteoporosis Project.

"These medications can dramatically reduce bone loss by bringing premature death to *osteoclasts,* the cells that break down and recycle old, worn-out segments of bone," she explains. However, bone breakdown and bone buildup are tightly coupled. So as Fosamax dramatically reduces bone breakdown, it also dramatically *decreases* new bone formation. In fact, studies show that the bone-forming surface of bone is suppressed by 60% to 90% by Fosamax.

Yes, Fosamax often appears to increase bone density. But, as Susan Ott, MD, explains, "This is because the bone is no longer remodeling and there is not much new bone. The older bone is denser than the newer bone—there is less water and more mineral in the bone, and radiographic techniques thus measure the higher density." So while this looks like added bone tissue—it is not. "Many people believe that these drugs are bone builders. But the evidence shows they are actually bone *hardeners,*" says Dr. Ott.

Surprising: Anti-resorptive drugs such as Fosamax and *risedronate* (Actonel) simply halt bone breakdown—they do not actually build new bone.

Vitamin K for Your Bones

Susan E. Brown, PhD, director of the Better Bones Foundation and author of *Better Bones, Better Body* (McGraw-Hill).

The newest nutrient for your bones is vitamin K. "This little-known nutrient is extremely important for bone health," says Dr. Susan Brown, director of the Osteoporosis Project.

Vitamin K (*phylloquinone*) is a fat-soluble nutrient (like vitamins A and D) found abundantly in leafy green vegetables, asparagus, green beans and vegetable oils. Vitamin K-2 (*menaquinone*) is formed in the body from K-1.

Vitamin K-1 helps the liver manufacture proteins that control blood clotting. Vitamin K-2 has many functions, including building collagen in bone—and preventing fractures.

Standout scientific evidence: Researchers from England analyzed the data from 13 studies on osteoporosis and vitamin K, given in a dose of 45 milligrams (mg) and a form called MK4. They reported vitamin K decreased hip fractures by 73%, spinal fractures by 60% and all non-spinal fractures by 81%. Their results were then published in the *Archives of Internal Medicine*.

Important: Medications called *corticosteroids* (*cortisone, prednisone, hydrocortisone*) are a synthetic version of cortisol, an adrenal hormone. They are often prescribed to help control the symptoms of chronic diseases with an inflammatory component, such as rheumatoid arthritis, inflammatory bowel disease, lupus and severe asthma. Taken regularly for six months or more, they can cause osteoporosis. Taking vitamin K with corticosteroids can help prevent or slow that bone loss.

Recommended: There is only one vitamin K supplement on the market in the US that contains the same amount and type of the nutrient used in clinical trials to decrease fracture risk—Osteo-K—which also contains calcium, vitamin D, magnesium and boron, says John Neustadt, MD, a naturopathic physician located in Bozeman, Montana. It is available at *www.nbihealth.com*.

Caution: If you are taking the anticoagulant *warfarin* (Coumadin) do not take Osteo-K or any other type of supplemental vitamin K, which can block the action of the drug.

Also helpful: Dr. Brown has created a nutritional supplement program that provides all 18 of the nutrients (including vitamin K) research shows are vital to maintaining and building bone. You can find out more about the supplement program by calling the Better Bones Foundation at 877-207-0232.

Natural Ways to Boost Energy—and Feel 10 Years Younger

Woodson C. Merrell, MD, chairman of the department of integrative medicine, Beth Israel Medical Center as well as assistant clinical professor of medicine at Columbia University College of Physicians and Surgeons, both in New York City. He is also an author, with Kathleen Merrell, of *The Source: Unleash Your Natural Energy, Power Up Your Health, and Feel 10 Years Younger* (Free Press). Dr. Merrell's Web site is *www.woodsonmerrell.com*.

Exhaustion is an underrecognized epidemic in the US. As many as 75 million Americans report feeling "extreme" fatigue at work. Fatigue is among the top five complaints that people talk about with their physicians—even though it is estimated that two-thirds of people with chronic exhaustion never mention it to their doctors.

Every physical activity, from the beating of the heart to running to catch a train, depends on *adenosine triphosphate* (or ATP), chemical energy produced inside of cells. Nearly everyone can significantly increase daily energy by increasing the cellular production of ATP and decreasing unnecessary consumption of ATP. *Most people realize that exercise helps to boost energy—but you also can boost your ATP in other ways...*

STRESS REDUCTION

Stress stimulates the sympathetic nervous system, which triggers thousands of chemical reactions that consume tremendous amounts of energy—energy that is then unavailable to the body. People who experience chronic stress may have insufficient energy even for normal body repairs. It is estimated that up to 80% of all illnesses are due in part to stress. *What to do...*

• **Keep a stress log.** Every day, write down the events or situations that put you over the edge. These might encompass rush-hour traffic or dealing with a difficult boss. Once you recognize your flash points, try to eliminate them—by taking a different route to work, for example, or avoiding unnecessary encounters with difficult people.

• **Create the perception of control.** People who feel helpless experience more stress than those who take a proactive approach—even when they're exposed to stressful events that are similar.

Example: Maybe your job involves daily, high-pressure meetings. The source of stress won't go away, but you can blunt the impact by deciding to do something about it—by taking a brisk walk before each meeting, perhaps, or simply telling yourself to stay calm.

• **Take frequent breath breaks.** Harvard mind-body researcher Herbert Benson, MD, found that the body's expenditure of energy dropped by as much as 17% during meditation. A less formal approach, when you notice signs of stress, is to take a "breath break."

How to do it: Inhale slowly to the count of four, pause for one second, then exhale slowly and completely to the count of six. Pause for one second, then repeat four more times.

People who take a breath break every one to two hours usually notice that they have more energy throughout the day. They also have a slower pulse, lower blood pressure and lower levels of *cortisol* (the primary stress hormone).

HIGH-ENERGY FOODS

A Harvard study found that the majority of American adults are deficient in vitamins and minerals. These deficiencies usually aren't severe enough to cause diseases, but they can impair the body's ability to manufacture usable forms of energy. *Helpful...*

• **Choose a "rainbow diet"**—including blueberries, broccoli, carrots, spinach, tomatoes and even dark chocolate. A variety of colors is important because different plant pigments, such as *carotenes* and *flavonoids,* help prevent metabolic by-products from damaging mitochondria (energy-producing machinery) within cells.

• **Eat fish two to three times a week.** The omega-3 fatty acids in cold-water fish reduce inflammation—saving the energy that is normally needed to fight it. To avoid the risk of excessive mercury, eat small fish, such as sardines, anchovies and trout. Large, predatory fish, such as tuna and sea bass, tend to have the most mercury.

• **Avoid refined carbs.** White bread, sweets and other refined carbohydrates are rapidly converted to blood sugar. This causes an energy surge that is followed by a longer-lasting energy decline. Spikes in blood sugar also cause *glycation,* a process that prevents cells from working efficiently.

Better: Whole grains, lentils, beans and other foods high in complex carbohydrates. These are digested more slowly and provide the materials for longer-lasting energy.

• **Drink water**—at least six glasses a day. The majority of my patients are dehydrated. Water supports the body's ability to eliminate free radicals (cell-damaging molecules) and other toxins that impair energy production.

THE JUICE CLEANSE

Juice fasts allow the digestive tract to rest while promoting detoxification, decreasing inflammation and dramatically increasing energy. One study even found that people who fasted once a month were 39% more likely to have healthy hearts than nonfasters.

Once a month, consume nothing but juice for an entire day. Use a juicer to combine a variety of organic vegetables, such as spinach, carrots and broccoli. Add a small amount of apples, cherries or other fruits as a natural sweetener.

It's normal to feel a little worse during the day of the fast. That's when the body is shedding the most toxins. Most people feel much more energized and clearheaded on the day after the fast.

Caution: If you have a severe chronic disease, diabetes or are pregnant, consult your physician before fasting.

SUPPLEMENTS CAN HELP

I recommend supplements only to patients who don't notice significant energy improvements within a few weeks of eating a healthier diet or making other lifestyle changes. *If this is the case for you, try...*

- **Ashwagandha.** It's an "energy-balancing" herb that improves the body's ability to metabolize sugars as well as cortisol.

Standard dose: 250 milligrams (mg) twice daily.

- **Probiotics that include acidophilus and bifidophilus.** People who take probiotic supplements have improvements in immunity and digestive function.

Standard dose: One to two daily supplements containing at least 10 billion organisms per dose.

- **Multivitamin that includes at least 400 international units (IU) of vitamin D.** People who have been diagnosed with low vitamin D require 1,000 IU to 2,000 IU daily. Vitamin D is very important for immune strength and cardiovascular health—and is crucial for maintaining healthy circulation and energy.

The Superfoods That Relieve Allergies to Pollen, Dust, Mold, More

Leo Galland, MD, founder and director of the Foundation for Integrated Medicine in New York City. An internist, he treats many patients with chronic allergies and specializes in integrating nutrition and herbs with conventional medicine. He is author of *The Fat Resistance Diet* (Broadway) and *Power Healing* (Random House). His Web site is *www.mdheal.org*.

The right foods can help relieve allergies to dust, pollen, mold and other spores in the air—easing symptoms that include sneezing, stuffy nose and wheezing.

Recent finding: Allergy symptoms are less common on the rural Greek island of Crete than elsewhere in Greece, even though there's no shortage of allergens blowing around. According to one study published in *Thorax* in 2007, the people of Crete can thank their diet. Researchers tested 690 island children for airborne allergies and asked their parents to answer questions about their children's diets and symptoms. Eighty percent of the children ate fruit at least twice a day, and 68% ate vegetables that often. Those who ate more nuts, grapes, oranges, apples and tomatoes—the main local products—had fewer allergy symptoms than those who ate less.

Allergy symptoms will occur when an overactive immune system responds to harmless substances as if they could cause disease. Inflammation is an early step in the immune response. Most of the foods that relieve allergies are anti-inflammatory, modulating the immune system response.

FOODS THAT FIGHT ALLERGIES

The following foods help to battle airborne allergies...

- **Fruits high in vitamin C,** an antioxidant, may help to reduce inflammation. Year-round, eat two pieces of fruit daily. When you're especially congested, choose from these twice a day—an orange, one cup of strawberries, an apple, one cup of grapes or a medium-sized wedge of watermelon.

Bonus: The skins of red grapes are loaded with the antioxidant resveratrol and were found to relieve wheezing in the Crete study.

- **Nuts, in particular almonds, hazelnuts and peanuts,** are a good source of vitamin E, which helps minimize inflammation. Eat a single one-ounce serving of any of these nuts daily year-round to help prevent symptoms. If you do have symptoms, increase the servings—try two tablespoons of peanut butter and one ounce each of hazelnuts and almonds a day.

- **Cold-water fish** (wild salmon, mackerel, trout, herring and sardines), as well as walnuts and flaxseed, all contain omega-3 fatty acids, which help fight inflammation. Eat at least two servings of cold-water fish each week year-round and three servings during the seasons when you experience airborne allergies. Also have 12 walnuts and one tablespoon of ground flaxseed a day.

• **Oysters, shrimp and crab, as well as legumes, whole grains and tofu,** are all high in zinc, which has antibacterial and antiviral effects that provide relief for immune systems overtaxed by fighting off allergies. Have six oysters, six shrimp or a few crabs every week, and twice that when your allergies bother you. Also have one serving of whole grains and one of beans or tofu a day.

• **Tea, whether green, white or black, is full of flavonoids,** plant compounds that reduce inflammation. Tea also increases proteins in the body that fight off infection, again relieving an overtaxed immune system. Enjoy one cup daily, and increase to two when your allergies are a problem.

Helpful: Drink your tea first thing in the morning with lemon and honey to stimulate the *cilia*—the tiny hairs in the nose that sweep pollen and dust out of the way.

• **Horseradish,** hot mustard, fennel, anise and sage also help stimulate the cilia and act as natural decongestants. Add a dash to food whenever possible.

FOODS TO AVOID ALL YEAR

If you experience congestion or other symptoms year-round, ask an allergist to conduct a skin test to identify allergies to dust, mold and foods. *Then consider the following changes in your daily diet...*

• **Mold and yeast in food can aggravate an allergy to mold in the air.** If you're allergic to mold, avoid foods that contain yeast, such as bread and baked goods (unless they are labeled "yeast free")...wine, beer and spirits...fermented foods, such as sauerkraut and cider...foods that tend to get moldy, such as cheese and mushrooms...vinegar and sauces that contain vinegar, such as mayonnaise, barbecue sauce, mustard and salad dressing.

Helpful: Use lemon juice and spices in dressings instead.

• **Milk and dairy products,** such as yogurt, butter and ice cream, could be making you feel worse if you get congested year-round, which is a symptom typically caused by an allergy to dust. One explanation is that *casein,* the protein in milk, can promote the formation of mucus. Although there isn't strong science showing that milk aggravates congestion, it's worth experimenting by cutting all dairy from your diet for at least two weeks. If your allergies improve when you avoid dairy products, eliminate dairy year-round. You will then need to take a calcium supplement, typically 1,000 milligrams (mg) a day, to compensate for the decreased calcium intake that accompanies a dairy-free diet.

• **Soy, corn and wheat.** Soy, including soy milk, tofu, soybean oil, edamame and soy sauce, may aggravate chronic congestion, according to clinical observations. Even if you do not appear allergic to soy on a skin-prick test, experiment by eliminating soy from your diet for at least two weeks.

The same is true for corn (including cornflakes, corn chips and corn oil) and wheat (including all breads and baked goods unless they are marked "wheat-free" or "gluten-free"). If you find that your symptoms are alleviated when you stop eating any of these foods, eliminate them year-round.

Red Flag Warnings: Symptoms That Can Save Your Life

Neil Shulman, MD, associate professor of internal medicine at Emory University School of Medicine in Atlanta. He is coauthor of *Your Body's Red Light Warning Signals: Medical Tips That May Save Your Life* (Dell) and author or coauthor of more than 30 other books, as well as more than 100 scientific papers. Go to *www.redlightwarningsignals.com* for more information.

Some symptoms are signs of a true emergency—but we put off getting prompt medical attention, believing that if we wait a bit, they will go away. *Here, symptoms never to ignore...*

EMERGENCY SYMPTOMS

The following symptoms can indicate a potential emergency. Call for an ambulance (usually 911). If one's not available, have someone drive you to an emergency room.

• **Fever and significant pain** (often tender to touch) in the center of the back (over the spine or bony area), especially with numbness down one or both legs. There are many possible causes of fever and back pain—the fever could be due to a common ailment, such as the flu, and back pain due to another cause, such as back strain.

Possible danger: There is a possibility of an infection near the spinal column, especially if there is numbness down one or both legs. The back often is tender to the touch, and movement is painful. The infection can spread quickly to the rest of the body, causing a life-threatening emergency.

The emergency room (ER) doctor may order image studies of the back. Other tests may include blood and/or urine cultures and a spinal tap. Antibiotics usually are effective.

• **Sweet or fruity-smelling breath often accompanied by confusion or disorientation.** Sometimes mistaken for alcohol, this smell may be a sign of accumulating chemicals in the blood caused by uncontrolled diabetes. Additional signs of out-of-control diabetes include frequent urination and extreme thirst.

Possible danger: A diabetic attack (uncontrolled diabetes) can end in coma and death if untreated.

Important: Victims may smell and act intoxicated (confused and/or disoriented), but it is important to rule out uncontrolled diabetes, rather than assuming intoxication from drugs or alcohol.

In the ER, if your blood test indicates severe diabetes, you will be given an intravenous (IV) drip with fluids, insulin and minerals before being referred for comprehensive diabetic care.

• **Sudden, agonizing headache.** There are many causes of headache, including sinus infections, seasonal allergies, dehydration, caffeine withdrawal, eyestrain, lack of sleep and low blood sugar. Take immediate action if you have the "worst headache of your life" that hits suddenly. It may be followed by sleepiness or confusion.

Possible danger: Bleeding in the brain from any of a number of problems, including congenital weakness of a blood vessel, injury to the head or cocaine or amphetamine abuse causing a blood vessel to rupture. At least 20% of people hospitalized with bleeding from a brain aneurysm (a weak point in a blood vessel that swells) die.

Important: Don't take aspirin—it prevents blood from clotting and may lead to more bleeding. Usually the ER doctor will order an imaging study of the brain.

DANGER SIGNS

The following symptoms usually are not a 911 emergency, but they should be evaluated by a physician as soon as possible...

• **Fever, often with a headache and/or muscle pain,** within a few weeks of spending time in a wooded area. Sometimes there are pink-to-dusty-red spots (they're darker on the skin of African-Americans) on the palms of the hands and the bottoms of the feet or other body parts. However, this rash often appears later or may not appear at all.

Possible danger: There is a risk that you have Rocky Mountain spotted fever, which is transmitted to humans by tick bites. It usually occurs between April and September. If untreated, this condition can be fatal.

The doctor will order blood tests to help make the diagnosis. Antibiotics can eliminate the infection.

• **Blood in stool or on toilet tissue.** The blood may make the stool appear maroon or black. It can originate anywhere from the mouth to the anus.

Possible danger: Blood may come from an open sore in the gastrointestinal (GI) tract, such as an ulcer or a small bulging sac called a diverticulum, but cancer is also a possible cause. Cancer of the GI tract, most often involving the stomach or colon, is potentially fatal.

Important: Even if you have hemorrhoids (swollen and inflamed veins in your anus or lower rectum), the bleeding still could be caused by cancer, so have any bleeding checked.

Possible emergency: Depending on the severity of the bleeding and how long you have been bleeding, this could be an emergency.

Also, the elderly and those with other severe illnesses may be especially prone to complications. If you feel dizzy, light-headed or weak, call 911.

If necessary, the doctor will order screening tests. Any growths will be biopsied and examined for cancer.

• **Blood in the urine, without pain.** The usual causes of blood in the urine are kidney stones or a bladder or prostate infection, typically accompanied by pain. When there is no discomfort, people sometimes take the "wait and see" approach. Women might think that they are having an irregular period.

Possible danger: Cancer of the uterus, kidney, ureter, bladder or prostate, which can be fatal if not treated early.

Important: Do not dismiss bleeding from the vagina as simply an irregular period or blood from the rectum as hemorrhoids. You may have cancer of the uterus or the GI tract.

A family doctor or internist can determine whether the blood is coming from the vagina, rectum or urinary tract so that you can obtain the appropriate evaluation and care.

• **Yellow tinge to the skin and/or whites of the eyes,** often with insomnia, fatigue, loss of appetite and/or generalized itching.

Possible danger: A blocked bile duct, due to cancer of the duct, cancer of the pancreas, liver disease, a breakdown of red blood cells or other conditions.

Blood work and an ultrasound (an imaging study) of the liver and bile ducts usually are the first tests.

• **Cold fingers that can last for hours or even days after exposure to cold water or air.** Lingering coldness in the fingers can be caused by anemia or by *Raynaud's syndrome,* in which the small blood vessels that supply blood to the tips of the fingers narrow.

Possible danger: Raynaud's can indicate rheumatoid arthritis, lupus or other serious autoimmune disorders. Anemia can indicate cancer and other serious problems. Or you may have serious heart and/or lung problems.

Your doctor will perform an exam and order tests to make a diagnosis.

What Doctors Won't Tell You: A Physician Reveals Why Many Popular Treatments Don't Work

David H. Newman, MD, emergency-room physician and director of clinical research, department of emergency medicine at Mt. Sinai School of Medicine, New York City. He is author of *Hippocrates' Shadow: Secrets from the House of Medicine* (Scribner).

Doctors today use sophisticated tests and treatments that would have been unimaginable a generation ago. This benefits many patients, but there is also a downside. By focusing too narrowly on technology, there is a temptation for doctors to always do *something* even when they're not entirely sure why they're doing it—or when doing nothing might be a better choice.

The truth is, doctors guess a lot of the time. They order tests even when they don't know what they're looking for. They perform procedures that are unlikely to help. They give drugs that have been proven to work in general but are unlikely to help a particular patient.

What doctors don't always admit—or don't know...

Fact: Tests may not help. Doctors used to spend a lot of time with patients. They asked questions about their personal lives as well as their medical histories. They often could make a diagnosis before the patient left the office.

That seldom happens today. The usual approach is to quickly order tests.

Example: Several years ago, my mother went to the emergency department with severe stomach pain. Within several hours, she was given chest and abdominal X-rays and tests for liver disease, gallstones, internal bleeding and pancreatitis.

After all that, she was diagnosed with "undifferentiated stomach pain," a fancy way of saying that she was probably fine, but no one could figure out what had caused the pain. Did she need all of those tests? Probably not.

The tests were at least partly warranted, but physicians sometimes order tests because they don't know what else to do. Tests should be used mainly to confirm a hypothesis, not merely to "fish" for possible problems.

Self-defense: If your doctor orders a test, ask what he/she is searching for. If the answer seems nebulous—"We're searching for something that might explain your symptoms"—get more information. What you want to hear is something specific, such as, "I'm pretty sure you have a lung infection, but I don't want to start treatment until I'm sure."

Fact: Most infections clear up without treatment. It's estimated that at least 80% of all outpatient antibiotic prescriptions don't help.

Reason: Most infections are caused by viruses, not bacteria—and antibiotics have no effect on viruses. The vast majority of upper respiratory infections, for example, are viral. Yet half of patients who see a doctor with one of these infections are given antibiotics.

Even when patients do have a bacterial infection, such as bronchitis, antibiotics may not be necessary. Infections often clear up on their own.

Antibiotics are not harmless. They kill beneficial organisms in the body that help curtail harmful microbes. Also, the unnecessary use of antibiotics may be responsible for an estimated 24,000 life-threatening allergic reactions annually.

Self-defense: If you have an infection, ask your doctor if it has to be treated. Take antibiotics only if an untreated infection—something such as bacterial pneumonia or a wound with spreading redness—is likely to cause serious complications.

Fact: Herniated discs seldom cause back pain. Magnetic resonance imaging (MRI) is the test of choice to evaluate back pain. But there is a secret about MRIs and back pain. The most common problems physicians see on MRIs and attribute to back pain—herniated, ruptured and bulging discs—are seen almost as commonly on MRIs of healthy people without back pain. This means that herniated discs usually have nothing to do with back pain. They are a normal finding, suggesting that discs rupture with some frequency and our bodies repair them uneventfully.

Surgery to fix or remove a disc usually is performed in the hope that a herniated disc is compressing a nerve and causing the pain, but it carries a poor overall success rate. Even after the nerve is decompressed or freed by removing the disc surgically, half of the time the patient's low back pain is not relieved.

Self-defense: Studies show that most people with back pain will improve within six months with standard medical care, such as physical therapy and the use of anti-inflammatory drugs.

Surgery should be considered primarily for those patients with a herniated disc that clearly is causing a neurological deficit, such as foot weakness or a loss of bowel or bladder control, in addition to pain.

Fact: Prescription medicine may not help. There's no question that modern medications represent some of the most important developments in medicine. Yet few doctors understand that commonly used drugs are unlikely to help certain patients.

Example: Doctors routinely recommend a daily aspirin to prevent heart attacks. This is reasonable advice for a select group of patients. Among those at high risk for heart attacks and strokes, a daily aspirin will help about one patient out of 100. The other 99 won't benefit. This isn't an optimal situation, but the risk for a heart attack is so serious that it is probably worth it even if 99 patients get the drug who don't need it.

There is a statistical concept called the *number needed to treat* (NNT) that researchers use to measure the impact of a medication. It estimates the number of patients who have to take a particular drug in order for one person to benefit. The NNT for aspirin in high-risk patients, as described above, is about 100. The ratio for other drugs isn't that favorable. If drugs were free and produced no side effects, the NNT wouldn't matter, but aspirin (along with most drugs) can cause serious side effects.

Self-defense: Always ask your doctor about a drug's NNT. A drug with a low NNT is more likely to be helpful for you than one with a high number. But always discuss the risks and benefits of a drug with your doctor.

How to Leave the Hospital Alive: Dr. G's Vital Strategies

Jan Garavaglia, MD, chief medical examiner for the District Nine Medical Examiner's Office in Orlando, Florida. Dr. Garavaglia is the host of Discovery Health channel's top-rated series *Dr. G: Medical Examiner* and is author of *How Not to Die: Surprising Lessons on Living Longer, Safer, and Healthier from America's Favorite Medical Examiner* (Crown, *www.hownottodie.com*).

As a medical examiner, I discover during autopsies why some people die unexpectedly. Significant numbers of them die from mistakes made in the hospital. A report from the Institute of Medicine (part of the National Academy of Sciences) found that between 44,000 and 98,000 Americans die each year from medical errors made in hospitals. Some errors are hard to prevent, but many can be avoided by alert patients or their families.

Some of the main dangers—and how to prevent them...

DRUG MISTAKES

It is estimated that up to half of adverse drug reactions are caused by errors. Sometimes it's the patient's fault, such as neglecting to inform the hospital staff about a known allergy. Sometimes doctors aren't as careful as they should be. A patient might be given a medicine that is inappropriate for his/her condition—or given the right drug but the wrong dose. A "standard" dose isn't necessarily the right dose.

Example: Older adults metabolize drugs slowly. A dose that is safe for a 40-year-old might be too high for someone who is 65. A patient's size also makes a difference. A large man will generally need a larger dose than a petite woman.

My advice: Tell the hospital staff about every supplement and drug that you're taking, including over-the-counter medications. Better yet, bring a written list to the hospital.

Also, ask your doctor if drug doses should be adjusted for your body weight/metabolism. And confirm that you really need a particular drug. Sedatives, for example, frequently cause side effects, including increasing risk for falls, yet they are commonly prescribed to hospital patients who don't really need them.

In addition, ask anyone who gives you a medication or intravenous infusion what it is for. This will make him/her think twice before administering it—which helps prevent errors.

INFECTION

This is the number one cause of unexpected hospital deaths. According to the Centers for Disease Control and Prevention (or CDC), 1.7 million Americans suffer a health-care–related infection each year. An extremely virulent organism, *methicillin-resistant Staphylococcus aureus* (known as MRSA), kills up to one in five hospital patients who get it.

My advice: Ask about a surgeon's infection rates. Do this before choosing a surgeon. For "clean" procedures, such as a knee replacement, the infection rate should be 2% or less. Infection is more likely during "dirty" procedures, such as those involving the intestines. You always want the number to be as low as possible—less than 10%. *Also...*

- **Do not let the staff touch you unless you've seen them washing their hands before putting on fresh gloves.** Everyone should wash his hands as soon as he enters the room. If anyone doesn't, ask him to do so.
- **Exercise your lungs.** Bacterial pneumonia is common in hospitals. Up to 30% of patients placed on a ventilator develop pneumonia, and up to 50% of these patients die from it.

Self-defense: Ask for an *incentive spirometer,* a tubelike device that increases bronchial pressure. This helps remove the mucus and fluids that bacteria require to proliferate. Also, walk as soon as possible, even if it is not comfortable.

- **Avoid urinary catheters.** These are the main cause of hospital urinary tract infections. If you can't walk to the bathroom, ask if you can use a bedpan or wear diapers. Men can request a urinal or condom catheter, which slips over the penis and doesn't require inserting a tube into the urethra.

DEEP-VEIN THROMBOSIS (DVT)

About 10% of hospital patients who stay in bed for a week and up to one-third of patients in intensive care units (ICUs) develop DVT, a life-threatening condition in which a blood clot in the leg can travel to the lungs and cause a *pulmonary embolism* (when an artery in the lung becomes blocked).

Immobility is the main cause of DVT. The risk is highest in hospital patients because tissue damage—either from surgery or underlying medical problems—increases the body's production of clotting factors.

My advice: Before checking into the hospital, tell your doctor that you want to move around as soon as possible after your procedure. Simply flexing your legs and sitting up in bed can help prevent DVT. Walking is better—try to do it once an hour if your condition permits. Even if you're in an ICU, ask the staff to help you stand up and walk.

Also important: Ask for leg-compression devices. Known as "squeezers," they are pneumatic devices that inflate and deflate at regular intervals to help prevent clotting.

FALLS

They're among the leading causes of unexpected hospital deaths. The risk is higher if you're taking sedatives, have recently had anesthesia or are taking multiple drugs, including laxatives and diuretics.

My advice: Don't get out of bed without help even if you think you're well enough to do so. Wear nonskid slippers when walking around your room or down the halls.

Also important: Keep the bed rails raised and the bed low. Make sure the nurse's call light is within reach. If you need to get up, call the nurse for assistance.

WITHHOLDING INFORMATION

No one likes feeling embarrassed. Men with chest pains, for example, may hesitate to admit that they have taken Viagra—which may be dangerous when combined with nitrate drugs used to treat chest pain.

It is common for alcoholics to say that they don't drink. This is extremely risky. Alcoholics can die from withdrawal unless they're given medications to prevent this and are carefully monitored.

My advice: Be sure to tell your doctor everything. Do not withhold any information about drug use, alcohol abuse, etc.

Helpful Psychotherapy For Lots Less

Joseph A. Rogers, founder and executive director of the National Mental Health Consumers' Self-Help Clearinghouse, Philadelphia, which is funded by a grant from the US Department of Health & Human Services, *www.mhselfhelp.org*. He also is chief advocacy officer for the Mental Health Association of Southeastern Pennsylvania. He served on the Congressional Task Force on the Rights and Empowerment of Americans with Disabilities.

Psychotherapy can help us to cope with emotional and psychological problems. The trouble is that the same economic problems that are causing anxiety and depression also are making it difficult for people to afford professional therapists.

How you can find affordable high-quality counseling...

SLIDING SCALE FEES

Some therapists decrease their hourly fees for clients who cannot afford to pay the full amount. Call therapists recommended by your doctor or family and friends. Explain why you are seeking therapy...be up front about your limited financial resources...and ask if they will charge on a sliding scale.

If a therapist says yes, ask for details about the sliding scale policy to make sure that your bills will be manageable. If the therapist does not have a sliding scale, ask if he/she knows a local therapist who does.

GROUP THERAPY

Ask local therapists if they offer group therapy appropriate for your needs. Five to 10 patients typically meet with the therapist at one time. That allows the therapist to charge each patient significantly less. If the therapist does not offer relevant group therapy, ask if he can recommend a therapist who does.

COMMUNITY MENTAL HEALTH AGENCIES

Many regions now have community mental health organizations run by either the county or city government or a nonprofit organization. These agencies often provide low-cost counseling for perhaps $5 to $50 per hour. If your local mental health agencies do not provide low-cost counseling, they might be able to refer you to area counselors who do.

To find resources in your community, check your local Yellow Pages under the heading "Mental Health." You also can search for organizations in your area at the Web site of the nonprofit group Mental Health America (*www.nmha.org*, click on "Get Help," then on "Find a local mental health professional"). Or reach out to my organization, the National Mental Health Consumers' Self-Help Clearinghouse (800-553-4539, *www.mhselfhelp.org*).

EMPLOYEE ASSISTANCE PROGRAMS

Your employer might provide free or low-cost access to local therapists through an "employee assistance program." These programs sometimes are available even to members of employees' immediate families. Ask your employer's benefits coordinator if such a program exists at your company.

Therapy provided through an employee assistance program typically is covered by the employee's health insurance or paid for by the employer. At the very least, the employer likely has negotiated a below-market therapy rate.

Participation in these programs normally is confidential.

LOCAL UNIVERSITIES

Universities that have schools of psychology, counseling or social work sometimes offer inexpensive therapy to members of the public. The therapy typically is provided by graduate students who need experience to earn counseling degrees or licenses. Their efforts will be overseen by qualified professors.

Contact the school of counseling or social work at any local university and ask if they provide low-cost counseling to the public.

HELP HOTLINES AND "WARM" LINES

The National Suicide Prevention Lifeline (at 800-273-8255) offers free counseling over the phone, 24 hours a day, for people in severe emotional distress and suicidal crisis.

Some local mental health organizations offer "warm lines," which are like hotlines, only they provide nonemergency phone counseling. These call centers typically are staffed by volunteers, not professionals, but are useful. Ask your county's mental health agency if there are any warm lines in your region.

How You Can Reverse Prostate Cancer

A low-fat diet may reverse prostate cancer. Eating a 10%-fat vegan diet, in combination with moderate exercise, meditation and yoga, reduces levels of *prostate-specific antigen* (PSA) in men with early-stage nonaggressive prostate cancer. Be sure to consult your doctor before making changes to your diet.

Dean Ornish, MD, clinical professor of medicine, University of California, San Francisco, and leader of a study of 84 men with prostate cancer, reported at the International Scientific Conference on Complementary, Alternative and Integrative Medicine Research.

Best Time for Prostate Test

A *prostate-specific antigen* (PSA) test is best performed at least 48 hours after having sex. Ejaculation can make a PSA reading jump. The test might then indicate possible prostate cancer. PSA readings return to normal 48 hours after ejaculation.

William J. Catalona, MD, director, Clinical Prostate Cancer Program, and professor, department of urology, Feinberg School of Medicine, Northwestern University, Chicago.

7

Money You Didn't Even Know You Had

More Money for You: America's Experts Share Their Secrets

It makes sense to review your financial strategies, especially when many rules affecting investments, credit cards, taxes and more have changed in tricky ways. We asked top personal-finance experts what single thing most of us can do now to improve our finances. *Their best ideas...*

INVESTMENTS

Dan Solin

Invest no more than 60% of your overall portfolio in stocks. In the hopes of making up for bear-market losses, I see many investors increasing their stock exposure to as much as 80% to 90% of their portfolios, but it's not necessary or wise. A mix of 90% stocks and 10% bonds averaged gains of 8.36% annually over the past 20 years through 2008, while a 50/50 mix averaged 7.24% with much less volatility.

Bill Staton

Focus in on large-cap stocks that have increased dividend payments for at least 10 consecutive years. The few dozen stocks that meet this test will beat the broad market's returns with less volatility while providing steady income. Over the past 10 years, I focused exclusively on investing in about three dozen stocks whose dividends had increased for at least 10 consecutive years. This portfolio generated a total return of 140%, compared with a loss of 1.5% for the S&P stock index. For stocks that qualify, go to "S&P 500 Dividend Aristocrats" at *www.sandp.com.*

Dan Solin, senior vice president at Index Funds Advisors, Bonita Springs, Florida.

Bill Staton, founder and president of Staton Financial Advisors, Charlotte, North Carolina.

Curtis Arnold, founder and CEO of US Citizens for Fair Credit Card Terms, Inc., a consumer advocacy organization, Little Rock, Arkansas.

Richard Barrington, CFA, personal finance expert for MoneyRates.com, Foster City, California.

James Lange, JD, CPA, an estate-planning attorney and accountant based in Pittsburgh.

CREDIT AND DEBT
Curtis Arnold

If you have credit card debt, apply for the Simmons First Visa Platinum credit card and transfer your debt to it. This card has no transfer fees, low interest rates and no annual fee* (800-272-2102 or *www.simmonsfirst.com*).

If you don't have any credit card debt, apply for the Fidelity Rewards American Express card (866-598-4971 or at *www.fidelity.com*, click on "Investment Products," then "Cash Management"). It provides 2% cash back on all purchases without limits or annual fees. The money goes into a brokerage account or, if you choose, into an IRA or a 529 college savings account.

SAVINGS
Richard Barrington, CFA

Consolidate all your bank assets. In years past, it made sense to divide your bank assets among different banks to avoid exceeding the $100,000 FDIC insurance ceiling and to take advantage of good deals on banking products wherever they could be found. But the Federal Deposit Insurance Corporation (FDIC) ceiling on insured accounts is now $250,000...and many banks offer higher interest rates and lower fees for sizable combined checking, savings, CD and money-market balances. Call banks to find out whether you would qualify for special terms if you give them all of your banking business.

TAX AND RETIREMENT PLANNING
James Lange, JD, CPA

If you want to convert traditional IRA assets to a Roth IRA, consider opening a separate Roth account for each type of investment that you convert. The rule that previously prevented high-earners from converting has now been eliminated, but you still pay income tax on the assets that you convert based on their value at that time. By creating separate Roth accounts—one for bonds, one for stocks or perhaps even one for each stock or stock sector—you gain more flexibility. If the value of a particular Roth account that you have converted decreases between the conversion date and October 15 of the following year, you could "recharacterize" that particular asset back to a traditional IRA. This could save excessive income tax on an asset that has declined in value.

*Offers and rates subject to change.

Note that once you pay the tax on converted IRA assets, you won't be taxed on the Roth assets or gains ever again.

Claim Your Property Now

Learn if a state is holding unclaimed property for you. Every year, state governments take possession of billions of dollars worth of unclaimed property such as utility deposits, unclaimed state tax refunds, uncashed paychecks and dividend checks, and other kinds of items. Reach the appropriate government office in your state through the Web site of the National Association of Unclaimed Property Administrators. Go to *www.naupa.org*.

Extra Income with Perks!

A low-wage, part-time retail position is not most people's idea of a dream job, but the weak economy is forcing some to consider this option. It can bridge the gap until jobs in one's own field open up again...be a second job to balance a stretched family budget...or serve as a retirement job to rebuild lost savings.

Part-time retail jobs typically offer low pay and limited benefits, but some do provide an attractive perk—an employee discount. Unlike most benefits, employee discounts might be available to part-time and seasonal help.

Employee discounts tend to be treated as a small afterthought by job seekers, but these discounts can significantly increase the total compensation.

Bob Cartwright, CEO of Intelligent Compensation, LLC, Pflugerville, Texas, *www.intelligentcomp.net*.

Want to Net Some Extra Cash? What It Takes to Sell Avon, Fuller Brush And More

Nicole Woolsey Biggart, PhD, a former dean of the Graduate School of Management and a professor of management and sociology at University of California, Davis. An expert in social network industries, she is author of *Charismatic Capitalism: Direct Selling Organizations in America* (University of Chicago).

Historically, a bad economy is good for direct-sales companies, such as Mary Kay, Avon, Fuller Brush, Tupperware, The Pampered Chef and others, that rely on independent, work-from-home salespeople to sell their products and services. In troubled times, more people work for these companies because of job layoffs or because they want to earn extra income.

The current downturn is no exception, with many direct-sales companies reporting sharp increases in new recruits, people who are eager to become their own bosses and earn income from both commissions and/or bonuses based on recruiting others into their ranks.

However, although recruiting numbers may be up, the Direct Selling Association (DSA) reports a downturn in overall sales to consumers in recent years—$28.5 billion in 2010 from a 2006 peak of $32 billion.

Result: A greater number of salespeople competing for a smaller chunk of business.

While making a go at direct selling could be harder than ever, it still is a good opportunity for certain people—could it be for you?

REALITY CHECK

At any given time, some 15 million Americans work in direct sales.

Product sales commissions generally range between 25% and 50% of the retail price. In some companies, you can earn an additional 3% to 5% commission on sales made by others you recruit.

Yet most people who try direct sales soon give up. After expenses—including the cost of buying inventory and transportation to make sales calls—most people will end up earning $10 to $15 an hour, typically working fewer than 20 hours a week. These people earn a median wage of $2,400 annually, according to the DSA.

In rare cases, those who are very good at selling can make $30,000 annually by working a 40-hour week. Only about 10% manage to make direct sales a full-time job.

WHO CAN SUCCEED?

Ultimately, these jobs are all about selling —and you will make real money only if you are an effective salesperson. Companies will not provide a listing of potential sales contacts, so most people who succeed in direct sales already have a large social network.

Those who do well also tend to have the "right" personality. If they are not outgoing, they are at least comfortable knocking on doors or calling people they may not know...have a "thick skin" that can handle frequent rejection ...and are self-motivated and disciplined.

MAKING IT WORK

Before you choose a direct-selling company to represent, consider the following...

- **Be product-practical.** At the very minimum, you should choose a well-known, established company that sells products you know about, have a passion for or would personally use. Your passion for, or knowledge of, a specific product will make you a more effective salesperson. To find a potential fit, visit *www.directselling411.com* to learn about possible companies. The best direct-sales products appear to be those that benefit from personal in-home demonstrations.

Examples: Knives (shoppers can't experiment with knives in retail stores)...cosmetics (it's impractical and can be intimidating to try them out in public)...and water purifiers (in regions where water quality is an issue).

- **Talk to veterans.** Research a company's reputation with an online search. Look for Internet communities of sellers.

Examples: *www.mydswa.org...http://internetbasedmoms.com/direct-sales...www.directsalesmoms.com.*

You also can check the Better Business Bureau (*www.bbb.org*) for filed complaints against a company you are thinking about.

If you are interested in working for a specific company, ask to be put in touch with several of its longtime direct sellers. New recruits tend to be enthusiastic but lack the experience to be realistic about their success. Speak to people who have had direct-selling experience with that organization for years. Ask these veterans about the difficulty finding customers...their opinion of the products...and the company's payment process. (Direct selling is a cash business, and money should flow back to sellers quickly—or they should be able to keep their share of the receipts.)

• **Look for DSA membership.** Companies that belong to the DSA (at *www.dsa.org*) need to subscribe to minimal industry standards. These include a "buyback" policy if you decide to quit the business, which allows you to return unopened and unsold products purchased within the prior 12 months for 90% of the price you paid for them (so you are not stuck paying for a large amount of inventory that you can't sell).

Another industry standard is having payment structures based chiefly on sales to consumers, not from recruiting other sellers (so your main job is not to recruit more members but to sell goods).

Most companies require all new recruits to purchase an initial startup kit—typically for $100 or less—that includes a sample inventory of their most sellable products, "how-to" information, and brochures and materials for customers.

Avoid working for any company, including members of the DSA, that charge more than $150 for a startup kit. Good direct-selling companies make money by getting you into a position to sell, not by loading you down with products that sit in your garage.

Turn What You Know Into Dough: Earn $1,000 a Month in Your Spare Time

Loral Langemeier, CEO for Live Out Loud, Inc., a coaching and seminar company with offices in Nevada, California and Utah. Langemeier regularly appears on the *Dr. Phil* show as a money expert and is author of many books about finance, including the best-seller *The Millionaire Maker* (McGraw-Hill) and, most recently, *Put More Cash in Your Pocket* (Harper). Her Internet site is *www.liveoutloud.com.*

If you want more cash, consider starting a part-time business. Almost everyone has the skills and time required to launch a business that's capable of generating an extra $500 to $1,000 per month.

With a part-time business, the smart strategy is to get it up and running within a week or two for no more than a few hundred dollars.

How to do it...

LOW-COST BUSINESS IDEAS

Identify skills that you already possess that could be turned into a service-oriented business. *Possibilities...*

• **Tutoring.** Tutor individuals or help high school students prepare for their SATs or ACTs. Teachers, former teachers, professors and those with degrees from prestigious universities are particularly likely to attract clients.

• **Auto care/repair.** If you're good with cars, offer to do auto-maintenance and basic repair services.

• **Computer.** Provide tech support to individuals or small businesses. Set up computer networks, solve problems, optimize computer performance or create and manage Web sites.

• **Foreign language.** If you're fluent in a foreign language, tutor those who want to learn it or students struggling with their foreign language classes.

• **Handyman.** Home maintenance and repair services always are in demand.

• **Music or acting.** Tight budgets are forcing many public schools to cut back on music and theater programs, creating openings for private tutors.

• **Photography.** Offer portrait or wedding photography services.

• **Sewing/alterations.** Alterations are on the rise as people choose to repair, not replace, clothing.

• **Sports.** Help promising young athletes to hone their abilities. Those who played a sport professionally or for a prestigious college program are most likely to attract clients.

• **Woodworking.** High-quality handcrafted wooden bowls and other carved kitchen items can fetch attractive prices in boutiques and at arts and crafts fairs.

If you do not have a particular skill that is likely to be in demand, there are service businesses that do not require extensive training or skills (though experience is, of course, helpful). *Possibilities include...*

• **In-home elder care**

• **Child care/day care**

• **Lawn and garden care**

• **Carpooling/driving services**

• **Pet walking/pet sitting**

• **House-sitting**

• **Housecleaning**

BUSINESSES TO AVOID

Certain businesses are best avoided by people seeking to earn extra cash with little risk...

• **Retail stores.** Retailing typically requires an expensive inventory, long hours, employees and leased commercial property. Retailers must compete with Internet sellers and massive chains.

• **Franchises.** Any profitable franchise charges big up-front franchise fees that part-time business people typically cannot afford.

• **"New idea" businesses.** It can take lots of time and marketing dollars to convince consumers to spend their money on something that they've never spent it on before. The failure rate for such businesses is very high. More than 485,000 applications for US patents were filed last year and only a few of these will be successful. It is better to provide a service that people already understand.

SETTING PRICES

Contact companies that provide similar services in your region, and inquire about their rates without mentioning that you intend to enter the same business. Avoid the inclination to undercut the competition's prices. Offering the lowest price for a service creates the impression that your services are less valuable. It is better to charge comparable prices and explain why your services are superior.

Examples: Establish that your qualifications are more extensive...or offer a money-back guarantee.

Exception: Offer lower prices to customers who sign up for extended service packages. Locking customers into long-term arrangements can help beginning businesses build reliable cash flow. It also is a way to make your service seem like a bargain without creating the impression that it is low quality.

Example: Someone starting a part-time car-maintenance business could offer a discount package to customers who sign up for a full-year auto-maintenance program.

MARKETING YOUR BUSINESS

The most cost-effective marketing tool is word of mouth...

• **Visit local businesses that offer related but not overlapping services.** Tell the owners or managers of these businesses what your business does. Ask if you can post a flyer in their windows or leave a stack of flyers on the counter.

Examples: Someone starting a house-sitting or lawn-care business could contact real estate agents.

• **Consider sharing a storefront location.** Ask area businesses that are in some way related to your intended field if they have extra space that they are willing to sublet to you. This can be much cheaper than renting your own space, and you'll have an inside track on that existing business's customers.

Example: Someone starting up a sewing and alterations business could sublet space at a dry cleaner.

• **Contact organizations that work with your intended customer base.**

Example: If you intend to provide tutoring or music lessons to students, contact local schools and youth clubs.

• **Volunteer your services to local nonprofits.** It's a good way to make contacts and show off your skills.

• **Offer satisfied customers a discount on their next purchase** if they refer someone who also becomes a customer.

TAXES, LICENSES AND INSURANCE

Don't worry about taxes at first. New businesses typically have 90 days from the date they start taking in money to get tax payments squared away. It's best not to get bogged down in such details sooner than necessary, but do ask your accountant if you need to charge tax on any of your goods and/or services. Don't worry about hiring a lawyer or incorporating your business until your business is up and running.

A few details do need to be sorted out before your business gets going...

• **Contact your town or county offices to find out if you need any licenses or permits.**

• **Set up a separate checking account for business expenses and receipts.**

• **Ask your insurance agent about professional liability insurance,** particularly if your business involves anything that could cause injury or trigger a lawsuit.

• **Contact your auto insurance provider if you plan to use your personal vehicle for business.** Your existing policy is unlikely to cover business use.

Rent Out a Room and Make $5,000 or More

Jacqueline Grossmann, co-president of the National Shared Housing Resource Center, a national clearinghouse for consumer information about shared housing programs. She also is homesharing coordinator of the Interfaith Housing Center of the Northern Suburbs, a nonprofit organization serving the north suburban Chicago region, *www.interfaithhousingcenter.org.*

If you need extra cash, you may be able to turn to your home for help. Renting out a spare room can provide very good income—perhaps $450 to $600 per month, though this varies by region and room quality.

First step: Check the rooms-for-rent listings in your local newspaper classifieds or online at Craigslist.org to find out how much other home owners are asking in your area.

Though renting out a room is a potential income source for any home owner, it's most likely to pay off if...

• **You can provide a room with a private bathroom and/or private entrance.**

• **Your home is located near public transportation sources.**

• **Your region offers employers that hire temporary and/or seasonal employees,** such as colleges and universities.

SELECTING A TENANT

Renting out a room means inviting a stranger into your home. The wrong tenant could make you feel uncomfortable...rob you...or fail to pay rent. *Strategies for finding the right tenant...*

• **Work with a nonprofit home-sharing organization.** These local organizations match home owners with room renters, usually for free. They have experience spotting potential problem tenants and even may conduct background checks on prospective tenants.

• **Links to home-sharing organizations** can be found on the National Shared Housing Resource Center's Web site (*www.nationalsharedhousing.org*). Click the "Program Directory" link, then search for programs in your region coded "MU," for "Match-Up Program."

• **Contact employers in your region.** Companies that hire temporary employees or that transfer employees to the region from other offices for temporary assignments sometimes keep track of local housing options.

• **Contact local universities' housing departments.** They might know of graduate students or visiting professors in need of rooms for a semester or longer. Contact school principals. Schools sometimes hire temporary replacements from out of town when teachers take maternity leave. Contact hospital human resources departments. Hospitals often hire temporary nurses, sometimes from overseas.

• **Contact local houses of worship.** Ask if they know any trustworthy people in need of affordable housing.

• **Insist that any potential tenant supply proof of stable income, such as pay stubs.** Also get his/her employer's contact information so that you can get a reference. And be sure to get at least two other references, including one from a previous landlord.

If you want to avoid tenants who have criminal histories, lean toward applicants in fields such as teaching or nursing, where background checks and drug tests are the norm. If you want to conduct your own check, search online for "background check" to find a company. Be sure to have the renter's Social Security number so that you are checking the right person. To see if the person is a sex offender, go to *www.nsopw.gov/core/publicregistrysites.aspx.*

• **Don't wait until the last minute.** Home owners often wait until their financial situations become desperate before renting out a room. This desperation forces them to accept almost any person who knocks on their door. Better to advertise your room for rent several months before your financial situation becomes tight so that you can be selective.

HOUSE RULES

Home owners should explain all the house rules to would-be tenants before agreeing to let them move in…

• **Identify the sections of the house and grounds that are off-limits to the tenant.**

Example: The master bedroom, den and the garden on the east side of the house are private areas.

• **Explain if and where smoking will be allowed.**

Example: Smoking is not allowed in the home, but it is permitted on the back patio.

• **Explain whether pets are allowed.**

Example: Cats and dogs are not permitted, but smaller pets confined to cages or aquariums are acceptable, subject to the home owner's approval.

• **Describe where the renter can park.**

Example: The renter can park a vehicle on the driveway's left side, leaving room for other vehicles to pass.

• **Explain whether overnight and daytime guests are allowed.**

Example: Daytime visitors are permitted in the renter's private room but not in the home's common areas. Overnight guests are not permitted.

• **Lay out the tenant's access to the house TV and other electronics**…the refrigerator…the washer/dryer…and the house phone.

Example: The tenant can use the TV and stereo between 10 am and 10 pm if they are not being used by the home owner. One shelf will be made available in the refrigerator for the tenant's use. The tenant has the right to do two loads of laundry per week. The tenant cannot use the house phone without specific permission from the home owner.

• **Set certain hours as "quiet time."**

Example: The tenant agrees to be quiet between 10 pm and 8 am.

• **Explain whether the tenant has any right to change the thermostat…**and, if not, at what temperature the home will be kept.

Example: The home will be heated to at least 68° in the winter and cooled to stay below 75° in the summer. The tenant cannot change the thermostat without permission.

• **Go over any restrictions on food storage, preparation and consumption in the tenant's private room.**

Example: The tenant can eat in the kitchen or in his private room, but all food will be stored and prepared in the kitchen. No hot plate, microwave or refrigerator is permitted in the private room.

• **Explain who is responsible for household utility bills.**

Example: All utility bills will be paid by the home owner. (Room renters generally prefer the certainty of a fixed charge.)

ROOM RENTING AND THE LAW

Five legal considerations…

• **Landlord law.** A long list of state and federal laws govern relationships between landlord and tenant.

Examples: Many jurisdictions have laws restricting a landlord's right to evict a tenant or enter a tenant's room or apartment…restricting security deposits and fees…and requiring the disclosure of lead paint and other health risks.

The Web site of the US Department of Housing and Urban Development offers details for federal fair housing laws and links to sites that cover laws in the states (*www.hud.gov/offices/fheo/FHLaws/yourrights.cfm*).

Exception: If you are renting out a room in your own residence, you are not subject to the same strict federal anti-discrimination laws that other landlords need to follow. You could choose to rent only to someone of your own gender.

• **Zoning laws.** Some towns and neighborhoods have rules limiting the number of unrelated people who can live together under one roof. These rules typically do not prevent home owners from renting out one room to one unrelated roommate, but it's worth checking with your town offices.

• **Taxes.** The rent your tenant pays to you is income that should be reported to the IRS. However, you likely can deduct a portion of your home's depreciation...home repair and maintenance expenses...utility bills and homeowner's insurance premiums from this rental income. See IRS publication 527, *Residential Rental Property*, for details. You can download it at *www.irs.gov.*

• **Insurance.** Contact your homeowner's insurance provider to make sure that your policy will not be voided if you take in a tenant...and that you will be covered if the tenant causes damage to your house or is injured on your property and sues.

• **Contracts.** Prepare a written lease to be signed by both you and your tenant. Suitable forms can be picked up in do-it-yourself legal guidebooks...or downloaded from law Web sites, such as Nolo.com, typically for $10 or $25. This lease should spell out each party's responsibilities, including the house rules... the amount of rent and the day of the month on which rent is due...whether a security deposit is required...and the terms under which the lease can be ended. Room-rental agreements typically allow either party to terminate the lease with 30 days' notice.

The Yard Sale Queen's Guide to Getting Cash For Your Clutter

Chris Heiska, who edits the Yard Sale Queen Web site, *www.yardsalequeen.com.* She lives in Lusby, Maryland, and attends 10 to 15 yard sales most Saturdays from spring through autumn, and she holds three or four sales each year. She has been quoted about yard sales everywhere from *The Wall Street Journal* to CNN.

Holding a garage or yard sale can be a great way to clear out clutter and earn some cash. *Here's how to increase the odds that your sale will be a success...*

SCHEDULING

The best time to schedule your sale is on a weekend when a local church or civic group is staging a large rummage sale. These large sales draw bargain hunters from surrounding towns, and many of those shoppers will visit nearby garage sales as well. Post signs with arrows leading from the exit of the big sale to your own sale.

Otherwise, choose a weekend when a large number of garage sales are scheduled in your neighborhood...or ask your neighbors to join you in a multifamily or block-wide sale. The more sellers in the area, the more buyers who will visit.

Saturday morning usually is the best time of week for a garage sale because that is when the most garage sale shoppers will be on the prowl. Other times are acceptable only if sales are commonly held at those times in your region. *Also...*

• **Start your sale 30 minutes earlier than other sales.** This will encourage shoppers to begin their garage sale day with you.

• **Avoid scheduling your sale for a holiday weekend when people leave town**—unless your home is in a resort community or located on a heavily used route to, say, a local beach.

• **If there's one big employer in your region,** schedule your sale for a weekend that closely follows its payday. That's when people are most likely to be in a spending mood. To find out when payday is, ask someone who works there or try calling the company.

• **If it rains on sale day, take down your signs and postpone your sale.** You can proceed with your sale if all of your merchandise is protected by a garage roof, but expect business to be slow. Many garage sale shoppers make other plans when it rains.

MERCHANDISE AND PRICING

Small, inexpensive items, including housewares...tools...costume jewelry...DVDs and CDs...books...and child-related products, sell well at garage sales. Large items, such as furniture, typically do not sell well, because most shoppers cannot fit them into their cars. Items priced above $10 or $20 tend not to sell well either and are better sold through eBay, Craigslist or a newspaper classified ad.

Before holding your sale, visit a few garage sales in your area to determine appropriate prices. Relatively new, clean items can bring as much as one-third of their original prices, but most goods sell for much less.

Examples: Used hardcover books rarely sell for more than $1 or $2 apiece...used adult clothing rarely brings more than $2 or $3 per item. Used designer clothing is likely to fetch a better price in a consignment shop.

Shoppers do not like to have to ask the prices of merchandise. Attach a price sticker to each item...or post price signs when multiple items all cost the same amount.

Example: "Paperbacks 50 cents each."

Goods bring better prices when they have been cleaned, but consider the value of your time before you start scrubbing. Cleaning a child's toy might increase its sale price from $1 to $3—but the 10 minutes you spend cleaning might be worth more to you than $2.

Other smart sales strategies...

• **Scan newspaper circulars for store ads offering the products that you are selling—** particularly if you are selling things that are relatively new or priced beyond $10. Clip out these ads, and attach them to your items so that shoppers can see what good deals you're offering.

• **If you sell electrical items,** have an outlet and extension cord handy so you can show that they work.

• **Put in cheap batteries.** Items powered by batteries bring much higher prices when they contain working batteries. If an item requires many batteries or large batteries, however, the cost of these batteries could eat up much or all of your profit. Buy cheap generic batteries at a dollar store...or pull used batteries near the end of their lives from electronics that you are not selling and buy new batteries for these.

• **Place all of your merchandise (except larger items) on tables,** even if this means borrowing folding tables from neighbors...or improvising tables from upturned boxes or boards placed across cinder blocks. Goods are less appealing when displayed on the ground, and many shoppers won't bend down to examine merchandise.

• **Be sure to have a "man's table."** Have at least one table of merchandise that's likely to interest the stereotypical man, such as tools, DVDs, electronics and books. If possible, also position a lawn mower, barbecue grill or large tools near the front of your sale, where they can be seen from the road. Many garage sale shoppers are married couples, and these couples are more likely to stop at your sale—and remain longer—if there is something for the man to examine.

ADVERTISING

Spread the word about your sale through ads in your local newspaper classifieds...on the free classified ads Web site Craigslist.org... and on community bulletin boards in local stores. Emphasize the size of your sale in these ads. Use words such as "huge" or "multifamily" if appropriate.

On the morning of your sale, post signs on the roads around your home. Provide large, easy-to-follow arrows that point toward your sale, along with the words "Garage Sale" (or "Yard Sale") and your address in big, thick print so that it can be read from a moving vehicle.

Caution: Do not post your signs any earlier than the morning of your sale...and don't leave them up after your sale ends. Many towns and neighborhood associations do prohibit private signs along roadsides. Garage sale signs often are ignored by the authorities and accepted by neighbors, but the longer you leave your signs up, the greater the odds that you will face a fine. Ask the homeowners association or town about garage sale sign rules in your area.

SALE DAY

Greet people who visit your sale, then give them space to browse undisturbed. Chat with customers only if they initiate conversations. Background music can make customers feel more comfortable. Garage sale cash boxes can get stolen, so carry all the cash generated by your sale (along with plenty of $1 and $5 bills for change) in a carpenter's apron or pouch worn around your waist. Be wary of accepting checks, which might bounce. Do not let strangers into your house to use your bathroom or make phone calls—they could be thieves.

Secrets of the eBay Millionaire's Club: Easy Ways for Sellers To Boost Profits

Amy Joyner, the author of several books about eBay, including *The eBay Billionaires' Club: Exclusive Secrets for Building an Even Bigger and More Profitable Online Business* (Wiley). Joyner has conducted more than 1,000 transactions.

The Professional eBay Sellers Alliance is an organization of eBay "power sellers" who together generate nearly a half billion dollars in annual sales. *eBay enthusiast Amy Joyner has interviewed more than 30 of these online auction stars to learn their favorite strategies...*

PRICING AND SELLING

• **Start the bidding at 99 cents.** Experienced eBay sellers recognize that more bidders are drawn to listings when the bidding starts out very low, even when selling merchandise worth hundreds of dollars. More bidders tend to mean a higher final price, because some bidders are likely to get carried away by the auction excitement and bid more than they originally intended. Setting your opening bid at just 99 cents instead of $1 or more also means you do not have to pay the insertion fee. ("Final value" fees based on the auction's closing price also apply.)

Exception: Do not set an ultralow opening price if there are numerous items similar to yours already for sale and they are not attracting multiple bidders. When sellers outnumber buyers, buyers sometimes win with their opening bids. This is particularly common with DVDs and books.

• **Skip the reserve.** In a "reserve auction," the item is not sold if bidding does not reach a seller-selected reserve (minimum) price. Cautious sellers use reserve auctions to protect themselves from selling items at far less than they are worth. However, top eBay sellers tend to agree that setting a reserve is a very bad idea. Most eBay bidders are bargain hunters. When they get the message "reserve price not met," they conclude that the seller will not part with this item at a bargain price and they move on to other auctions. Setting a reserve price also adds to your eBay insertion fees.

Helpful: If you simply cannot live with the risk that your item will sell for a very low price, increase the opening bid instead of adding a reserve. High opening bids are the lesser of two evils.

• **Don't gouge buyers on shipping.** Some eBay sellers inflate shipping charges to increase their profits. Top sellers rarely do this. They have learned that many potential buyers consider excessive shipping costs a sign of an untrustworthy seller. The proper amount to charge for shipping is slightly more than your actual cost of postage and packing materials.

Helpful: If you have an eBay store (a personalized Web page on eBay, where you can sell merchandise at a fixed price), encourage more sales by offering discounts on shipping when buyers purchase more than one item.

• **Get the gallery photo but not the bold print.** When you list products for auction on eBay, you are offered numerous "listing upgrades" that are meant to help your auction catch shoppers' attention. All top sellers agree that the free "gallery photograph"—the small picture that appears next to the title when listings are displayed—is key. Buyers tend to skim right past listings that lack these.

Don't opt for bold print titles. They do not draw enough extra attention to justify the $2 fee.

• **Offer second-chance auctions when you sell multiple quantities.** If you have more than one of the same item to sell, don't list each in a separate auction. Auction one of the items, then send an e-mail through eBay to the bidder who made the second-highest bid, offering him/her the chance to purchase an identical product for the amount of his final bid.

Second-chance auctions save you fees because you will be charged an eBay insertion fee only on the first item (final value fees do apply to each item sold)...they provide you a guaranteed selling price on the second item, assuming that the bidder accepts the offer... and they let you choose a bidder you trust, based on positive feedback scores. If the second-place bidder has negative feedback, make your offer to the third- or fourth-place bidder instead.

BUSINESS STRATEGIES

Would you like to turn eBay selling into a business? *To make it work...*

• **Stay in touch with customers.** Inexperienced eBay sellers often fail to take full advantage of their satisfied customers. Ask buyers for permission to add their names to your e-mail list so that you can update them about future auctions.

• **Include a free gift with purchases to foster goodwill.**

Example: One successful camera seller adds free lens cloths to shipments.

• **Don't waste time at the post office.** Long post office lines can be major time drains for people who sell on eBay regularly. Instead, schedule free post office package pickups at your home/store through the post office's Web site (*www.usps.gov*). The site also lets you print shipping labels and pay shipping costs with a credit card. You can even order free priority mail shipping boxes.

Important: You will need an accurate scale to weigh your shipments.

• **Protect your feedback score at all costs.** Top eBay sellers know that a high eBay feedback score is a necessity to get high bids. Adopt a policy of "the buyer is always right"—even when he is not. Even if just a few buyers leave you negative feedback, potential bidders in future auctions might not trust you.

Provide money-back refunds to unsatisfied customers whenever possible.

Do not type bitter responses when you receive undeserved negative feedback. If you explain bad feedback in a calm, rational manner, future bidders are more likely to assume that the buyer was to blame for the problem.

Be responsive to bidder questions. Try to be at your computer as your auctions draw to a close so that you can answer any last-minute questions.

Do not list negative-sounding policies on your auction pages. State your sales policies in a positive way.

Example: Write "I accept only PayPal," rather than "Under no circumstances will I take a check or money order."

• **Select appropriate auction management software.** These programs can take the grunt work out of posting multiple items for auction by offering tools to quickly create, edit and format multiple listings. Turbo Lister from eBay is appropriate for most sellers (free at *pages.ebay.com/turbo_lister*).

Those who sell hundreds of items or more a month might choose a more sophisticated program, such as eBay's Blackthorne Basic. It is $9.99/month at *pages.ebay.com/blackthorne.*

• **Become a consignment seller.** Let friends know that you can handle their eBay sales for them, and ask them to recommend you to their friends.

Consignment sellers typically charge between 35% and 50% of the net sale price, after eBay fees. The item's owner should pay the auction fees if the product doesn't sell.

Helpful: Check completed auctions of similar items before posting a consigned item for sale. If you can let the item's owner know what price the product is likely to fetch, you will reduce the risk of disappointment.

For more information, go to *www.ebay.com* and click on "Sell."

sh for All Those Old Books

Type in the ISBN numbers (you can find them on the back cover of the book or on the copyright page) of books that you no longer want at Cash4Books.net, and the site will make an offer on each. When you are ready to ship, you print out a prepaid mailing label (shipping is included), package the books and send them off. Cash4Books.net will send you a check or deposit a payment into your PayPal account within three business days after receiving and processing your books.

Or donate books to your library. The tax deduction could be more than the books would sell for.

Money for Old Gadgets

A site such as Gazelle.com will buy old gadgets that you no longer use. This site takes laptop computers, cameras, cell phones and digital music players. Answer a few questions about your device (its condition, whether you have the original software, cables, etc.), and the site will quote you a price. Free shipping is offered for most items, with prepaid shipping labels sent by e-mail to the sender.

Best Way to Barter

Consider joining one of the barter exchange programs, such as *www.SwapTreasures.com*, *www.FavorPals.com* and *www.SwapTree.com*...or try going it alone by bartering with local merchants.

Example: Barter baked goods with your mechanic for an oil change.

Woman's Day, 1633 Broadway, New York City 10019.

Bulletproof Your Job... And Ride Out the Rough Times at Work

Stephen Viscusi, the president and founder of BulletProofYourResume.com, a résumé-writing company that creates both traditional and video-streaming résumés, in New York City. Viscusi started his career as a headhunter and is author of *Bulletproof Your Job: 4 Simple Strategies to Ride Out the Rough Times and Come Out on Top at Work* (Collins, *www.bulletproofyourjob.com*).

Millions of US jobs were lost as the nation slid deeper into a recession. And, more layoffs are likely.

In an economy this bad, even doing one's job well is no guarantee of job security. Many skilled hardworking employees will find themselves out of work. *How to decrease the odds that you will be among them and maybe even get a promotion...*

- **Be "low maintenance."** You will be among the first shown the door if your boss considers you to be a complainer...thinks you require handholding or special attention...or listens to complaints about you from your coworkers. Bosses don't lose sleep about laying off high-maintenance employees such as these—they dream about it. Cutting such people loose can make life easier for them and everyone else in the office.

To avoid the "high maintenance" label, accept without complaint all assignments that come your way...do not ask for special treatment or argue about your rights as an employee ...learn to endure your workplace's minor annoyances in silence...and get along well with all of your colleagues.

- **Be upbeat.** Black humor is common when layoffs loom. Don't join in—others might not have any sense of humor about this economy or the business's current struggles.

Speak with optimism about the company's future—especially when the boss is around. It sends the message that you want to be part of that future.

- **Make sure your boss knows you as a human being.** It is easier to fire an employee whom you don't know. Share details of your life with your boss. Your goal is to humanize yourself to make it harder for your boss to fire you.

Also, be sure that your employer is aware of your personal financial responsibilities. Your boss might be less likely to lay you off if he/she knows that the layoff would cause financial catastrophe for you because you have kids...a spouse with a serious health problem...a parent who is financially dependent on you...or some other major financial commitment.

Sparing the job of someone who is especially unable to afford unemployment allows the employer to think of himself as a big-hearted boss who is doing his best to look after his employees during difficult times.

Best: Don't sound desperate or needy when you discuss your financial situation. Just mention it in a conversation with your boss should a natural opportunity arise.

If you are single and debt-free, don't advertise this. Your employer will not feel as guilty about firing you.

• **Make a friend in the human resources (HR) department.** HR employees often know about layoffs months before they occur. If you have an ally in HR, this colleague might be able to warn you about which departments will be hardest hit in time for you to transfer to a safer position. In some layoffs, HR employees even have a say in who stays and who goes.

• **Volunteer to take on all tasks that your boss dislikes.** This might mean managing a headache project...training any employees who transfer in from other departments...or representing your company during conferences and charity outings. If you don't know which aspects of your boss's job cause him the most displeasure, ask.

If you're in charge of these tasks, your boss won't be able to let you go without worrying that he will have to take on these unloved responsibilities once again. That's powerful motivation to keep you around.

• **Don't let your boss catch you not working.** Employees who are seen as slackers usually are among the first to be let go. Don't take long lunches, and do not get caught shopping online...playing computer games...or making long personal phone calls.

• **Arrive at least five minutes before your boss every morning, and stay five minutes after he leaves.**

• **Add value to the company.** Employers lay people off to save money. If it's clear that you earn or save your company more than you are paid in salary and benefits, there's nothing to be gained by letting you go.

If you are not in a sales position and cannot easily bring more money into the company, search for ways to assist your employer contain costs. Take on additional responsibilities to save the company the cost of hiring an additional employee. Brainstorm creative ways to trim company expenses.

• **Become your employer's specialist on a crucial chore.** Your job is much safer if your boss sees you as the one person in the office who can keep the computer system running... the most important client happy...or the files organized.

• **Watch for warning signs that your specialized role might become obsolete.** Have a plan in place to transition to another vital role if this occurs.

Example: You always have managed one particular client's account, but now the client's struggling in the recession and could go out of business. Start cultivating a relationship with another key client so that you will not be expendable if the first one disappears.

• **Build allies.** Layoffs are rarely distributed evenly across large corporations. One department might lose 30% of its staff, while a more profitable department might lose no one at all.

Give colleagues in your organization's most promising departments reason to like you. If your own department appears particularly vulnerable to layoffs, contact your allies in these safer-seeming divisions and ask them whether a transfer might be possible.

• **Try to negotiate a layoff into a pay cut or a part-time job.** If you are laid off, tell your employer that you would consider a pay cut or a part-time position if one were offered. In this economy, an underpaid job is better than no job at all.

"I Didn't See It Coming": Warning Signs That You Might Lose Your Job

Amy Dorn Kopelan, president of the conference management organization Bedlam Entertainment, Inc., in New York City, and coauthor of *I Didn't See It Coming: The Only Book You'll Ever Need to Avoid Being Blindsided in Business* (Wiley). Her 20-year career at ABC included nine years as programming manager for *Good Morning America.*

Even the most secure-seeming job is never completely safe. Changes in a company's direction...petty office politics...a strained relationship with one's boss...or any of a host of other factors can cost even the most competent worker his/her job.

Amy Dorn Kopelan lost her position as head of morning programming at ABC in 1995, when Capital Cities Communications acquired the network. She had thought her job was safe because of the high ratings of the morning programs. She failed to consider that Capital Cities already had a skilled morning programmer and had no need for two.

Kopelan, along with two other high-powered executives who lost their jobs, decided to write a book on warning signs of workplace trouble. *Here are six career-threatening events and what to do about them...*

1. Your company merges or it is acquired. Top-performing employees often assume they will survive the layoffs that follow a merger or acquisition, but an entire division might be eliminated, taking the stars out the door along with everyone else...or the acquiring company might already have someone in your role. Do not feel completely secure even if your boss "guarantees" you that your job is safe—in the new company, your boss might not have the power to make the final decision.

What to do: Consider how your skills and talents could be applied elsewhere in your organization, and discuss this with executives in those divisions. This increases your odds of finding a safe haven should your current division or position be eliminated. Also prepare an exit strategy.

2. Your boss loses power. If your boss falls out of favor with the company's top brass, his career is not the only one at risk—yours could be threatened as well. Your whole department might be viewed negatively, stalling the careers of all assigned to it...your boss's favorable opinion of you will carry little weight, making it harder for you to advance...and your boss's fall from grace could mean a new boss will soon take over, which can create its own problems (see number three below).

Signs a boss is losing power...

- His demands become uncharacteristically unrealistic as the pressure to produce forces him to ask the impossible of underlings.
- A consultant is brought in to study your department.
- The departmental budget is slashed.
- Your boss suddenly has trouble getting access to top executives.

What to do: The safest strategy for you is to attempt to transfer to a different department with a more highly regarded leader. The more aggressive strategy is to put yourself forward for your boss's job. You could talk to a division head you know or someone you have befriended in human resources to decide how best to go about this. Attempt it only if you have specific ideas for improving the department and a track record that suggests that such a promotion is merited.

3. You get a new boss. It is not enough to show your new boss that you are intelligent and hardworking. To ensure that your career remains on course, you also must match your style to that of your boss. Does he like to receive daily e-mails from people who report to him or just the occasional verbal update? Does he prefer to have an informal atmosphere or a buttoned-down workplace? Does he like hard-driving go-getters or easygoing team players?

What to do: New bosses often form lasting opinions of their employees within minutes of meeting them, so it is best to get the answers to these questions before the boss walks through the door. As soon as you learn your new boss's name, start tracking down employees, clients and colleagues from his previous positions who can fill you in. Be aware that word might get back to the new boss, so frame your queries in a very positive way.

Example: "I'm really excited about working with John and want to make a good impression. What can you tell me about him?"

4. A coach is brought in. If your employer hires a coach to help you improve your communications or conflict-resolution skills, the appropriate response is to fear for your job. These coaches typically are hired to spend time with executives whom companies intend to fire. A report from an outside coach stating that an executive was unwilling or unable to address his serious communication problems will make it more difficult for this executive to sue the company for wrongful termination later.

What to do: Listen to the coach, and implement his advice even if you consider it silly or unnecessary. Your company might have hired this coach to push you out the door, but if you show improvement and maintain a positive attitude, management might let you keep your job.

Exception: Consider it a very positive sign if a coach is hired to help you with your marketing skills. Marketing skills coaches generally are hired when companies think an executive has excellent ideas but needs to learn how to present them better. (If you are not sure whether a coach hired to work with you is a positive or negative omen, find out which department is paying the coach's bill. Your career could be in danger if it is the human resources department.)

5. You remind your boss of someone he is/was partial to. It can seem like a huge career boost when a boss takes a liking to you based on a perceived similarity with someone else, such as a son or daughter, spouse, protégé or even himself at your age.

In the long run, however, this is more likely to damage your career than help it. Your colleagues could come to resent your seemingly undeserved special treatment, making it difficult for you to work with them. Or your boss could start to base his evaluations of you on the abilities and actions of someone else, taking your future out of your control and possibly hindering your career.

What to do: Consider whether there's something in particular about your behavior or appearance that triggers the association with this other individual. Then take steps to alter this similarity.

Example: If your boss treats you like a son and you find yourself being deferential toward him, reposition yourself. Say something like, "I've been thinking about what we discussed last week, and I have a very different approach." *Also...*

- Establish boundaries if the boss seems to be trying to get too close. If you are asked to join the boss for drinks or dinner more often than your colleagues, thank him for the invitation but say that you have previous plans.
- Keep colleagues on your side by standing up for their interests with the boss.

6. You are promoted ahead of your peers. Being promoted in your department bodes very well for your future—but if mishandled, it could derail your career. Some of your colleagues will resent you for getting the promotion that they had hoped for. Others might have trouble treating a previous equal as the boss. If you cannot convince the entire team to treat you with respect, you lose effectiveness as a manager and your career could stall.

What to do: Do not celebrate your promotion in front of your colleagues. This will only deepen any animosities. *Also...*

- Meet with each member of your new team one-on-one, and reassure each individual that you respect his talents.
- Let team members take the glory when your team achieves success. You should claim credit primarily for leading your troops.
- If any member of your group cannot adjust to your new role, try to find the person another position elsewhere in the company.

It is important to prepare an "exit strategy" if you think your job might be on the line. Network with others in your industry...update your résumé...contact headhunters...and try to quickly acquire any important skills that you lack. This way, you're all set to look for a job if you need to—and you might even land a position before you are let go.

Should You Take a Job Buyout Offer?

Robert Barry, president, Barry Capital Management, a financial-planning firm based in Hackettstown, New Jersey. He is a past president of the Financial Planning Association. His Web site is *www.barrycapital.com.*

Some of the big automakers have offered as much as $140,000 to tens of thousands of workers willing to give up their jobs. Automakers aren't the only ones paying employees to not show up. Many other companies have "bribed" employees to quit in recent years. And the pace of such offers may pick up if the faltering economy doesn't. Organizations provide these "buyout offers" and "early retirement packages" to trim their payroll, pension and health-care obligations without resorting to layoffs.

How to determine whether to accept...

FIRST, EVALUATE YOURSELF

Even before you analyze the financial details of the buyout offer, ask yourself these important questions...

- **What do I want to do with the rest of my life?** Have you always dreamed of trying a different career...working for a different company...moving to a different part of the country...or retiring early? A buyout offer might be a great opportunity to do so.
- **How employable am I?** If you are confident that you could find a good job fast, accepting the buyout probably makes financial sense. But if it appears that finding an equally or more attractive new job will take a long time or require a relocation that you and/or your spouse would dread, you may want to reject the offer.
- **Am I financially ready to retire in the manner I desire?** If you consider a buyout your ticket to early retirement, first make sure you have enough money saved to never work again.

SECOND, EVALUATE THE RISKS OF STAYING

- **How financially secure is my company?** If there's a significant chance that your employer might soon go out of business or be forced to implement large-scale cutbacks, the buyout might be a smart way to exit the sinking ship. Consider what may happen to your job.
- **Will there be future buyout offers?** And if so, might their terms be less attractive?
- **Will your job change?** A shrunken workforce may mean more work or less desirable work.

LASTLY, EVALUATE THE OFFER

Not all buyout offers are created equal. *Important considerations...*

- **Do I get to keep my health insurance?** This is a vital issue unless you are eligible for Medicare or have access to an affordable insurance plan through another source, such as a spouse's employer. Individual health insurance policies can be prohibitively expensive, so this may be enough reason to reject the buyout.
- **How will my pension be affected?** If you have a defined benefit pension plan, which promises specific monthly benefits at retirement, the size of your pension is likely determined in part by the number of years you have been employed by the company. In some buyouts, employers agree to add a few years to service time in pension calculations. If not, it may pay to stick around.

Important: If you have a defined contribution pension plan, such as a 401(k), your pension should not be a major issue. You can simply roll over your retirement savings to a new employer's retirement plan or into an IRA.

- **Is there a lump-sum option, instead of a series of smaller payments over the coming years, and if so, should I take it?** The lump-sum option might push you into a higher tax bracket in the year of the payout and thus create a larger total lifetime tax bill—but the option may be the prudent choice if there's any chance that the company could go bankrupt before you receive the last of the deferred pension payments.

Negotiating Better Severance: What Companies Don't Want You to Know

Jason Stern, Esq., an attorney located in New York City, who specializes in severance negotiation. He previously served as a judge and hearing officer in New York City. His Web site is *www.severanceattorney.com.*

Severance packages have become much stingier as employers struggle to fit large-scale layoffs into ever-tighter budgets. At the same time, obtaining attractive severance packages is more important than ever for terminated employees because finding a new position could take many months in the current economy.

Laid-off employees often fear that the initial offer will be withdrawn if they attempt to negotiate, but this almost certainly will not occur. Employers do not provide severance out of kindness. They do this in exchange for the employee's signature on an agreement not to sue for wrongful termination. Obtaining that signature has value to the company.

To get all you can if you are let go...

DON'T SIGN RIGHT AWAY

Do not sign a severance agreement when it is initially presented to you. Tell the human resources (HR) representative that you need time to review it with an attorney. Using this phrase is an excellent negotiation tactic even if you do not expect to hire an attorney. If the HR rep acts upset that you intend to involve an attorney, point out that the company certainly has its attorneys review such documents. Then scan the final paragraphs of the agreement—there is usually a clause near the end stating that the company encouraged you to consult with an attorney. If you see this, point it out to the HR rep.

A warning: If your employer encourages you to resign rather than get laid off, politely decline unless you are offered a substantially improved severance package for doing so. Resigning may deprive you of your right to collect unemployment insurance...or to sue for wrongful termination.

WEIGH YOUR PRIORITIES

Which component(s) of the severance offer would you most like to improve?

- **Cash.** Many companies now offer only one to two weeks for every year you have worked for the organization. It is reasonable to request one month of severance pay per year.
- **Pension benefits.** If you are within five years of retirement age, ask the company to continue funding your retirement account until that time.
- **Health insurance premiums.** If you do expect to use COBRA (*Consolidated Omnibus Budget Reconciliation Act*) or any similar state program to remain on your employer's health insurance plan, ask your employer to pay some or all of the insurance premiums.

Employees with valid claims against the company and employees with more than 10 years of employment should request the standard 18 months of paid COBRA premiums.

- **A written waiver of your noncompete agreement.** A noncompete (or noncompetition) agreement prohibits an employee from working in a related business. Other employers might be wary of hiring you if you don't have a waiver of this agreement—even though your former employer probably cannot legally enforce your noncompete agreement after laying you off.
- **Office equipment.** Keeping your company laptop or BlackBerry can help you with your job search.

Helpful: Offer to let the company's technician wipe clean the computer's hard drive.

- **Vacation days.** Ask to be paid for any unused days. Some states require employers to pay for unused vacation time. Sick days have less protection than vacation days. Most states do not require employers to pay for unused sick days.
- **Reference letter.** Decline to sign any severance agreement until you receive a "mutually acceptable" letter of recommendation—a tactic that typically yields a far more favorable recommendation.

EVALUATE YOUR NEGOTIATING POSITION

You might have a lot more leverage than you realize...

• **Have you been offered any severance benefits that you don't need?** Ask the HR rep to estimate the value of these benefits, then try to trade them for severance benefits that are of greater use to you.

Examples: COBRA insurance premium payments may be of little value to you if you have access to a spouse's insurance plan. Outplacement services are of no value if you intend to retire or already have another job lined up.

• **Is there any hint of discrimination in your firing?** Women who have young children or who are of childbearing age...employees beyond age 40...and minorities should consider whether their group seemed to be singled out for termination or whether the workplace was hostile to them. If so, the threat of a lawsuit could make your former employer more open to negotiation on the severance package.

• **Have other terminated employees been offered more than you?** This is no time to be shy about talking with peers about money. If others got more, you probably can, too.

• **Do you have a friend in upper management?** The HR rep is likely to treat you well if you can convince a highly placed executive to call and tell him/her how valuable you have been through the years. HR employees worry about their jobs, too—they won't want to risk angering any high-level executives by treating their friends poorly.

• **Did you receive favorable performance evaluations throughout your employment?** Bring copies of these with you when you meet with the HR rep. Better-than-average employees typically receive better-than-average severance packages.

Best Workplaces

Top workplaces for people age 50 and older feature wellness programs, flexible schedules, telecommuting and other benefits that make life easier for employees.

Number one: Scripps Health in San Diego, California offers a toolkit to help mature workers maximize their retirement and provides an on-site nurse case manager to employees returning to work after an illness.

Number two: Cornell University, because it allows telecommuting and compressed work weeks...provides access to campus fitness centers and nutrition and exercise classes...and gives time off for caregiving.

Other top workplaces: National Institutes of Health in Bethesda, Maryland...First Horizon National Corporation in Memphis, Tennessee... West Virginia University in Morgantown.

For the full list, go to *www.aarp.org* and enter "Best Employers" in the search box.

Deborah Russell, director of workforce issues, AARP's 2011 Best Employers for Workers Over 50 list, Washington, DC.

Unemployment Insurance Update

Rick McHugh, midwest coordinator and staff attorney in the Ann Arbor, Michigan, office of the National Employment Law Project, a national advocacy organization for employment rights, *www.nelp.org*. An expert on unemployment insurance law, McHugh has been widely quoted in national publications and has written and testified extensively on this topic.

Millions of Americans are likely to be jobless this year. For many of them, unemployment insurance (UI) will be a financial lifeline while they hunt for work.

Here's what you need to know now about unemployment benefits...

WHAT YOU GET

Generally, states aim to replace half of your prelayoff wages up to a maximum amount set by individual states. Currently, Mississippi provides the lowest maximum weekly benefit of $235, while Massachusetts offers the highest maximum of $653 per week.

Typically, state unemployment benefits last up to 26 weeks. Congress has voted several times to extend the benefits. After 26 weeks expire, the jobless can get additional weeks of unemployment (the amount depends on the unemployment rate in the specific state). The most recent extension is scheduled to end December 31, 2013, but the program stands to lose as much as 11% of its funding this year because of political gridlock in Congress.

WHO QUALIFIES?

Although UI is meant to help those who involuntarily lose their jobs anywhere in the US, each state has its own rules. In addition to those laid off for economic reasons, some individuals who have been fired or who quit can receive unemployment benefits depending on where they live. If you are out of work for any reason other than a layoff, don't assume that you don't qualify. Instead, file a claim and review your state unemployment agency's decision. If you are turned down, file an appeal.

All states recognize that there can be valid job-related reasons for quitting.

Examples: A big cut in pay and/or work hours...material change in job duties or working conditions...or sexual harassment.

In some states, you also may qualify for unemployment payments if you quit a job for a wide range of "compelling" personal reasons. The most lenient of these states include Alaska, Arizona, California, Pennsylvania and Rhode Island. Most other states either do not accept personal reasons or put varying degrees of restrictions on what qualifies as a "compelling" personal reason.

Common examples of valid personal reasons: To give care to an ailing relative...to escape domestic violence...to move with your spouse who is transferred within a company. (In some states, you qualify even if you move because your spouse gets a job with a different employer.)

Most states use a standard of "misconduct" to decide whether to pay benefits to people who have been fired for noneconomic reasons. Generally, those who are fired for "poor performance" do not lose benefits. All states try to decide whether the reasons for a discharge indicate "willful" misconduct or "reckless" conduct on the employee's part, and in those cases, benefits often are denied. On the other hand, when the employee is fired because he/she simply couldn't perform up to the employer's expectations, benefits are paid. And in most states, being fired for missing a few days of work for valid reasons is not grounds for denying benefits, especially if the employee called in and can document the reasons for missing work.

Part-time workers qualify as long as they've earned (over a 52-week period) the minimum required amount set by the state, which tends to be between $400 and $4,000. Various states have different job-search requirements for UI recipients to remain eligible. In some states, recipients can look for just part-time positions, while in others, they must look for full-time work.

HOW TO FILE

Contact your state's UI agency. You can file your initial claim either by phone or, in many states, through the agency's Web site.

Because of the large number of claims during this recession, most states are encouraging workers to file on the Internet whenever possible. Filing information for every state is found on the US Department of Labor's site at *www.servicelocator.org/OWSLinks.asp.*

Look for work, and be prepared to document your efforts. Report any earnings, even if you have temporary work. Each state uses its own formula for adjusting your benefits according to how much money you earn while collecting benefits.

THE APPEALS PROCESS

All states provide written notices when they grant or deny benefits. This notice will state how many days you have to file your appeal. Appeals must be in writing and filed as instructed on the notice.

What to do: Always open your mail from the agency immediately. Read the entire decision. Allow sufficient time for delivery if you are mailing your appeal. Clearly express that you are disagreeing with the unfavorable decision and include your name and identifying information, but do not feel that you must cover everything. Save that for the hearing.

Important: File benefit claims while your appeal is pending, or you will not get paid for those weeks even if you win your appeal.

The most important stage of appeal is your hearing before an administrative law judge or hearing officer. You will receive prior written notice of the date, time and place. Many states conduct hearings by phone.

Take the time to review the notice. Think about the issues that the notice says will be considered at the hearing. Speak very clearly, and stay focused on the issues at hand. For example, in a discharge case, the issue is not whether your previous employer should have fired you. The issue is whether the reason is valid for disqualifying you from benefits.

Turn Small Talk into BIG Deals

Don Gabor, communications trainer based in New York City. His clients include Marriott Hotels, American Express, Time Inc. and Viacom. He is author of several books on communications, including *Turn Small Talk into Big Deals* (McGraw-Hill Professional). His Web site is *www.dongabor.com.*

Small talk is widely considered a waste of time. Used properly, however, it can be a great way to find new business clients, network for a new job and/or form new friendships.

When we engage in chitchat, we send the message that we are open for communication ...we build trust and rapport with strangers... and we identify areas of common interest, the building blocks for lasting relationships.

Here's how to move from small talk to productive dialog in just minutes, using eight simple steps...

1. Establish eye contact, then raise a non-threatening small-talk topic. The best topics usually are found in the immediate vicinity—where you are and what's going on around you are two things that you are certain to have in common with people you meet.

Examples: If someone is walking a dog, ask about the dog's breed. If you're both in line at the bank, mention the length or speed of the line or the quality of the bank in general.

Warning: If your small-talk topic could be construed as a complaint—such as the slow speed of a bank line—phrase it in a lighthearted, joking manner. People are less likely to want to interact with you if you seem negative.

2. Target the person's interests, and match his/her communications style. Your primary goal early in small talk is to make those you speak with feel comfortable. Does this person perk up whenever a particular subject comes up? Steer the dialog that way even if it's not what you want to discuss. Is this person immediately open and warm or initially cool and reserved? Match his conversation style, body language and speaking tone.

Exception: Smile whether or not your conversation partner smiles back.

3. Listen for a keyword (or phrase) that is in some way related to the topic that you would prefer to discuss with this person.

Example: If the person you are chatting with is a potential employer and you need a job, listen for words such as employee, staff, hiring, manpower, associates, productivity or anything that's related to being busy or working long hours.

4. Refer back to this keyword at the next natural break in the conversation. Subtly remind the person you are talking with that he/she said this word, then ask an open-ended question related to it that encourages the other person to speak. This creates the impression that your conversation partner raised the subject, not you—which makes it less likely that this person will resist the transition...or that he will become annoyed with you later if it becomes clear that you have a self-serving motive for discussing this subject.

Examples: Say, "You mentioned going in to the office this Sunday—is business that brisk?" if your goal is to steer the conversation toward giving you a job interview. Or, "You mentioned the cold weather. Is your house hard to heat?" if you run a furnace-cleaning business.

5. Determine what the person believes he needs related to your topic of interest. Once you've steered the chat to the topic you wish to discuss, ask probing, open-ended questions that get at what your conversation partner requires in this area.

Examples: If your goal is to land a job interview, try to get potential employers to discuss what their companies most need. If your goal is to convince a neighbor to take better care of his lawn, steer the conversation toward landscaping or home maintenance, then encourage the neighbor to talk about what he needs to better handle these chores.

Probing questions include, "What are your biggest challenges with that?"..."Why is that a problem?"..."In the best of all possible worlds, what would you like to have happen?"..."What do you see as your options?"..."How is your current approach working?"

At this stage, do not attempt to offer solutions to any challenges mentioned (unless you are invited to do so)...and do not criticize the person's past or current strategies. Simply listen and think to yourself, *How could I help this person solve this problem?*

6. Link yourself to the person's needs. Mention similar situations that you have been involved with in the past...or research that you have done in the area.

Resist the desire to bombard your listener with your experience or suggestions—this can comes across as pushy. Just provide a thumbnail sketch of your relevant background, then wait for the person to ask for your assistance or advice.

Example: "That's interesting. I've worked as a consultant for 20 years, and I see companies facing precisely that issue all the time."

If the person does not ask for your advice or assistance, take it as a hint that he does not want to discuss the matter any further.

Backup plan: If you cannot serve as the solution to this person's needs, think about who else you know who could help. Making a referral could establish you as someone who has this person's interests in mind, strengthening the relationship.

7. Postpone further discussions if the person wants to get down to business right away and there are others present. Exchange business cards or phone numbers, and set up an appointment to consider the matter in greater depth, optimally within a week. Declining to discuss serious matters in social settings prevents alienating others present...and reduces the impression that you were angling for this all along (even if you were).

8. Before parting, shift the conversation to something else that you have in common with this person. It's okay if this is something minor that's completely unrelated to the matter you have been discussing. People who have multiple areas of common interest are much more likely to view one another as potential friends and allies than those who have only one thing in common.

Example: "Is that Cadillac CTS yours? I drive a Cadillac myself."

The Secret to Finding A Job When "There Are No Jobs"

Richard Nelson Bolles, a leader in the career development field for more than 30 years. He is author of *What Color Is Your Parachute?*, the best-selling job-hunting book of all time (revised annually). His latest book is *The Job-Hunter's Survival Guide: How to Find Hope and Rewarding Work, Even When "There Are No Jobs"* (both published by Ten Speed). He lives in the San Francisco Bay Area. His Web site is *www.jobhuntersbible.com.*

Finding a job is difficult enough in this economy, but many job hunters reduce the odds of their success by using common job-search strategies that often fail. *Here's what doesn't work so well—and what does...*

COMMON STRATEGIES

Five popular job-search strategies that do not work for the majority of those who try them...

• **Mailing out résumés/submitting or posting résumés online.**

Odds of success: 7%.*

Problem: Employers receive huge numbers of unsolicited résumés. Virtually all of these are filed away without a second look.

*The "odds of success" percentages cited in this article are based on industry studies and other sources. They reflect the percentage of job hunters who eventually find work by pursuing the strategy.

Might work if: Your résumé is handed to an employer by someone the employer knows and trusts—particularly if this individual adds a personal recommendation.

• **Responding to ads in professional or trade journals.**

Odds of success: 7%.

Problem: Employers tend to place ads in these journals only for low-wage jobs and other positions that they have had trouble filling. Also, because most trade journals are national, jobs listed there often require relocation.

Might work if: You have a specific skill set that is difficult for employers to find and you are willing to relocate.

• **Responding to ads posted on Internet jobs sites.**

Odds of success: 10%.

Problem: Employers tend to post jobs on Internet job sites only as a last resort, because these ads tend to bring a flood of responses from mostly inappropriate or low-quality applicants. A significant percentage of jobs posted on employment Web sites are outright scams, and competition tends to be very fierce for the legitimate openings.

Might work if: Your field is information technology (IT). Attractive IT jobs often are advertised online because employers recognize that tech-savvy employees tend to use the Internet for everything.

• **Responding to ads running in the local newspapers.**

Odds of success: Between 5% and 24%, depending on your salary requirements.

Problem: Most employers consider newspaper classifieds an out-of-date way to find applicants. Few bother to list attractive jobs there anymore.

Might work if: You're willing to work for close to minimum wage. Many low-paying jobs still are listed in local newspapers.

• **Working with an employment agency or search firm.**

Odds of success: Between 5% and 28%, depending on your salary requirements.

Problem: With the economy struggling, employers don't see the need to pay search firms to locate qualified applicants—there are more than enough coming in to them. Also, there is little evidence that agencies do a particularly good job of finding work for clients.

Might work if: You are looking for a low-wage office position, such as a secretarial or clerical job.

BEST WAYS TO FIND WORK

Five job-hunting strategies that offer excellent odds of success, ordered from the least to most successful...

• **Networking for leads.**

Odds of success: 33%.

Advantage: Employers love to hire based on personal recommendations from employees and trusted contacts—it vastly improves the odds that the applicant will be talented and suitable.

Limitation: The success of your networking depends on the size and quality of your network. Don't give up if at first no one you know has heard of a job. Continue to expand your network when you are unemployed by asking your contacts to put you in touch with their contacts...and remaining active in your community.

• **Knocking on doors unannounced at employers of interest.** Express an interest in the company or sector, and ask for five minutes of the boss's time.

Odds of success: 47%.

Advantage: It is more common than you might think to find an employer who is about to list an opening, and he/she might hire you without even interviewing other candidates. Small-business owners tend to be go-getters who respect the moxie of those who knock on doors and ask if there is a need for their skills and experience.

Limitation: You must anticipate that you will likely get rejected to your face. Also, this knock-on-doors strategy doesn't work well at large companies, where it is hard to get a meeting with an executive without an appointment. Stick to smaller companies with 50 or fewer employees. Midafternoon is the best time to do this. Dress in attire appropriate to that particular business.

• **Calling companies of interest that are listed in the local Yellow Pages (or white pages business section).** As with the strategy above, ask for the owner, very briefly explain your background or relevant skills, then ask if he/she knows anyone in the industry in need of someone like you...or if you could come in and talk with him about the industry. To present yourself in the best light, review your skills before each call and remind yourself that you would be a productive, useful employee.

Odds of success: 69%.

Advantage: This is a great way to get to know businesses in your region. You could be hired for a position that has not yet been advertised.

Limitation: This is ineffective with large companies that have computerized phone systems and operators who make it difficult to reach those in charge.

• **Partnering with other job hunters.** Put together a group of job hunters who agree to keep an eye out for opportunities suitable for others in the group. Meet at least weekly. To build your group, team up with job hunters you know or go to job fairs to meet attendees.

Odds of success: 70%.

Advantage: More eyes looking for opportunities can mean more opportunities coming your way. And working with a group makes it harder to slack off on the job search.

Limitation: This works best when members are looking for employment in fields that call for different skills and career goals, so they are not in competition for the same jobs.

• **Taking inventory of yourself, then targeting the employers where you ought to be working.** Spend at least a weekend considering which of all of your skills you most enjoy using...in which fields you would most enjoy putting those skills to work...which organizations have these jobs to offer...which people at those organizations possess the power to hire you...and how best to approach them.

Odds of success: 86%.

Advantage: Job hunters who utilize this systematic process tend to appear more confident to employers, which makes them more appealing hires. They also are better able to articulate why they would be an asset to the organization.

Limitation: It takes time to do this properly. The secret is to define your skills and the type of work you wish to do in as much detail as possible. In poor economies, many job hunters assume that they must cast a broad net and look for any available job. These people come off as desperate. The most successful job interviewees write a detailed inventory of what they have to offer an employer and analyze times when they were successful before they actually go to an interview.

Where the Jobs Are Now: "Hot" Sectors

David DeLong, a doctor in business administration (DBA), president of David DeLong & Associates, a research and consulting firm that specializes in accelerating knowledge transfer across generations to reduce the risks for skill shortages, Concord, Massachusetts. He is author of *Lost Knowledge: Confronting the Threat of an Aging Workforce* (Oxford). He is a research fellow at MIT AgeLab. For more information, go to *www.lostknowledge.com.*

Despite the news about unemployment and layoffs, there still are good jobs to be found in today's economy. *Employers have positions to fill immediately, even for older workers...*

HOTTEST SECTORS

• **Federal government.** In 2010, almost 60% of supervisors in the federal government and nearly half of all nonsupervisory workers became eligible to retire. That's because the huge baby boomer population is beginning to reach retirement age. While concerns about healthcare costs and the economy may keep many from leaving, a significant number will retire. So federal agencies are hiring now, and not only in the nation's capital. Five out of six federal employees work outside Washington, DC, with the next largest concentrations of federal jobs in Atlanta, Baltimore, Chicago, Los Angeles, New York City, Salt Lake City and San Diego.

The government is looking for human resources managers, office clerks, accountants, information technology security workers, engineers, scientists and policy analysts, among other types of positions. The Veterans Health Administration needs many human resources specialists. People under age 31 can apply for jobs as air-traffic controllers for the Federal Aviation Administration, where thousands of controllers are about to retire.

All federal jobs now are listed on one Web site, *www.usajobs.gov.*

• **Health care.** Next to government work, the best job security is in health care, an expanding industry as the baby boomer population ages. If you can afford to invest some time in training, consider studying for a certificate to work as a medical records specialist or a pharmacy technician. Community colleges offer two-year associate degrees in these fields—online courses can be completed in a few months and cost less than $1,500.

Hospitals and nursing homes need many people to fill a variety of positions, including positions for information systems and human resources professionals, cleaning people and clerical workers. Rural hospitals tend to be especially shorthanded.

• **Education.** Schools will require approximately 2.8 million new teachers in the next eight years, according to the National Center for Education Statistics. Like federal government workers, today's older teachers who have spent their careers within school systems have good pensions that will allow them to retire. Although budget cuts mean many local school districts won't be able to replace every retiree and some have instituted hiring freezes, they can wait for only so long. Eventually, there will be a huge push to locate good teachers, particularly in math and science. The experience of older teachers could be a real asset, especially in areas with the greatest demand. If you have technical skills or experience in a trade, look into openings for teachers at vocational schools and community colleges.

GROWING DEMAND

Other potential employers include security service providers, accounting firms, grocery chains and companies that benefit from investments in roads and bridges funded by the economic stimulus package.

• **Security.** Hard times often lead to crime. The 2009 stimulus package included funds for 100,000 police officers over eight years. Even cash-strapped local governments are looking today to fill positions related to public safety. Also, security services for computer systems are expanding and private security guards are in demand.

• **Accounting.** While Wall Street jobs now are scarce, people with a background in finance still can get work. Many of the regional and community banks, for instance, are doing just fine. And lots of major accounting firms, such as KPMG (*www.us.kpmg.com*), PricewaterhouseCoopers (*www.pwc.com*) and Ernst & Young (*www.ey.com*), will continue to aggressively hire accountants and administrators and will be looking for a mix of recent graduates and experienced workers. Consulting firms, such as Booz Allen Hamilton (*www.boozallen.com*) and Accenture (*www.accenture.com*), are hiring thousands of people with information technology skills in specialties including Java and SAP. There will be bigger demand for personal financial planners as new baby boomer retirees will need help managing investments and planning for old age.

• **Grocery/discount store chains.** People are buying food to cook in the home—and grocery chains need cashiers, retail clerks, managers and other professionals for back-office functions. Chains include Wegmans Food Markets (*www.wegmans.com*), a 79-store chain, Publix Super Markets (*www.publix.com*), Whole Foods Market (*www.wholefoodsmarket.com*) and Wal-mart (*www.walmart.com*).

• **Going green.** An explosion in green jobs seems on its way, although the credit freeze is slowing things down. Consider specialized training to help companies respond to new environmental-safety laws and demands for green products. Go to *www.greenbiz.com* for information about educational resources on sustainable business practices.

HIRING DURING LAYOFFS

Don't write a company off your list just because it's laying off some workers. Companies can be actively hiring even while downsizing. Big corporations require many kinds of specialized skills and operate in many locations—a freeze in one department may not prevent another from staffing up.

WHERE THE JOBS AREN'T

Every sector presents opportunities if your skills, personality and passion give you a competitive advantage in that area. *Still, there are some job categories where the odds definitely are stacked against you today...*

- **Automotive parts assemblers.**
- **Stockbrokers.**
- **Home builders.**
- **Real estate agents.**
- **Manufacturing jobs.**
- **Journalists.**

Add a P.S. to Your Cover Letter...and Other Tactics To Jump-Start a Stalled Job Search

David E. Perry, managing partner of Perry-Martel International, Inc., an executive-recruiting firm in Ottawa, Canada. Perry is a coauthor, with Jay Conrad Levinson, of *Guerrilla Marketing for Job Hunters 2.0: 1,001 Unconventional Tips, Tricks, and Tactics for Landing Your Dream Job* (Wiley). For more job-search tips and a free "Guerrilla Job Search Secrets Revealed" DVD ($7 shipping and handling), visit *www.putamericabacktowork.com/dvd.*

According to the Bureau of Labor statistics, the average job search in America now takes 28.5 weeks. But if you've been searching for a job for six months or longer, it is time to switch tactics. We have found that the typical "Guerilla job hunter" who follows our strategies finds a job in 12 weeks. *What to do...*

TARGET YOUR TOP 20

While the other job seekers are competing against one another for a limited number of advertised positions, you can create your own private job market. Start by making a list of 20 companies that you would like to work for. Ask friends, family members, colleagues and former classmates for their suggestions. Also, use Google to locate "best employers for women," "best companies for minorities," "best companies for disabled veterans," "the most admired companies" and so on. Refine your search by adding city and state names ("best companies to work for in Houston," "best employers of women in Springfield, Illinois"). Refine it even further by adding the kind of job you want ("mechanical engineer," "paralegal," "medical records database supervisor," "tax attorney"). If you do not come up with 20 companies, expand your list by going to Hoovers.com. Enter the name of a specific company, then click on "Competition" for a few of the company's competitors. (You need a subscription for the full list.)

Once you have zeroed in on your top 20, get each company's full mailing address and phone number (from the organization's Web site, Superpages.com or the Yellow Pages), and the name, title and contact information of a decision-maker who can offer you a job. At a small company, one with 50 or fewer employees, get the name of the president. At a larger company, find out who your boss would most likely be—then get the contact information for that person's boss. Someone who is higher up will have a better overall picture of the organization and more hiring authority. Most likely, you'll want to contact a divisional vice president or senior manager.

TALK TO PEOPLE WHO HAVE LEFT THE COMPANY

We all know that it's important to learn as much as you can about each organization—through company Web sites, annual reports, industry newsletters and journals. I also recommend seeking out the "newly departed"—people who left a target company within the last year. People currently working at an organization may be less likely to talk with you—and describe the needs of that company—than those who have left. You can locate hundreds of résumés, with contact information, for the newly departed by conducting a quick search on Google.

Example: If you want to find out who recently left the mechanical engineering department at Boeing, type in "Boeing résumé experience mechanical engineering –apply" into the Google search bar. Typing "–apply" will tell Google to exclude search results that have the text "apply" on the page, so you will get fewer pages about applying for positions and more résumés.

Or you can access ZoomInfo.com's directory. Available as a Microsoft Outlook plug-in, this search tool gives job hunters free access to an expanding database of 50 million business contacts at 5 million businesses. Go to *www.zoominfo.com/business* or phone 866-904-9666, for more information.

When you have found six to eight people you would like to speak with, call them. Say something like, "Hi, my name is David Perry, and I just pulled up your résumé on the Internet. I'm thinking of going to work for ABC Corporation. I wondered if you would be willing to answer a few quick questions."

You will find that people generally are happy to talk about a past employer and fill you in on the problems or challenges that a department is facing. And that's what you are going after. You want to know about the problems because where there's a problem, there's a hidden job. Usually, that job is in the employer's head. He/she just hasn't had time to figure out what kind of person he needs to hire to solve the problem. That's where you come in—you're going to be the solution to the problem.

WRITE A STAND-OUT RÉSUMÉ

You'll need a stand-out résumé that piques employers' curiosity and compels them to call for more details. You can tweak it to fit each company you target. *Here are the basics...*

- **Include all your work experience**—one line for each position in bullet format (title, company dates). Be sure to keep the résumé to one page.

- **Include the top three to five things you accomplished at your previous job,** specifically what you did to save the company time or money—or help it make money. Those are the top three things employers are looking for. They should be bulleted, taking only one line each.

Examples: "Saved XYZ Corporation almost $500,000 in the first quarter of 2010." "Increased productivity by 30% between January and June 2010."

- **Back up your claims with testimonials.** If you saved XYZ Corporation $500,000, use the left-hand margin of your résumé to cement that with a quote from a former employer, "David dramatically cut our costs by increasing worker productivity and eliminating unnecessary expenditure for overtime."—John Adams, vice president, sales, XYZ Corporation. Try to include three to five testimonials in the left-hand margin of your résumé.

- **If possible, use recognizable company logos in your résumé** (place them in the left-hand margin). You can piggyback on a company's success by using its logo, and logos set your résumé apart. Download logos using a "Google Images" search.

- **Once you've written your master résumé, tailor it to meet an employer's needs/problems.** If you have found, from talking with XYZ Corporation's newly departed, that the engineering department is having a hard time meeting deadlines, one of your "accomplishments" should focus in on how you made or helped to make a similar department operate more efficiently.

DELIVER THE GOODS

Make sure that your résumés and cover letters reach the right people by sending them via UPS, FedEx or two-day mail. Ask for the recipient's signature—and also ask to be notified via e-mail when your letter has been signed for. Then wait a half-hour before you pick up the phone and call that person. If you can't get him/her on the line, leave a voicemail message saying, "Hi, this is David Perry. My number is 555-1212. I see that you just received my package. I'd like to meet with you for coffee to talk about how I can help your company achieve (fill in the blanks)."

CREATE AN ONLINE PRESENCE

While you are doing all of this, create—or punch up—your online presence. The professional-networking site called LinkedIn.com is important. Use this tool to post your contact information, résumé, key PowerPoint presentations and any articles that you've written (or that have been written about you).

Being on ZoomInfo.com also is important. Both professional and in-house company recruiters go to ZoomInfo.com to access profiles of people with the experience they are looking for. You may already be on ZoomInfo.com and not know it. If so, update your profile. Or create a free profile. You don't need to post your résumé. Just get yourself on the site with your correct title.

Important: Upload your photo onto both your LinkedIn.com and ZoomInfo.com pages. A photograph tells recruiters that you want to be found.

ADD A P.S. TO YOUR COVER LETTER

Instead of focusing in on "you," your cover letters should concentrate on prospective employers and their needs.

Example: Rather than starting off with, "I've had 20-plus years of experience...," say something like, "You will benefit from my 20 years of experience because I've helped companies like yours grow their people, sales and shareholder value."

Always end with a "P.S." A reader's eye automatically goes to the P.S.

Examples: "P.S. I'd like to sit down with you to explain how I can increase your division's productivity by at least 25%."

Or "P.S. Call me at 555-1212 to learn why my last boss said, 'Dave is a brilliant strategist.'" This last statement may seem cocky, but it isn't if it is true.

How to Get Your Online Résumé Noticed

Margaret Dikel, a consultant in Rockville, Maryland, who helps college career offices, outplacement firms and other organizations improve their use of the Internet as a job search tool. She is coauthor of *The Guide to Internet Job Searching* (McGraw-Hill). Her Web site is *www.rileyguide.com.*

The job openings now posted on major employment Web sites can attract thousands of responses. Many firms have turned to résumé analysis software and other high-tech tricks to cut candidate pools down to manageable numbers. *Here is how to help your résumé survive the culling process...*

INCLUDE KEY PHRASES

Make sure that each job requirement is addressed in your résumé.

Example: If the employer is asking for "management experience," somewhere in your résumé should appear the exact phrase "management experience."

Anticipate other keywords and phrases that employers might stress by checking which terms appear repeatedly in job listings in your field.

Example: If job listings for your profession often request "problem-solving skills" or "project management experience," find a permanent place for these phrases in your résumé.

SELECT A SMART FORMAT

Format your résumé as a text-only (also called "plain text") document before you submit it online. (Go to my Web site, *www.rileyguide.com*, or look in the help section of your word-processing program to get instructions.) This reduces the odds that the résumé will become garbled in transmission.

Use a familiar font—either Arial or Times New Roman—and select a conventional résumé layout.

Example: The work-experience portion of your résumé should be arranged with your most recent job first.

TRY THE SMALLER JOB SITES

The biggest employment Web sites are Monster.com and CareerBuilder.com. Jobs posted to these popular sites generally receive the largest number of responses. Devote more of your online job-search time to smaller sites. The Internet sites of professional associations, trade journals and recruiters specializing in your industry or profession typically list job openings.

Or search for jobs in your region through local newspaper Web sites, chamber of commerce Web sites or state job boards (go to *www.jobbankinfo.org,* then select your state).

Many employers also list job openings on their corporate Web sites. *To submit a résumé via e-mail...*

- **Get the name and e-mail address of a specific person to send it to.**

• **Mention your job function and interest in job openings in the subject line.**

Example: "Structural engineer interested in employment opportunities."

• **Start the e-mail with a short introduction explaining who you are in just three or four sentences.**

• **Put your résumé in the e-mail—don't attach a file.** Attachments often go unread, due to the effort it takes to open them and risk of computer viruses.

The 5 Words Never To Say During a Job Interview

Paul Powers, EdD, a management psychologist located in Wellesley, Massachusetts, who has 30 years of experience in career counseling. Powers is also former chairman of the Massachusetts Board of Psychologists and was the original "answer man" for job seekers on the job search site Monster.com. He is also author of *Winning Job Interviews* (Career). His Web site is *www.drpaulpowers.com.*

Job hunters greatly outnumber job openings these days, so even a seemingly minor slip of the tongue can cut short your employment opportunities. *The five words that can undermine your job chances...*

• **Crisis.** Job applicants often trumpet their ability to respond calmly and intelligently to all workplace challenges. Trouble is, when they use the word "crisis" to describe a past professional challenge, they send exactly the opposite message. Epidemics and hostage standoffs are crises—an employer's budget crunch or public relations headache is not. Calling an ordinary workplace situation a crisis will make you seem like an alarmist—the sort of employee who often blows problems out of proportion and infects those around you with panic. You'll seem more poised and reliable if you instead use words such as "challenge" or "problem" to describe these situations.

• **People person.** Interviewers often cringe inside when applicants describe themselves as "people-oriented" or "a people person." This is like saying that your worst flaw is that you work too hard—it's such a cliché that it will make you seem uninteresting or evasive to an experienced interviewer. Worse, "I'm a people person" is so general and unverifiable that it tends to be offered up by applicants who have no actual skills or accomplishments to discuss. Saying something similar could cause the interviewer to subconsciously associate you with this group even when you have an impressive résumé.

If interpersonal abilities are an important part of what you have to offer, find a more specific, less clichéd way to convey this. You could identify your talent as "conflict mediation," "coordinating teams" or "soothing upset customers." Cite specific examples of the times that you have used this skill successfully.

• **Can't.** Using negative words and phrases such as "can't," "there's no way" or "impossible" during an interview could make you seem like a negative person. Few qualities turn off potential employers faster than negativity. If you must tell an interviewer that what he/she wants is impossible or that you need a larger salary or budget than he is proposing, find a way to phrase this in a positive way.

Example: The interviewer says that the company is looking for someone to expand its Web site, but your experience tells you that the budget or time frame being discussed is insufficient. Rather than say, "It cannot be done," or "That's not going to work," you might say, "Let's discuss some of the options we would have for getting that finished." Mention outsourcing certain functions...or focusing initially on only the most important elements of the project.

• **Irregardless.** It isn't really a word at all. The correct word is *regardless.* If the interviewer is a stickler for correct grammar, using this nonword might create the impression that you are ignorant. Another frequently misused word that could hurt your chances is "literally," which often is used by people who really means figuratively.

Example: "I was literally putting out fires all year." No, you weren't—unless you were a firefighter.

• **Fired.** Interviewers often ask applicants why they left their previous jobs. It's fine to say your position was eliminated in a workforce reduction or that you were laid off, but never say that you were "fired." Though you might consider "fired" and "laid off" synonymous, the former has a much more negative connotation—that you messed up—in most people's minds.

Free Money to Go Back To School

Gen Tenabe, coauthor with his wife, Kelly, of *501 Ways for Adult Students to Pay for College* (SuperCollege). He is cofounder of SuperCollege, which provides resources and tools for college-bound students of all ages. He lives in Belmont, California.

When the going gets difficult, many adults go back to school. With unemployment rising and industries shrinking, workers are finding that they need to boost their skills, retool their careers and, in some instances, start over—and that means heading back to the classroom.

These days, adults have more educational options than ever. College admissions officers tell me that in the last 12 to 18 months, they have seen an explosion in the number of applicants over age 35. At the same time, retraining programs for adults, which help those who are unemployed learn new skills needed to return to work, are cropping up at community colleges, community centers and even on the Internet.

Problem: The need for more education hits when many people, especially those who have lost their jobs, have the most trouble bearing the cost of tuition.

Here is how you can pay for the training you need...

GO FOR THE FREE MONEY

Scholarships aren't just for teens—they defray adults' tuition bills, too. For most scholarships, there are no age limitations. That means you're eligible for much of the same free money that high school seniors are hunting for! There also are both need- and merit-based scholarships specifically for adults. *To find money...*

• **Search on the Internet.** Free Web sites to search for scholarships include FastWeb.com and SuperCollege.com, the site my wife and I founded. Once you locate a scholarship for which you might be eligible, contact the sponsoring organization for details on how to apply and deadlines.

Many colleges and universities also provide scholarships specifically for adults who are returning to school. A visit to the college or university's Web site will provide a list of all the available scholarships.

• **Check out professional organizations.** Adults have the advantage when it comes to applying for scholarships and grants through professional and trade associations. Unlike teens going off to college who have no idea what they are going to do, adult students usually know exactly why they're going back to school and can easily show the commitment that these groups look for.

Start with the local trade and professional associations in your area to see if they offer scholarships.

Example: Members of the Kentucky Farm Bureau, an organization of farm families, are eligible for a variety of grants. The San Diego Foundation also has several scholarships for adults.

Also look into national organizations.

Example: The American Association of University Women Educational Foundation offers a grant of $2,000 to $12,000 to college-educated women who want to advance or change their careers or reenter the workforce. Go to *www.aauw.org* for details.

FILL OUT THE FAFSA

The only way for you to determine if you qualify for need-based aid from the institution that you'll be attending and/or for federal loans is to fill out the Free Application for Federal Student Aid (FAFSA), which schools use to determine a student's financial need. For more information, visit *www.fafsa.ed.gov.*

Almost everyone qualifies for some kind of federal loan, so it's really worth doing all the paperwork.

New: Federal guidelines are now making it easier to repay federal student loans.

Important: Federal student loans usually carry lower interest rates than those from private lenders, such as banks. And because they are guaranteed by the federal government, your credit rating will not be taken into consideration—a potential plus in these troubled times.

Note that this year's FAFSA contains a new question about whether the student is a "dislocated worker" (someone who has been laid off, for example), which may help you qualify for more aid.

MONEY FROM YOUR STATE

Your state may provide grants for state-sponsored retraining classes and other skill-building programs. States that have been hardest hit by the recession tend to have the most active and generous programs.

Example: In Michigan's displaced workers program, participants are given up to $5,000 annually to cover tuition and other costs.

Best sources: Log on to *www.careeronestop.org*. Sponsored by the US Department of Labor, it offers links to all of the state retraining programs and new information for individuals looking for "reemployment." Also, to help unemployed adults who are returning to college, the Obama administration has created a new Web site, *www.opportunity.gov,* which includes information about paying for college.

MONEY FROM YOUR EMPLOYER

Tuition assistance from your employer is a huge benefit for workers who qualify. Often the employee must show how the educational program will improve his/her job performance.

Examples: McDonald's and Starbucks provide generous tuition assistance to both part- and full-time employees.

"LIFE CREDIT"

The fewer classes you have to take, the less you'll pay in tuition. Schools routinely waive requirements for certain classes if you can show that your previous professional background or life experience taught you material similar to the course's curriculum. An accountant seeking advanced training, for instance, might be able to skip basic finance courses.

There are several types of standardized exams, including the College Level Examination Program (CLEP), available through the College Board (*www.collegeboard.com*), which will test you on, and gives you credit for, knowledge that you already have. Schools do not use any set formula to assign such credit, so you need to work closely with the admissions officer to determine what's best for you.

Social Network Alert

Your employer may check out your online profile to make sure that you're not bashing the organization or acting in any way that reflects on it poorly. Even when your privacy settings are tight, you never know who might see your profile, so never post inappropriate or potentially offensive photos, videos, wall posts, updates or other content on Facebook or other social networks.

Consensus of human resources executives, reported online at CBS MoneyWatch.com.

8

Make More, Keep More, Live Well on Less

The $100 Start-Up—How to Launch a Business for $100 or Less

The old adage "It takes money to make money" isn't always on the money! You can start a successful business without a lot of start-up capital.

I identified 1,500 people who earn $50,000 or more each year from businesses they founded with an initial investment of $100 or less. *Their secrets…*

SELL INFORMATION

Most successful $100 start-ups sell information. Unlike most businesses, information providers typically don't require expensive inventory, equipment, employees or leases.

What information should you sell? If you're an expert in some aspect of your profession, that's likely your best bet. *If not, ask yourself…*

- **What's a task that many people consider inscrutable and aggravating that I understand and enjoy?** People are happy to pay those who can alleviate their major annoyances.

Example: Most people consider redeeming airline frequent-flier miles extremely frustrating. Gary Leff, the CFO of a Virginia University research center, enjoyed the challenge of mastering his frequent-flier miles. He began charging other travelers $150 per trip to help them get the most from their miles. Last year, this second job earned him $75,000 in his spare time. *www.BookYourAward.com*

- **What knowledge have I obtained by pursuing my interests that others might pay for?** The knowledge you've acquired might be salable.

Example: Ireland native Benny Lewis became adept at learning foreign languages while

---

Chris Guillebeau, author of *The $100 Startup: Reinvent the Way You Make a Living, Do What You Love, and Create a New Future* (Crown). Based in Portland, Oregon, he is the founder of The Art of Non-Conformity, a blog about changing the world by achieving personal goals. *www.ChrisGuillebeau.com*

traveling. He created a successful Web site and guidebook sharing his strategy for achieving fluency quickly. *www.FluentIn3Months.com*

• **When do I feel I lack the information that I need to make wise decisions?** If others feel the same way, they might be willing to pay you to provide the facts they lack.

Example: Those who use travel-bidding Web sites such as Priceline.com typically must blindly guess at what bids might be accepted. The Web sites BiddingforTravel.com and BetterBidding.com were created to help people gather the information they need to place more informed bids.

• **What do people ask for my help with?** If friends and family solicit your guidance on a topic, people you don't know might be willing to pay for it.

Example: A California man named Brett Kelly realized that people were asking for his help with Evernote (a note-taking software program that he used) in part because there was no English-language guide to the program. He wrote Evernote Essentials, an eBook that has generated more than $100,000 in sales so far. *www.NerdGap.com*

• **What information could I provide that would be useful to those participating in a new fad?** If something is new and popular, there might not yet be many resources available for those interested in it.

Example: The trendy Paleo diet (which mimics the diet of our hunter-gatherer ancestors) can be challenging to follow. Jason Glaspey of Portland, Oregon, launched PaleoPlan.com, a Web site that offers meal plans, grocery lists and other helpful resources.

HOW TO MAKE MONEY

Decide how you will make money from the information you provide. *Low-cost options include...*

• **Serving as a consultant or instructor.**

• **Writing and selling an eBook**—Amazon.com's Kindle Direct Publishing charges no up-front costs to publish eBooks (*http://kdp.amazon.com*).

• **Launching a Web site or blog,** then selling ads on it or providing links to Internet retailer Web sites that pay commissions—Amazon.com's Associates program pays up to 15% (*http://Affiliate-Program.amazon.com*).

• **Test the market for your idea before devoting much time to it.** *Two low-cost ways to make sure that there's as much demand for your idea as you think...*

• Contact people you consider potential customers. Ask if they would be interested in what you intend to provide...if there's any other related information or service that they would consider even more valuable...and what their biggest challenges and questions are in regard to this area. To locate these potential customers, brainstorm about where such people would be likely to gather, either in your region or online. If your intended customers are other businesses, simply call some of them.

• Do a Google search of the keywords someone might enter if he/she were looking for a business such as the one you intend to create. The results might give you a sense of how many people would be interested in your idea and whether there already are businesses that adequately serve their needs.

Example: If the Google search leads to a lot of questions related to the topic on sites such as Answers.google.com but few Web sites are providing adequate answers, you might be on the right track for a new business.

DON'T WAIT

If there does seem to be a market for your business, don't waste time with endless planning and don't try to achieve perfection before you start to sell. Get your idea into development and then onto the market as quickly as possible. The sooner you start making sales, the sooner you'll start receiving useful feedback from customers about how to refine and improve your offerings.

Example: Map designers Jen Adrion and Omar Noory responded to feedback from their early customers by expanding the range of maps they sold. *www.TheseAreThings.com*

If you go above and beyond for your initial customers, they might even become evangelists for your brand, spreading the word to their acquaintances about how great you are. That word of mouth is one of the most cost-effective ways to grow a young business.

THINK FREE

Many effective marketing options involve providing things for free...

• **Give freebies to tastemakers.** Send samples of your work to those who have the power to influence others.

Example: Megan Hunt, an Omaha-based dress designer, custom makes dresses for two or three fashion bloggers each year. Those bloggers inevitably are grateful for the freebies and write complimentary posts about her dresses.

• **Write free guest posts on popular Web sites visited by your prospective customers.** Many Web sites are happy to run well-thought-out content from people willing to provide it for free. Those who read your articles are likely to consider you an expert on the topic.

• **Offer free consulting.** Charge nothing (or very little) for information or services that usually come at a price, and you will attract prospective customers who later might hire you for paying jobs.

Example: An unemployed Seattle architect named John Morefield set up a booth in a farmers' market offering "Architecture 5¢." His advice impressed so many prospective clients that he soon had a flourishing freelance practice.

• **Use contests to provide free stuff on your blog.** It's amazing how attracted Internet users are to the possibility of free merchandise. Hold a drawing for something as simple as a free T-shirt with your company logo and dozens or hundreds of people might submit their e-mail addresses in hopes of winning. Those e-mails are prospective future customers.

Example: I recently received more than 1,000 entries in a drawing for a free copy of my book.

Finding a Work-at-Home Job—Most Are Scams, But These 7 Are for Real

Michael Haaren, CEO of Staffcentrix, a training and development company with offices in Annandale, Virginia, and Woodstock, Connecticut. Staffcentrix's clients have included the US Department of State, US Air Force and US Army. Haaren is coauthor of *Work at Home Now: The No-Nonsense Guide to Finding Your Perfect Home-Based Job, Avoiding Scams, and Making a Great Living* (Career Press). *www.RatRaceRebellion.com*

A growing number of employers are willing to use home-based employees, assuming those employees have access to a phone, computer and high-speed Internet connection. That's good news for people with disabilities or who are caring for children or an elderly relative or who live in an area where jobs are scarce. It's also good news for people who could find work outside the home but prefer to spend more time with their families and less time sitting in traffic.

The bad news is that there are roughly 60 "work from home" job scams on the Internet for each legitimate opportunity, according to our research.

Here's how to avoid the scams and land a good work-at-home position...

LANDING WORK-AT-HOME JOBS

• **Tweak your résumé before you start applying for work-at-home jobs.** Stress any work experience that shows that you can work productively without direct supervision or handle projects outside the workplace. Be sure to mention any experience you have with communications technology, such as video-conferencing tools and tablet computers.

If your work history is light on projects outside the workplace, consider taking a virtual volunteer position and listing this on your résumé.

Example: The United Nations Volunteers program offers plenty of volunteer-from-home opportunities and looks impressive on a résumé (*www.OnlineVolunteering.org*).

• **Interviews for online positions often are conducted via phone or Skype video call.** If you are not naturally comfortable speaking on the phone or you lack experience with Skype video calls, practice with friends before the interview.

Helpful: If the interview is a Skype video call, make sure that the backdrop behind you is uncluttered and looks professional.

HOME-BASED CAREERS HIRING NOW

Among the career opportunities open to the home-based...

1. Customer service agents field calls from their employers' customers and prospective customers—they do not place telemarketing calls. Major employers of home-based workers in this field include LiveOps (*http://Join.Live Ops.com*)...Alpine Access (*www.AlpineAccess.com*)...and Arise (*http://Partner.Arise.com*).

Other well-known companies that frequently hire home-based customer service agents include American Express (on *http://Careers.AmericanExpress.com*, click on "Search Jobs" and enter "Work At Home" in the keyword search box)...Amazon.com (on *www.Amazon.com*, select "Careers" from the "Get to Know Us" menu near the bottom of the page, then enter "Work At Home" in the keyword box)... and the Home Shopping Network (on *www.HSN.com*, select "Careers at HSN" from the "About HSN" menu near the bottom of the page, then select "Work At Home" from the "Why HSN" menu). To find other companies hiring in this field, select the "Call Center & Cust. Service" listing on the left of the home page of my company's Web site, *www.RatRace Rebellion.com*.

Pay typically is $9 to $12 an hour, though it can reach $20 an hour or more.

2. Internet ad assessors conduct Internet searches and make sure that search results are appropriate for the search terms used. Extensive tech skills are not needed—just basic Internet skills. Companies hiring home-based workers in this area include Google (on *www.Google.com/about/jobs*, search for the job "Ad Rater")...Lionbridge (on *www.Lionbridge.com*, select "Jobs," then "Work-at-Home Opportunities") and Leapforce (*www.LeapforceAtHome.com*). Pay is about $10 to $15 per hour.

3. Web site testers visit Web sites and record their impressions of those sites. It's like being part of a focus group except that you can do it from home. Employers offering home-based employment in the field include Userlytics (*on www.Userlytics.com*, select "Join Our Tester Panel" near the bottom of the page) and UserTesting.com (on *www.UserTesting.com*, select "We're Hiring!" near the bottom of the page, click the link under "User Tester").

Reviews typically take around 10 to 20 minutes apiece and pay perhaps $10 per review. But don't expect to make a lot of money or make this a full-time career—testers typically get occasional assignments, not regular work.

4. Online moderators oversee Web site communities, Facebook groups and interactive online games, stepping in to remove offensive comments or ban troublemakers. Employers that hire home-based moderators include LiveWorld.com (*www.LiveWorld.com/about/jobs/moderator*) and Zynga.com (on *http://Company.Zynga.com/about/jobs*, click "US Jobs," select "Community" from the "Category" list, then choose "Super Moderator"). The job requires tact, interpersonal skills and experience with social media. The pay for this work tends to be toward the lower end of the scale—often $10 an hour.

5. Virtual task freelancers perform chores posted on Web sites such as TaskRabbit.com. Some of the chores require travel and thus are not appropriate for the exclusively home-based—picking up a client's dry cleaning or assembling new IKEA furniture, for example. But others can be performed from home, such as conducting online research or doing data entry.

Job seekers typically bid on tasks. If their bid is accepted, they are paid directly by the individual or company that needs the work done.

Comparable Web sites include Amazon's Mechanical Turk (*www.MTurk.com*) and Clickworker (*www.Clickworker.com*). Also, the site Fiverr (*www.Fiverr.com*) lets people post tasks that they're willing to perform for $5.

6. Transcriptionists type verbatim accounts of board meetings, presentations, conference calls, etc., from audio recordings.

Some of the companies that hire home-based transcriptionists include Tigerfish (*www.Tigerfish.com/employment.html*)...Ubiqus (*on www.Ubiqus.com*, select "Working For Us")...and Cambridge Transcriptions (*www.CTran.com/employment*).

The pay for transcriptionists can vary with typing speed but generally is around $10 per hour.

7. Freelance posters are paid to post content to blogs. Topics vary widely, depending on the theme of the blog. Pay can range from a few dollars per post to $50 and beyond, and usually is made directly to the poster by the owner of the blog. Short posts on generic themes such as lifestyle and fashion generally pay less, while specialized posts requiring more research (on economic issues, for example) pay more. These are listed on such Web sites as Problogger.net (click on "Jobs") and BloggingPro.com (click on "Job Board")...Postloop (on *www.Postloop.com*, click "Join")...and Wired Flame (on *www.WiredFlame.com*, select "Writers").

More from Michael Haaren...

Work-at-Home Scam Alert

Some work-from-home scams are easy to spot—they promise big paydays without much effort, feature photos of people clutching big wads of cash or require applicants to pay up-front "membership" fees or similar fees—but other work-at-home scams are more subtle and can fool even savvy job applicants.

The best way to avoid these scams is to search for work-at-home jobs only on Web sites that make some effort to weed out scammers. These include Indeed.com (click "Advanced Job Search," type "Work From Home" without quotes into the "exact phrase" field, and leave the location field blank) and the Work From Home section of About.com (on *http://JobSearch.about.com*, select "Find a Job," then "Work From Home Jobs"). We've also posted more than 18,000 screened job leads on my company's Web site, *www.RatRaceRebellion.com*.

Warning: Con artists are constantly fine-tuning their scams, and occasionally a bogus offer will slip through at Indeed.com and similar "job aggregator" Web sites. Job seekers should always proceed with caution. Use a search engine to research the potential employer to make sure it appears legitimate before applying. Also visit work-at-home forums such as WAHM.com and WorkPlaceLikeHome.com to learn what other home-based employees and job seekers have to say about the employer. If your search turns up little or no mention of an employer, be wary—it could mean that it isn't really an employer at all.

How to Avoid Identity Theft

Frank W. Abagnale, president, Abagnale & Associates, secure-document consultant, and author of *The Art of the Steal* (Broadway Books). Mr. Abagnale's early life was the inspiration for the movie *Catch Me If You Can*.

Identity theft is the fastest-growing crime in the US. The Federal Trade Commission (FTC) estimates that more than 10 million people are victimized every year.

Each victim of identity theft spends months or years and thousands of dollars to clear his/her name.

PREVENTION STRATEGIES

What you can do to steer clear of identity thieves...

- **Don't disclose any personal information** until you find out how it will be used (including whether it will be shared with others).

- **Pay attention to billing cycles** so you can follow up with creditors if your bills don't arrive on time. A missing bill could mean that someone has taken over your credit card and changed the billing address to cover his tracks. If your card has expired and you haven't received a replacement, call the card issuer immediately—someone may have obtained your new card.

• **Shred every bill** and other documents that contain personal or account information. A shredder, available at office-supply stores, costs as little as $25.

• **Install a lock on your mailbox** to prevent someone from stealing your mail to obtain your account and other personal information.

• **Remove your name, phone number and address from marketing lists** by contacting the Direct Marketing Association (*www.thedma.org*). This does not remove your name from all lists, but from many of them.

• **Reduce the number of preapproved credit card offers you receive** by calling the credit reporting industry's prescreening "opt out" number at 888-567-8688.

• **Order a copy of your credit report once a year from each of the three major reporting agencies.** Make sure the information is accurate and that the report includes only legitimate transactions.

Contact: Equifax (800-685-1111 or at *www.equifax.com*)...Experian (888-397-3742 or *www. experian.com*)...TransUnion (800-888-4213 or *www.transunion.com*).

Note: You are entitled to one free report each year (*www.annualcreditreport.com*). And, if you have been turned down for credit, you can get a free report.

• **Consider subscribing to a credit monitoring service** that alerts you within 24 hours of any changes to your credit file (for example, an application for a new credit card).

Examples: PrivacyGuard.com (877-202-8828 or *www.privacyguard.com*)...and Identity Fraud, Inc. (866-443-3728 or *www.identityfraud.com*). Costs range from $30 to $160 per year.

• **Consider purchasing identity theft insurance**—a type of policy that is now being offered to help identity theft victims with the expense of restoring their good name and credit.

The insurance generally covers the cost of fixing credit records, lost wages for time away from work to talk with credit bureaus and investigators, long-distance phone calls, attorney fees and other costs.

Examples: Travelers (*www.travelers.com*) and Chubb Group of Insurance Cos. (*www. chubb.com*). Premiums for $15,000 of coverage with a $100 deductible range from $15 to $30 per year.

Note: This coverage is unavailable in some states.

• **Don't carry sensitive information,** such as your Social Security number, personal identification numbers (PINs) or passwords, in your wallet or purse.

• **Don't give out personal information over the telephone** unless you initiated the call.

• **Don't put your Social Security or driver's license number on your checks.**

• **Don't use easily available information,** such as your mother's maiden name, your birth date or the last four digits of your Social Security number, as your password for credit/debit cards, phone accounts, etc.

• **Don't have new checks sent to your residence.** Instead, pick them up at the bank or have them delivered by registered mail so that you'll have to sign for them.

• **Don't leave mail and personal information around your home** if you have outsiders there (workers, roommates, etc.).

IF YOU'VE BEEN VICTIMIZED

If you find out that someone has been obtaining credit using your personal information, do three things immediately...

1. Contact the fraud department of each of the three major credit reporting bureaus. Report that your identity has been stolen. Ask that a "fraud alert" be placed in your file and add a "victims statement" that creditors contact you before opening a new account in your name.

2. Contact the security department of the creditor or financial institution of any fraudulently accessed or opened account. Close the account, and change passwords on any new account. Tell the creditor or institution that this is a case of ID theft.

3. File a report with your local police or where the identity theft took place. Request a copy of the police report in case the bank, credit card company or other creditor needs proof of the crime later on.

After these initial actions, it's important to prevent additional injury as well as correct any adverse actions to date...

• **Cancel all current checking and savings accounts and open new ones.** See that the bank pays only outstanding checks that you've written and that it doesn't honor checks written by someone else. Contact the major check verification companies to alert them of the theft of your checks. They include Global Payments (800-638-4600, ext. 555), SCAN (800-262-7771) and TeleCheck & TRS (800-710-9898).

• **Get new ATM cards,** and use a new PIN.

• **Contact an attorney** if credit bureaus are unresponsive or if the title to your property has been changed. Ask him to send a letter to the credit bureau or county clerk of record.

• **Report the crime to the FTC** by calling its Identity Theft Hotline (877-438-4338) or visiting *www.ftc.gov*. Click on "File a Complaint," under the tab "Consumer Protection."

Important: If you are disputing fraudulent debts and accounts opened by an identity thief, the ID Theft Affidavit issued by the FTC now simplifies the process of cleaning up your credit history. Instead of completing multiple forms, you can use this affidavit to alert companies and the credit bureaus when a new account has been opened in your name. Download the affidavit from *www.ftc.gov.*

Bet on Biotech—One Of Three Stock Sectors Set to Shine

Janet M. Brown, president of FundX Investment Group, San Francisco, and managing editor of *The NoLoad FundX* newsletter. Based on risk-adjusted returns, the publication is ranked by The Hulbert Financial Digest among the top five mutual fund newsletters over the past 15 years. *www.FundX.com*

Gambling stocks and retail stocks have soared in 2012, while oil and gas producers have sunk—but wait awhile and that may change. Although betting heavily on specific industries is a tricky game, adjusting your portfolio slightly to recognize long-term trends can be a shrewd move from time to time.

Examples: Investors who put money into real estate funds as the economy began to show signs of recovery in 2009 have averaged a 44% annualized return on those investments. And $10,000 invested in an exchange-traded fund (ETF) focused on gold in 2005 would be worth more than $35,000 now.

Although I always recommend maintaining a broadly diversified stock portfolio, consider adding some small exposure (1% to 10% of your overall portfolio) to each of these three areas that have been heating up...

BIOTECHNOLOGY

Big pharmaceutical companies, flush with cash and facing expiration of profitable drug patents, are taking their most aggressive steps since the recession to strengthen their drug pipelines. In 2012, for instance, Bristol Meyers Squibb acquired hepatitis C drug developer Inhibitex, paying a 163% premium over the biotech firm's share price. The prospect of a wave of lucrative mergers and acquisitions has ignited a fire under biotech stocks. Investors also are excited by the record number of biotech products now in development—more than 900, according to Pharmaceutical Research and Manufacturers of America. *Worth considering now...*

• **T. Rowe Price Health Sciences Fund (PRHSX)** is a relatively tame way to gain exposure to volatile biotech stocks, which comprise one-third of the portfolio. Overall, fund manager Kris Jenner keeps nearly 45% of the portfolio in small- and mid-cap stocks and the rest in well-known health-care giants, such as Merck and UnitedHealth Group. Over the past decade, the fund has had about the same volatility as the Standard & Poor's 500 stock index but with much higher returns.

Five-year annualized performance: 14.86%. *www.TRowePrice.com*

For more aggressive investors...

• **iShares Nasdaq Biotechnology ETF (IBB)** offers more concentrated exposure to biotech, with about 120 mostly mid- and small-cap stocks in the portfolio. The fund has been 30% more volatile than the S&P 500, but the risk is worth it for many investors because the ETF has outperformed the index over the past one-, three-, five and 10-year periods.

Five-year annualized performance: 15.62%.

TECHNOLOGY

Tech stocks have heated up because of heavy consumer demand for products such as smartphones, computer tablets and thin computer ultrabooks...as well as highly anticipated events such as Microsoft's upcoming rollout of the Windows 8 operating system. There's also another long-term emerging trend at work here—investors have begun to view established tech firms as relatively safe stocks. Investors are attracted not just to their earnings growth rates, which are higher than the broad market's earnings growth rates, but also to their strong balance sheets, minimal debt loads and attractive dividend yields. *Worth considering now...*

• **PowerShares QQQ ETF (QQQ)** tracks the 100 largest nonfinancial stocks in the Nasdaq Composite Index. The ETF is composed of 60% tech stocks, with the rest split between health-care and consumer discretionary companies.

Five-year annualized performance: 9%.

For more aggressive investors...

• **T. Rowe Price Global Technology Fund (PRGTX)** tilts toward small-cap stocks and keeps one-sixth of its assets in foreign firms, such as Baidu, the Chinese Internet search provider, and Gameloft, a French maker of digital games for mobile phones. The fund ranks in the top 13% of its category over the past decade.

Five-year annualized performance: 10.5%.

HOME BUILDERS

Increasingly positive economic data is convincing investors that the long-awaited turnaround in these formerly hated stocks may be near. Lennar, one of the largest home builders, reported first-quarter sales that were the strongest in four years, with new orders up 33% year over year. Many home builders, which typically lost more than 80% of their value between 2007 and 2009, have become much healthier and more stable businesses by reducing their inventory, increasing operational efficiency and stockpiling cash. *Worth considering now...*

• **SPDR S&P Homebuilders ETF (XHB)** offers concentrated exposure to home-building and other construction stocks, as well as home-related companies such as The Home Depot and flooring manufacturer Mohawk Industries.

Five-year annualized performance: 5.54%.

Stocks Under $10 That Are Worth Much More

Hilary Kramer, New York City, editor in chief of the subscription newsletters *GameChangers* and *Breakout Stocks Under $5*. Formerly, she was CIO of a $5 billion global private equity fund. She is author of *The Little Book of Big Profits from Small Stocks* (Wiley) and *Ahead of the Curve: Nine Simple Ways to Create Wealth by Spotting Stock Trends* (Free Press). *http://GameChangers.InvestorPlace.com*

I love seeing a stock slip below $10 a share. *Reason:* That's the threshold at which many major investment firms sell or ignore a stock. Some mutual funds and pension funds actually are prohibited from owning shares that are trading below $10 because they are too hard to sell in large quantities.

That means these low-priced stocks provide the small investor with a rare edge because you can snatch up bargains while Wall Street is looking the other way.

A low stock price does not mean that you necessarily are investing in an unproven company. Nearly two dozen profitable corporations in the Standard & Poor's 500 stock index recently were trading in the sub-$10-per-share range. Nor does a low price necessarily mean that the company is headed toward bankruptcy, although in some cases—as with Eastman Kodak's bankruptcy filing in January—it does mean that.

Many of my biggest winners over the past decade started out as stocks that were trading under $10 per share when I began investing in them. That includes Priceline, which has topped $525...and Starbucks, which has topped $45.

Two types of low-priced stocks that I look for...

UNDISCOVERED GROWTH

These are great small businesses with stock prices that are low simply because many investors have never heard of the companies or have yet to realize their enormous potential.

These companies may be in unglamorous industries or tapping into growth trends that the public hasn't recognized yet. They typically are small-cap companies experiencing fast growth in revenues.

Characteristics I look for...

• **Likelihood of at least 15% annual growth in revenues** over the next five years based on a variety of positive signs.

• **A highly fragmented industry in which the company can keep gaining market share year after year,** not just from increasing revenue but also by acquiring small competitors.

My favorites now...

• **Destination XL Group (DXLG)** is a big-and-tall men's retailer that operates 500 Casual Male and Destination XL stores in the US and Canada. Wall Street has regarded the extra-large menswear category as a marginal retail niche, but the burgeoning waistlines of American men have made it into a $7 billion-a-year industry. Destination XL is the top retailer in its category but still has room for enormous growth with only a 7% share of that market.

Recent share price: $5.18.

• **Magic Software Enterprises (MGIC).** Magic Software is an information technology, consulting and software company based in Israel. It specializes in "cloud-computing" applications that help workers at large companies use their smartphones and other mobile devices to connect to their offices and to remote data servers wherever they are. The company, whose global network of business partners includes IBM and Microsoft, has increased revenue by double-digit percentages for eight consecutive quarters. The company is rolling out support for iPhones and Android phones and is making acquisitions of small consulting and staffing-services firms to gain more access to Asian markets.

Recent share price: $4.91.

• **Metalico (MEA)** is a scrap metal processor that buys discarded base metals (steel and iron) and more valuable ones (copper and platinum) from demolition contractors, then recycles and refabricates them. No one thinks of junkyards and waste disposal as a fast-growth business, but global steel mills are showing strong interest in US metal recyclers as low-cost suppliers. Recycling accounts for 2% of the nation's gross domestic product (GDP). That means billions of dollars in potential revenues. Metalico, which operates 30 locations across the US, is more diverse than many of the hundreds of small competitors that make up this industry, providing protection from price volatility in any one metal. It produces metal products for a range of uses, including radiation shielding, stained-glass windows, bridges and US Navy ships.

Recent share price: $1.42.

FALLEN ANGELS

Once-mighty or high-profile companies that have proved they can succeed sometimes encounter problems that send their stock prices plummeting to single digits. The reasons range from accounting scandals and management mistakes to the economic slowdown. The companies may be fixing their problems out of the spotlight and still have great potential—but fickle investors often want no more to do with them.

Questions I ask when considering a promising fallen angel...

• **Is the company profitable, and is it growing its revenues?**

• **Does the company have a clear and effective solution for what went wrong?** For instance, if the company expanded into areas where its executives have no expertise, have they acknowledged this and changed direction?

• **Are there specific catalysts that can jump-start the business again?**

My favorites now...

• **Cowan Group (COWN)** is a diversified financial services firm in New York City run by one of Wall Street's best-known deal makers, Peter Cohen, the former CEO of Shearson Lehman Hutton. It focuses on investment banking, asset management and brokerage services. Revenue is likely to grow by 10% annually over the next five years, and a likely increase in mergers-and-acquisition activity should boost Cowan's investment banking business.

Recent share price: $2.76.

• **Ruth's Hospitality Group (RUTH).** The owner of the largest upscale steakhouse chain in the US, Ruth's Chris Steak House, has seen its stock price stall since 2007 as the economy tanked and investors feared that wealthy diners and business executives would cut back on prime-grade steaks and $75-per-guest checks. But even in this tepid economic recovery, the company, with its exceptionally loyal customers, has managed to increase sales over the past two years. Many of its competitors have gone out of business, and consumer spending by the wealthy is rebounding. Its main competitor, Morton's Restaurant Group, was acquired at a 34% premium to its stock price in 2011, a sign that Ruth's shares are very undervalued.

Recent share price: $9.61.

Secrets of Paying Less Tax on Social Security Benefits

Stuart Kessler, managing director, RSM McGladrey, Inc., 1185 Avenue of the Americas, New York City 10036.

After many years of paying Social Security taxes on your earned income, you look forward to collecting retirement benefits someday.

Problem: Up to 85% of those retirement benefits may be added to your other income—and taxed again.

Solution: Careful planning may reduce—or may even eliminate—the tax on your Social Security benefits.

PROVISIONAL INCOME

To determine this tax, you must first calculate your "provisional income," which is the total of...

1. Adjusted gross income (AGI) as reported on your federal income tax return.

2. Tax-exempt interest income from municipal bonds and municipal bond funds. *And...*

3. One-half of your annual Social Security benefits.

Example: With an AGI of $25,000, tax-exempt income of $4,000 and $20,000 in annual Social Security benefits, your provisional income is $39,000.

On a joint return, you can have provisional income up to $32,000 without having to pay any tax on your benefits. For single filers, the threshold is $25,000. Over those amounts, up to 50% of your benefits can be taxed.

Even worse, if your provisional income is more than $44,000 on a joint return or $34,000 filing singly, up to 85% of your benefits will be taxed.

INCOME LEVELS

As you can see, the taxability of your benefits depends on your income.

Very low income: When your provisional income is less than $25,000 ($32,000 on a joint return), you won't owe taxes on your Social Security benefits.

Very high: If that income is above $44,000 ($34,000 on a single return), there may not be much you can do to avoid paying tax on 85% of your benefits.

Middle ground: If your income is neither very low nor very high, some planning may cut the tax on your Social Security benefits.

Problem: Planning techniques may be most effective before age 70½. Subsequently, you probably will have to take minimum distributions from your IRA, which might push your income up to a level where taxes on your benefits are inevitable.

ANNUITIES

One solution is to use an immediate annuity for income before you reach age 70½.

Example: You retire at the age of 62 with $500,000 in a municipal bond fund that you intend to use for income. At a 4% yield, that would be $20,000 a year—all of which would be counted in your provisional income once you start to receive Social Security benefits.

Better way: Use that $500,000 to buy a 10-year term annuity. Your income from the annuity would be about $5,000 a month, or $60,000 a year.

Of the $5,000 per month you receive, only $1,000 or so might be taxable. The rest will be considered a tax-free return of capital. (The exact amounts will depend on various factors such as current interest rates and insurance company competitiveness.)

Bottom line: Instead of $20,000 worth of provisional income per year, this strategy drops the amount you will report to about $12,000. Within the income range described above, this reduction could mean that 50% of your Social Security benefits will be taxed, rather than 85%. Or, your benefits might be completely untaxed.

Caution: The higher payout you get from investing $500,000 in an annuity rather than in a municipal bond fund results from your receiving a return of your own capital. Thus, you may want to spend only $20,000 a year and reinvest the rest.

OTHER OPTIONS

Additional strategies can help you reduce your provisional income and the tax you'll owe on Social Security benefits...

- **Seek shelter.** Inside deferred annuities or permanent life insurance, your earnings can build up without swelling your AGI.

As much as possible, try to minimize your sales commissions and avoid surrender fees.

- **Live on loans.** Tap a home-equity line of credit or a margin account. Take out a reverse mortgage or refinance investment property. Borrow against your life insurance.

All of these techniques will provide cash flow but won't boost your provisional income.

- **Sell stocks.** Take losses on depreciated stocks and stock funds to raise cash. Not only will you avoid boosting your AGI, you'll also harvest tax losses that you can use now or sometime in the future.

- **Stagger your income.** If you are withdrawing from your IRA or liquidating appreciated investments for retirement income, double up to skip years.

Example: You can increase your withdrawals and sales in 2013, boosting your tax bill this year. In 2014, though, you can tap this pool of cash while keeping your AGI to low levels.

A FINAL THOUGHT

Before you reach full retirement age (65 or later, depending on the year of your birth), you will face yet another problem with your Social Security benefits.

At ages 62 (the minimum starting age), 63 and 64, you lose $1 in Social Security benefits for every $2 you earn over $15,120 in 2013. The earned income threshold rises each year.

If you keep your earnings to that level, you'll reduce this effective taxation in addition to the actual taxation of your benefits. If your earnings will be well over $15,120, you're better off deferring your benefits. The longer you defer benefits, the larger your initial checks will be.

Once you reach your full retirement age (66 for those born between 1943 and 1954), you can earn any amount and still keep all your Social Security benefits. Thus, it may pay to defer compensation, including any bonuses, from ages 62 to 64 to until after age 65.

Tactic: From full retirement age to age 70, you're better off taking Social Security benefits than tapping your IRA for spending money. No more than 85% of your Social Security benefits (and perhaps less) will be taxed while 100% of any IRA withdrawals will be added to your taxable income.

Moreover, deferring your IRA withdrawals will permit you to receive more tax-deferred compounding.

How to Invest in Stocks and Still Sleep at Night

Tom Lydon, president of Global Trends Investments, Irvine, California, which manages more than $80 million of assets in all-ETF portfolios. He is founder of ETFTrends.com and coauthor of *iMoney: Profitable ETF Strategies for Every Investor* (FT Press).

After the investment world's wild ride of the past several years, many investors are aching for more tranquility. Wall Street is addressing that yearning with a range of new exchange-traded funds (ETFs)* that are designed to smooth out the wild swings. More than a dozen of these low-volatility ETFs now are available.

And lower volatility doesn't mean that you have to settle for lower returns. Over the past decade, the Standard & Poor's 500 Low Volatility Index returned 7% annualized versus 4% for the S&P 500 stock index.

Here's how low-volatility ETFs can be right for you...

HOW THEY WORK

By investing in low-volatility stocks, these ETFs can reduce the impact of the market's jolts.

Example: When the S&P 500 moves up or down by 1%, a low-volatility version of the index tends to move 0.7% in the same direction.

Major investment companies that offer low-volatility ETFs, such as Blackrock, Russell and Invesco, focus on several factors to choose the low-volatility stocks that make up the ETFs. *These factors include...*

- **How much the stocks swing up and down** relative to their average long-term price
- **How much the stocks move relative to the larger index that they track**
- **How correlated or uncorrelated they are to one other.**

*ETFs are funds that typically track a particular investment index but can be bought and sold on an exchange like individual stocks. They tend to have lower annual expenses than comparable mutual funds.

In response to these considerations, low-volatility ETFs often load up on stocks that are in stable sectors, such as household goods and utilities that consumers don't eliminate even during difficult economic times. But even when various low-volatility ETFs seem similar, they are not simply clones of one another. They cover slightly different indexes... reevaluate their holdings at different intervals...and sometimes impose restrictions on how much they allocate to particular countries or sectors.

Important: Despite their appeal as safer investments with possibly better returns, low-volatility ETFs are all-stock offerings, which means that they still will be significantly riskier than funds that include bonds or a mix of bonds and stocks in their portfolios. Also, you are better off holding these ETFs in tax-deferred accounts, since most adjust their portfolios several times a year, which is likely to lead to higher turnover and more tax implications than many index funds.

Finally, if you invest in a low-volatility ETF, you probably will need to adjust your expectations downward in bull markets. While these ETFs can provide some protection and returns in down times, they are unlikely to keep pace with the overall market when stocks are rising sharply.

HOW TO USE THEM

Low-volatility ETFs can be very useful tools to help you accomplish the following...

- **Reduce overall risk without getting out of stocks completely.** During rough times, investing in low-volatility ETFs is a less drastic alternative than trying to time the market by shifting assets to cash or bonds.
- **Gain exposure to riskier asset classes that can boost your long-term returns.** For example, if you are a retiree invested mostly in bonds but still need substantial growth in your portfolio, you may feel more comfortable adding a low-volatility foreign stock fund than a standard one.

Here are a variety of low-volatility ETFs for you to consider. *They all are from reputable money-management firms that use a disciplined selection process...*

LARGE-CAP

• **PowerShares S&P 500 Low Volatility Portfolio (SPLV).** The largest of the low-volatility ETFs, it has attracted $4.3 billion in assets. It consists of the 100 stocks from the S&P 500 with the lowest volatility. Every three months, the portfolio is reevaluated and stocks are replaced if necessary.

Recent share price: $31.18.

• **Russell 1000 Low Volatility ETF (LVOL)** picks from the 1,000 largest US companies and can hold up to 200 stocks. It uses more complex criteria than the PowerShares ETF to choose stocks and keeps a tighter rein on volatility in both up and down markets. To ensure it remains focused on low-volatility stocks, the portfolio is reconstituted every month.

Recent share price: $53.62.

SMALL-CAP

• **Russell 2000 Low Volatility ETF (SLVY)** currently is the only small-cap ETF devoted to low-volatility stocks. It holds up to 400 of the least volatile stocks in the Russell 2000. The ETF has about 19% of its portfolio in real estate and utilities, and it is reconstituted every month.

Recent share price: $52.02.

FOREIGN

• **iShares MSCI EAFE Minimum Volatility Index (EFAV)** tracks the MSCI EAFE Minimum Volatility Index, which attempts to create the least volatile portfolio of up to 200 stocks from the MSCI EAFE Index. That index includes developed nations in Europe, the Australia region and the Far East. The ETF reevaluates and reconstitutes its portfolio only twice a year. In attempting to reduce the ETF's volatility, it imposes certain constraints that its competitors don't, such as limiting the percentage of assets that can go into any one sector or country. The ETF also has one of the lowest annual expense ratios of any low-volatility ETF, just 0.2%.

Recent share price: $59.70.

• **PowerShares S&P International Developed Low Volatility Portfolio (IDLV).** This ETF tracks the 200 stocks in the S&P Developed Ex.-US-Korea LargeMidCap Index** that have exhibited the lowest volatility over the past 12 months, with 16% of its portfolio currently devoted to Canadian firms. The ETF is rebalanced and reconstituted quarterly and is a more conservative offering than the iShares MSCI EAFE Minimum Volatility Index ETF. (**Although South Korea sometimes is regarded as a developed country, it is not included in this index because of the high volatility of its stock market.)

Recent share price: $30.53.

Sneaky Fees Can Reduce Your 401(k) by 10%—But These New Rules Will Help You Fix That

Peter Philipp, CFP, CFA, who specializes in employee benefits and investment management for businesses and individuals at Cambridge Investment Research, Inc. Based in San Francisco, he is an instructor in wealth management with the UC Berkeley Personal Financial Planning program. *www.CambridgeSF.com*

Employee retirement plans have drawbacks as well as advantages. Several new rules from two departments of the federal government—Labor and Treasury—are designed to reduce some of the drawbacks and provide new opportunities.

Here's a closer look at how your retirement plan is about to change and what you can do...

FEE DISCLOSURES

A recent AARP study found that 71% of 401(k) participants are unaware that they are paying any fees at all in their 401(k) plans, even though those fees can have a major impact on their retirement nest eggs.

Example: Paying an extra 0.5% in annual fees throughout a 30-year career can reduce the amount in a 401(k) at retirement by 10%, according to the fund company Vanguard.

The Labor Department has issued new rules that start within the next few months that are meant to make it easier to figure out how much you're paying in fees and expenses in 401(k) plans and in 403(b) plans that are covered by the Employee Retirement Income Security Act (ERISA). *Here are some of the fees you'll be hearing about...*

• **Administrative fees are what you pay just to participate in your 401(k) plan.** These include recordkeeping and accounting expenses, among other costs. Although employees at large companies often are not charged these fees, employees at smaller companies typically are. An employee at a company with 10 employees might be charged an amount ranging from $50 to $200 per year.

What's new: Any administrative fees imposed on plan participants now must be revealed in the annual disclosure statement. When plan providers debit these fees from participant accounts, they also must be clearly listed in the "account activity" section of the next quarterly statement.

What to do: If you're charged significantly more than $50 per year (perhaps $100 if you work for a company that has fewer than 10 employees), encourage your employer to explore lower-cost 401(k) providers. Suggest that your coworkers make the same request.

• **Asset-based fees are what you pay to invest in specific mutual funds (or other investments) in your 401(k).** They are a percentage of the amount invested and can vary significantly. When insurance companies manage 401(k) plans, they typically impose a "wrap charge"—sometimes called an "asset charge"—of as much as 1% or 2% annually on top of mutual fund fees. That charge often has not been disclosed to plan participants.

What's new: The fees and expenses charged in each investment now must be clearly disclosed in a chart for easy comparison. Annual expenses also must be listed both as a percentage and as a dollar figure per $1,000 invested. Any wrap charges must be included. Shareholder fees, such as up-front sales commissions and redemption fees, also must be listed.

What to do: Try to avoid investments that impose annual fees in excess of 1%. (It's reasonable to adjust that down to 0.5% for bond funds...or up to 1.5% to 2% for foreign stock funds.) Index funds should charge much less. Unfortunately, 401(k) plans typically offer very limited investment options, and there might not be any options appropriate for your goals that fall below these fee levels. If so, request that your employer seek out a 401(k) provider offering lower-cost investments. Also, check whether your 401(k) offers a "brokerage window" that allows you to invest in mutual funds or other investments that are not specifically included in the plan. If so, you can use this window to invest in lower-fee investment options.

Warning: You generally cannot arrange automatic contributions through a brokerage window, so you will have to make each share purchase yourself. Some 401(k) providers charge either a flat fee or a per-trade commission for using the brokerage window. Find out if yours does.

• **Individual service fees are charged when you take advantage of optional 401(k) plan services,** such as borrowing money from your account or requesting a check via overnight mail.

What's new: These fees now will be summarized in a straightforward table.

What to do: Refer to this table before requesting any special services.

NEW ANNUITY OPTIONS

In decades past, it was common for traditional pensions to provide retirees with a check each month for as long as they lived. Now most retirement plans are 401(k)s, which offer no guarantee of income for life. And even retirees who still have traditional pensions often opt for the flexibility of a lump-sum payout rather than monthly checks.

That lack of guaranteed retirement income—together with longer life spans, low bond interest rates and recent declines in the value of homes—has greatly increased the odds that retirees will outlive their savings.

The Treasury Department has proposed rules to reduce that risk...

• **Longevity annuities would be allowed in 401(k)s and IRAs.** Longevity annuities provide an income stream that starts when the buyer reaches a fairly advanced age—usually 80 or 85—and continues for the remainder of the buyer's life (or the life of the buyer and his/her spouse, in the case of a joint-life longevity annuity). These can be a lot more affordable than an immediate annuity that begins making payments soon after your initial investment.

Example: A 65-year-old might have to pay $277,500 to purchase an annuity that pays $20,000 per year starting immediately...or just $35,200 for a longevity annuity that pays out $20,000 per year starting at age 85, according to a report issued by the President's Council of Economic Advisers.

Trouble is, it currently is difficult or impossible to purchase a longevity annuity in a 401(k), 403(b), 457 plan or IRA—they run afoul of required minimum distribution (RMD) rules that force investors to begin taking money out of tax-deferred accounts starting at age 70½.

What's new: The proposed rules would exempt assets invested in longevity annuities from RMD calculations—as long as the annuity costs no more than 25% of the account balance...and as long as the cost of the annuity is no more than $100,000...and starts making payments no later than age 85.

What to do: A longevity annuity might be a viable option in certain cases—say, if you're healthy and come from a long-lived family. But that doesn't mean you should jump at the one offered in your 401(k).

While the plan provider might have used its market power to obtain better annuity terms than you could obtain on your own, it also is possible that you could find a better longevity annuity on the open market, outside your 401(k).

Compare the costs and monthly payments offered by several insurers before making any choice. Consider the financial health of the insurance company offering the annuity, too. If this company goes out of business, the value of your investment could be severely diminished—protections for annuity investors in the case of insurance company insolvency vary by state but often do not exceed $100,000, which might be much less than what you expected your longevity annuity to provide. (See *www.Ambest.com* and *www.StandardAndPoors.com* for ratings of insurers.) Married people should strongly consider a joint-life longevity annuity, which makes payments until both spouses pass away.

Be aware that today's low interest rates mean longevity annuities currently are relatively expensive. There's something to be said for delaying a purchase or seeking out another way to ensure that you don't outlive your retirement savings, such as delaying the start of Social Security benefits, which increases your monthly checks by 7% to 8% for every year you delay from age 62 to age 70.

• **Those with traditional pensions will be allowed to take two forms of payment.** Currently, employees with old-fashioned pensions are offered a choice upon retirement—either monthly payments or a lump-sum payout.

What's new: The Treasury proposal would make it simpler for employers to offer the option of taking part of the pension as a monthly check and part as a lump sum, something that currently is difficult and rare.

What to do: Taking part of your pension as an annuity for safety and part as a lump sum for flexibility could make some sense. But it's wise to hire an actuary to examine the plan's lump-sum offer first to make sure that it is as large as it should be. There's a lot of money on the line, and it is very hard for the average person to gauge whether he/she is getting a good deal. Unfortunately, the lump sums offered by pension plans sometimes are significantly lower than the present value of the monthly pension checks surrendered to acquire them.

How to Guarantee Income for Life

Robert Kreitler, CFP, registered investment adviser, Raymond James Financial Services, and president of Kreitler Associates LLC, 195 Church St., New Haven, Connecticut. He is author of *Getting Started in Global Investing* (John Wiley & Sons).

Many retirees rely on bond investments in their portfolios to supplement their income. Then they cross their fingers, hoping that they won't run out of money.

But immediate fixed annuities guarantee a cash flow for life—one that retirees can't outlive.

HOW ANNUITIES WORK

The immediate fixed annuities are insurance vehicles—the same as those that companies use to finance lifetime employee pensions. Most of us are familiar with deferred annuities. These annuities grow capital tax deferred for retirement.

Immediate annuities generate cash *during* retirement. The income from the immediate fixed annuity is higher than the income of government bonds because it includes repayment of principal.

What's the catch? First, there is no principal remaining upon the annuitant's death. This is the trade-off for higher monthly payments and a lifetime guarantee. Keep the money for your heirs separate from your annuity portfolio.

Remember to obtain a *term-certain provision*. This guarantees payments for a specified number of years, usually 10, even if you die soon after buying the annuity. After the annuitant's death, the remaining funds go to a named beneficiary.

An annuity is irrevocable. You can't sell it like a bond. And, like most bonds, it doesn't protect you from inflation. Therefore, keep a portion of your nonannuity portfolio in stocks.

HOW TO ANNUITIZE

Most retirees can benefit from immediate annuities. The smaller their savings, the greater the need. Generally, those who have assets in excess of $2 million probably don't need immediate annuities.

The older you are—and the shorter your life expectancy—when you buy the immediate fixed annuity, the more generous the monthly payments. Retirees can receive even more generous payments by buying a new annuity every five or 10 years, starting at age 65.

COMPARISON SHOPPING

Research the financial health of the insurers on the Web sites of independent ratings agencies, such as A.M. Best Company (908-439-2200 or *www.ambest.com*).

Hidden Traps in the Health-Care Law—This Article Could Save You $10,000

Maura Carley, MPH, CIC, CEO of Healthcare Navigation, LLC, a patient advocacy and consultin company based in Shelton, Connecticut. She previously held senior management positions with Yale-New Haven Hospital, Stamford Hospital and Kaiser Permanente. She is author of *Health Insurance: Navigating Traps & Gaps* (Ampersand, Inc.). *www.HealthCareNavigation.com*

In June 2012, the Supreme Court upheld much of the Patient Protection and Affordable Care Act (ACA), the wide-ranging health-care law meant to substantially alter America's health insurance system.

You've probably seen hundreds of headlines about the best-known parts of the ACA—the fact that it will require most Americans to have health insurance or pay a "penalty"...will require insurance companies to offer policies to all who apply (even those who are sick)...and will raise the Medicare tax on people who earn more than $200,000 ($250,000 for married couples filing jointly).

But some important elements of the ACA have not made headlines or are commonly misunderstood. Depending on your situation, it may be very important that you know about these elements. *Among the ACA's lesser-known consequences and hidden loopholes are the following...*

• **Your retirement could cost your adult child his/her health insurance.** One of the much-ballyhooed aspects of the ACA is that it allows adult children to remain on their parents' health insurance coverage through age 26. But there's an important exception to this rule that hasn't received much attention—it usually does not apply to retiree health plans.

Vital: If your adult child is on your health insurance coverage and you expect to retire soon, confirm that your retiree plan will cover the child. If it won't, the adult child should start researching alternative coverage options well before your retirement date. Options might include individual coverage...COBRA coverage from the parent's former employer's plan...or Medicaid coverage if the adult child has very limited income and assets.

• **Preventive care sometimes isn't 100% covered despite news reports to the contrary.** One well-publicized aspect of the ACA is that insurers now are required to provide many forms of preventive care—things such as routine checkups, mammograms and colonoscopies—without the patient paying a penny out-of-pocket.

What's rarely mentioned is that this preventive-care provision is so loaded with confusing caveats that patients who seek "free" preventive treatments might end up with unexpected medical bills. For example, if your insurer has not made major changes to your plan since the ACA passed in 2010, the plan might be "grandfathered" and not obliged to fully cover preventive services. Preventive care also might not be fully covered if you seek treatment from an out-of-network provider... you have a limited-benefit plan that has obtained a government waiver freeing it from the preventive-care mandate...or the specific preventive treatment that you receive is not one covered by the ACA.

Self-defense: To avoid surprises, contact your plan provider or your employer's benefits department to confirm the coverage level before you schedule any preventive services.

• **The ACA's attempt to close the Medicare Part D "donut hole" has made selecting the right Part D plan more important—and more difficult.** Medicare recipients face a gap in their prescription drug coverage—the so-called Part D "donut hole." If you incur significant pharmaceutical bills during a year, you might have to pay thousands of dollars of drug costs out-of-pocket before your Part D benefits resume.

The ACA will slowly close that Part D donut hole over the coming years. It will force drug manufacturers to offer steep discounts to buyers who reach the donut hole and will require Part D plans to pay most of the remaining costs. Trouble is, drug manufacturers and the private companies that sell Part D plans inevitably will pass the cost of that expanded coverage along to Part D plan participants—and some will do so in subtle ways that might not be noticeable at first.

Example: An insurer might remove many brand-name drugs from its formulary—its list of covered drugs. You probably won't notice until you refill a prescription or receive a first-time prescription for one of these drugs.

As different insurance companies adopt ways to pass along the cost of closing the donut hole in the coming years, the differences among Part D plans will increase, making it more important than ever for patients to carefully examine available Part D options during the open-enrollment period. Do this every year even if you are pleased with your current Part D plan—your current plan might change substantially from year to year as insurers adjust to the ACA's rules. This is happening already—I have a client who would have faced $10,000 more in out-of-pocket costs this year with one Part D plan than with another.

Useful resource: The Medicare Web site, *www.MyMedicare.gov*, can help you analyze Part D options.

• **If you have a health condition that makes obtaining insurance on the individual market difficult or impossible, now might be the best time to find affordable coverage.** People with preexisting conditions will be able to purchase individual health insurance at the same rates as healthy people starting in 2014. Until then, government-subsidized high-risk pools are available to help these people get insurance.

These high-risk pools have attracted little attention and relatively few participants, in part because of their strict eligibility requirements—only people who have been without health insurance for at least six months can join, among other restrictions. But these pools can be a tremendous deal for those who qualify. Some states are running their own high-risk pools, while others offer pools run by the Department of Health and Human Services (DHHS). Rates vary, but in general, they are even lower than the rates likely to be available starting in 2014.

Example: A 50-year-old with serious health problems that make him otherwise uninsurable could obtain coverage for between $214 and $559 a month through a DHHS-administered pool, depending on his state of residence and other factors—less than many perfectly healthy people his age pay. Rates tend to be much steeper in high-risk pool programs that were created by states before the ACA. Those programs vary, too, but are not federally subsidized.

What to do: If you have a preexisting condition and have been without health insurance for at least six months, don't wait until 2014 to shop for coverage. Visit the government's high-risk pool Web site, *www.pcip.gov*, to find out if you qualify for appealing rates now.

Four Ways to Rebuild Your Retirement Nest Egg

Jonathan Clements, former personal finance columnist for *The Wall Street Journal.*

A weak economy has left many retirees strapped for cash. here are four strategies to bolster your finances...

• **Work part-time.** If you work part-time during retirement and earn $10,000 a year, it's like having an extra $200,000 in your retirement nest egg. Why? For every $100,000 in savings, you can expect to receive $5,000 a year in income. You also are giving your nest egg extra time to grow.

True, those extra earnings may make 50% to 85% of your Social Security retirement benefits taxable. Even after taxes, however, you still will have more money in your pocket.

• **Move to a less expensive home,** perhaps in a more affordable part of the country. You will slash property tax, homeowner's insurance and home-maintenance expenses, thus freeing up money for everyday expenses.

Caution: Buying and selling homes is expensive. Purchase a place that you expect to live in for many years to come.

• **Take out a reverse mortgage.** This allows people age 62 or older who own their homes outright to tap into the equity without actually selling. Provided you don't move or sell your home, the mortgage doesn't have to be repaid until after your death, at which time the amount owed can't exceed your home's value.

You can receive the money as monthly income, a lump sum or a line of credit.

Find more information on reverse mortgages at *www.aarp.org/money.*

• **Cut taxes.** Time withdrawals from retirement accounts and sales of taxable investments strategically. Aim to generate just enough income each year to get to the top of the 15% federal income tax bracket, but no higher. That means income of about $36,250 in 2013 if you are single, and $72,500 in 2013 if you are married filing jointly. These figures, which assume you take the standard deduction, are slightly higher if you are 65 or older or if you itemize your deductions.

Generate extra taxable income now—for example, by selling stocks—if you expect to be in a higher tax bracket in the future. Legally required retirement-plan withdrawals at age 70½ could push you into the 25% income tax bracket and possibly higher.

The Reverse Mortgage Boom

Tyler D. Kraemer, Esq., a real estate, finance and estate-planning specialist and principal in the law firm of Kraemer Kendall Benson Rupp Deen LLC, Colorado Springs, *www.k2blaw.com*. He is coauthor of *The Complete Guide to Reverse Mortgages* (Adams Media).

Reverse mortgages—a special kind of home-equity loan designed specifically for older home owners to let them stay in their homes and supplement their income—have soared in popularity among financially strapped seniors. Recent changes in the law have made these mortgages even more appealing.

Recent law: Congress has raised the maximum loan limit that you can borrow to $625,500 in certain areas...capped the fee lenders may charge to process your loan application (origination fee) at $6,000...and allowed you to use a reverse mortgage to buy a new home.

What you must know before you jump in...

THE FINE PRINT

Reverse mortgages, the most common of which is known as a Home Equity Conversion Mortgage (HECM), are loans available to qualifying home owners age 62 or older. They allow home owners to borrow money from banks and mortgage lenders against the value of their homes. The home owner continues to live in the home and retains title to the property.

Unlike with a traditional loan, your income and credit score don't matter. The lender pays you, typically in a monthly payment or lump sum or with a line of credit. The money you get is tax-free, can be used for any purpose and, if it is an HECM, is guaranteed by the federal government even if your lender is unable to pay in the future.

Interest rates that lenders charge on reverse mortgages are adjustable and based on a US Treasury rate plus a lender margin. Interest accrues over the life of the loan—but you don't have to repay anything until you move out or die, at which point the house is sold to pay off your debt. Best of all, the amount of debt you owe, including interest, cannot exceed the market value of the home. So even if your home loses value, you or your heirs aren't responsible for any shortfall. You are required to maintain your home while you live in it and pay your property taxes, homeowner's insurance and utility bills (otherwise the loan comes due immediately).

Actuarial tables determine how much a borrower can withdraw from the home. Calculations are based on the value of the home, interest rate, age of the borrower and location. For an estimate of what you might receive with your home, use the free online calculator at *http://rmc.ibisreverse.com*.

While the payouts you receive are tax-free, reverse mortgage income can make you ineligible for certain state and federal supplemental benefits, including Medicaid, though not Medicare.

DOWNSIDE

The main downside to a reverse mortgage is that it's expensive. Even though lenders can legally charge you an origination fee of no more than $6,000, you also have to pay an upfront insurance premium that could amount to thousands of dollars. In addition, closing costs on a $400,000 reverse mortgage typically are $2,000 or more.

For these reasons, it's often a better deal to take out a traditional home-equity loan or, if it's available, a loan from family members.

WHEN TO USE A REVERSE MORTGAGE

In the following situations, a reverse mortgage can make sense...

- **You are facing foreclosure.** In this circumstance, it's nearly impossible to get a traditional home-equity loan, and selling your house outright might leave you owing more than you get from the sale. A reverse mortgage can possibly save you from losing your house if you have significant equity built up. You can never be foreclosed on or forced to vacate your house because you "missed a mortgage payment."
- **Your savings have been depleted to a dangerously low level,** and you need the income from a reverse mortgage to cover healthcare costs or other critical monthly expenses.

For some retirees, this could provide the time needed for investments ravaged by last year's bear market to recover.

• **You plan to stay in your house for five years or more.** If you sell the house before then and pay back the reverse mortgage loan, then the cost of the loan will seem significant compared to the benefit. If you keep the loan for a long time, you spread the up-front cost over many years.

• **You want to buy a new home but would be forced to use all of your savings to do it.** A federal program called HECM for Purchase allows you to buy a new principal residence and obtain a reverse mortgage on it at the same time.

Example: An elderly couple lived in a two-story house valued at $600,000. They sold the home and wanted to buy a one-story home closer to their children for $600,000. Getting a traditional mortgage for the new property wasn't a good option, because they were on a fixed income and didn't want to make mortgage payments each month. They also needed some of the profits from their old home's sale to live on in the future.

Solution: The couple applied for, and received, a reverse mortgage of about $400,000 to buy the new house. That meant that to buy the new home, they had to put down only $200,000, which they acquired from the sale of the old house. The couple makes no monthly payments to the lender—instead, the lender will recover the loan principal plus interest when the home eventually is sold.

BEFORE YOU TAKE THE PLUNGE

Reverse mortgages are complex. Careful consideration and consultation with your adviser is critical before taking the plunge. In fact, federal law mandates that you attend a session with an independent financial counselor to ensure that you understand all the implications of what you're doing. *Also be sure to...*

• **Comparison shop.** Compare offers, including interest rates, and check the lender's credentials with state regulators and better-business agencies. As with traditional loans, you can save by getting quotes from different lenders. To find reverse mortgage lenders in your state, go to *www.hud.gov* (click on "Resources," then on "Lender Locator").

• **Know the warning signs of unscrupulous lenders.** Reverse mortgages can be tricky, and scams are becoming more common.

Examples: The broker or lender tries to get you to invest your reverse mortgage loan money in costly financial products, such as deferred annuities...or the lender asks you to sign loan paperwork that's not completely filled out.

The bottom line is that reverse mortgages are not for everyone. Spending money on the up-front fees usually makes sense only if you need the cash and you do not have another readily available source.

How to Save $3,000 a Year on Groceries

Phil Lempert, editor of Supermarketguru.com, a Web site that focuses on food and health news; host of the syndicated radio program *Before You Bite* and food editor for NBC's *Today* show. He is also author of *Phil Lempert's Supermarket Shopping and Value Guide* (Contemporary Books).

The key to cutting your grocery bills in a super-competitive marketplace is to think *value*...not just *price*. Here are some surefire ways to get the most from your shopping excursions—in every aisle, every time you shop.

GET TO KNOW YOUR SUPERMARKET

Value is a balance of four factors—quality, price, selection and service. Supermarket customers visit, on average, two different supermarkets a week and several different stores each month in search of the best value. But—53% of shoppers say they dislike supermarket shopping...and 14% downright hate it.

My aim: To help you get the best value from your supermarket and help you have more fun grocery shopping.

• **Choose one store to be your regular supermarket.** With more than 35,000 products available on most supermarket shelves, there's no reason to keep switching stores.

• **Front-end electronic marketing programs** are similar to frequent-shopper programs, but members are rewarded based on the amount they spend. Such programs are often one part of a broader preferred shopper program, rather than a stand-alone benefit.

• **Purchase-triggered coupon programs,** also called purchase-activated coupon programs, issue coupons at the checkout register that are good for future purchases at that particular chain of stores. The coupons are "triggered" by the purchases you have just made. These programs do not keep track of your personal shopping habits.

Example: If you just bought Brand X peanut butter, you may receive a coupon for Brand Y peanut butter or a larger size of Brand X...or a jar of jelly.

• **Instant electronic discounts are also called "paperless coupons."** Customers who use their membership cards at the checkout register automatically receive discounts on products that have been identified in mailers or by signs on the shelves. Some supermarkets also offer customers discounts at neighboring businesses, entries in contests and other electronic rewards.

• **Meet the store manager and/or customer service manager.** Be sure to tell him/her that you are a long-time regular customer. Mention what you like about the store—and suggest improvements. *Ask the following questions...*

- What are the best/worst times to shop here?
- What are your biggest sale items?
- What day do your weekly sales begin?
- Can I get an advance copy of your newspaper and circular ads and a schedule of in-store sales, product samplings and promotional events?
- How do I join your frequent-shopper program, and if there is a fee, will you waive it? (Usually, the answer is yes.)

• **Get to know the staff in the store—and save $100.** Exchanging friendly greetings with the people who work where you shop will always make your supermarket visits more enjoyable—and can save you $100 a year or more. Introduce yourself to the cashiers and to the people in the produce section, deli, bakery and other departments—*and tell them you are interested in sales and special offers.*

Once they get to know you, the supermarket staff will point out new products, special promotions and sales. They will direct you to in-store coupons, newspaper or circular coupons and rebate offers.

UNDERSTAND MARKETING EFFORTS—AND TRICKS

• **Use coupons**—and save $300. If you use just 10 manufacturer's coupons every week, at an average of about 60 cents each, you'll save more than $300 a year.

• **Buy store brands**—and save $2,000. Switching to your supermarket's "private label" or "store brand" is one of the best ways to save money with no loss of quality.

In most cases, when you compare the ingredients list of "store-brand" products to those of the national brands, you will find that the quality is equal, if not superior, to the name-brand product. Often, store brands are made by the same manufacturers as national brands. You'll have to try store-brand products to see if you like them.

If you spend $135 to $140 a week on groceries, you can save more than $2,000 a year by switching to store brands.

• **Outsmart supermarket display techniques.** *Don't fall for common supermarket display tricks...*

- Placing the highest-priced items at eye level.
- Piling up end-of-aisle displays with products that are close to their expiration date, but are not necessarily on sale.
- Grouping products to provoke impulse buying, like chips, dips and soft drinks.

• Making attractive arrangements of delicious precut fruit or salad items that are far more expensive than the unsliced versions.

• Creating an "international" cheese table or deli display when the same prepackaged products are available in the dairy case for much less.

• Placing staple items, such as milk, in the back of the store, forcing you to walk past the rest of the merchandise.

Strategy: If you need just a gallon of milk, avoid temptation by walking down an aisle stocked with items you rarely buy, such as automobile supplies, pet food or school supplies.

• **Stick to your list**—and save $300. Finally, the supermarket shopper's must—always shop with a list and control your impulse buys. This is an easy way to save $300 a year.

I limit myself to three impulse purchases per shopping trip, but otherwise stick carefully to my list. This strategy guarantees that I always have fun while I'm shopping—but I never exceed my budget.

You Can Find a Great Vacation Rental Online—A Travel Insider Tells How

Pauline Frommer, creator of *Pauline Frommer's Travel Guides* (Wiley) and cohost of *The Travel Show*, a nationally syndicated radio show. Based in Hoboken, New Jersey, she is a two-time winner of the North American Travel Journalists Association's Guidebook of the Year award. *www.Frommers.com/pauline*

Imagine spending your vacation in a two-bedroom luxury apartment on the Thames in London for as little as $1,020 per week...a furnished studio apartment in the heart of Paris for $540...or a cozy apartment near the water in Miami Beach for just $273.

Hundreds of thousands of privately owned properties now are offered as short-term vacation rentals, an increasingly popular alternative to hotels. They include everything from ordinary homes and apartments to ski chalets, beach houses and luxurious mansions.

HomeAway.com, the largest vacation rental site, reports 44% growth in rental listings over the past three years.

Rentals generally are significantly cheaper than hotel rooms of comparable quality, and they almost always offer more space, a homier feel and a kitchen. But choosing, booking and paying for a vacation rental are much trickier than staying in a hotel—and there are potential drawbacks that you usually don't face in hotels.

Here's what you need to know to save money and have a wonderful vacation rental experience...

THE CHALLENGES

Consider these possible drawbacks before booking a vacation rental...

• **You'll probably have to sign a contract and pay a security deposit well in advance of the trip.** It can be almost like signing a short-term lease. Read the rental contract carefully before signing—it likely spells out important details, such as additional fees and what you must do to ensure that your security deposit is returned.

Helpful: As soon as you arrive for your vacation, walk through the property and take digital photos or video of any problems or damage. Then confirm that the property owner is aware of these so that you don't get blamed. Take another set of photos and video as you leave to prove that you left the property as you found it.

• **Cancellation penalties can be stiff.** Canceling a vacation rental might mean sacrificing 50% to 100% of the rental price depending on the terms of the rental agreement and possibly on whether a replacement renter can be found.

Helpful: Travel insurance could cover this loss. Policies are available through some of the Web sites that list vacation rentals (see next page), but I recommend going through Squaremouth (800-240-0369, *www.Squaremouth.com*) or InsureMyTrip (800-487-4722, *www.InsureMyTrip.com*), both of which provide quotes from many different insurers.

• **Some vacation rentals are in violation of local laws or homeowners association rules.** Some sections of certain cities including New York, Paris and San Francisco have banned short-term rentals. In theory, that could result in a guest being forced to vacate—though I've never heard of such a thing happening.

• **Maid service usually is not part of the deal.** Guests often are charged a cleaning fee.

• **There might be other fees as well.** Some rental owners charge for linens and towels or for exceeding some preset limit on the number of guests. Others pass along the cost of electricity or charge extra when you arrive and/or depart on a weekend. These details might be buried in the fine print.

FINDING RENTALS

Searchable vacation rental Web sites enable travelers to quickly sort through many thousands of properties. These sites usually do not own the properties. They list them on behalf of property owners and property-management companies. The sites typically include online calendars indicating when a particular property is available—but property owners don't always update them. It usually is necessary to communicate directly with property owners or managers to confirm availability.

Some Web sites offer little more than classified listings, while others provide reviews from other travelers and safeguards to increase the odds that travelers get what they pay for. And while most sites don't charge travelers a penny—they typically charge property owners to list their properties—a few do impose significant booking fees.

Options include...

• **HomeAway** has more than 260,000 listings in 145 countries. It's particularly strong in the US, France and Spain. HomeAway doesn't charge travelers to use the service. Travelers sign rental agreements and make payments with the property owner or a local property-management company. *www.Homeaway.com*

• **VRBO** features 165,000 listings, especially US destinations such as California, the Carolinas, Florida and Hawaii. It is now owned by HomeAway and has very similar programs and policies—travelers do not have to pay to use it. *www.vrbo.com*

• **Airbnb** offers more than 100,000 listings worldwide, with an extensive selection in major tourist-destination cities such as New York, San Francisco, Paris and London. Unlike most sites, Airbnb processes payments so that travelers can pay with credit cards or PayPal rather than send money directly to a stranger. Airbnb holds payments until 24 hours after check-in so that travelers can confirm that the property is as described. It also offers a 24-hour support line in case anything goes wrong. These added services come at a price, however—Airbnb charges guests a fee of 6% to 12% of the reservation amount. *www.Airbnb.com*

Helpful: Some Airbnb listings are just spare rooms in people's homes. These listings can be quite affordable—I've had wonderful luck with them—but not everyone is comfortable sharing a home with a stranger.

• **FlipKey** has more than 120,000 rentals worldwide with the largest numbers in the US and Europe. Many FlipKey properties are represented by professional property managers, which sometimes are better equipped than property owners to cope with travelers' problems. The Web site takes steps to confirm that those who post reviews of vacation rentals actually stayed in the properties they're reviewing, decreasing the odds of fake reviews. *www.FlipKey.com*

• **Wyndham Vacation Rentals** features more than 90,000 properties, mostly in the US and Europe—especially in the UK. Unlike the sites above, which list properties on behalf of property owners and property-management companies, WyndhamRentals.com lists properties that Wyndham—one of the world's largest hotel companies—has an exclusive deal to manage on behalf of property owners. That means travelers can book stays online without having to contact a separate owner or manager to confirm availability. Guests have access to Wyndham's customer service department if they encounter any problems. *www.WyndhamRentals.com*

• **Zonder** offers about 10,000 properties, mainly in North America, Central America and the Caribbean. It has a toll-free customer service phone number in case travelers have questions or experience problems. It offers a guarantee that it will find alternate accommodations or issue a refund if a property's location or size is grossly misstated. Many Zonder listings feature extensive photos and video, making it easier to judge whether a property is right for you. Zonder does not charge travelers any added fees. *www.Zonder.com*

EVALUATING RENTALS

• **Favor vacation rental listings that feature lots of photos or videos of the property**—it indicates that the property owner or manager has nothing to hide.

• **Carefully read the property description**—and any reviews left by previous guests—before booking a stay.

Warning: Some property owners post reviews of their own properties. But Airbnb reviews are particularly likely to be legitimate because the site allows only people who actually have booked a stay at a property to review it.

• **Be extremely wary of rentals that ask renters to wire payments.** Once a payment is wired, there is no recourse if the property is not as described—or, worse, if the "property owner" actually is a scammer. Instead, rent from those who accept credit card or PayPal payments—and if you pay with PayPal, make sure that your PayPal account is linked to a credit card. Credit cards offer consumer protection in case of fraud or misrepresentation.

Worth asking...

• **Where, precisely, is this property located?** If you can get a specific address before booking—or at least a specific block—you can confirm that the rental is as close to the beach or downtown as its listing suggests. You also can use Google Maps' satellite and street view functions to examine the area.

• **What is included...and what isn't?** Some vacation rentals provide nice extras such as bikes or kayaks...while others don't even provide basics such as free towels, sheets, parking, Wi-Fi and a phone. Some have comfortable king-size beds, while others have lumpy mattresses on the floor or sofa beds. If you're renting on an upper floor, confirm that there is an elevator if you need one.

10 Secrets That Hotels Don't Want You to Know

Peter Greenberg, travel editor for NBC's *Today* show and chief correspondent for the Discovery network's Travel Channel, Studio City, California. He is author of *Hotel Secrets from the Travel Detective* (Villard) and editor of the newsletter *Travel News Today. www.travelnewstoday.com*

You want a hotel to be your home away from home, but many aspects of hotel pricing and policy are anything but homey. *Here's what you need to know...*

GETTING A ROOM

• **You get the best rate by calling the hotel's local number,** not the 800 number, which usually links callers to an off-site centralized call center. Instead of asking for the reservations desk, ask to speak with the manager on duty, the general manager or the director of sales. These people have the authority to negotiate room rates.

It's often possible to beat a hotel's best advertised price by 20%, particularly if you call just a few days before your visit. First, shop around for the best deal on a third-party Internet travel site, such as Expedia.com or Hotels.com. Don't take the deal—just jot it down.

Then call the hotel and explain to a manager or director that you know these Web sites mark up room prices by 20% to 40%. Tell the manager you would like to split the difference—say you'll pay 20% below the price you found online. Unless the hotel is filled to capacity, the manager is likely to take you up on your offer.

• **Everything is negotiable.** Think parking is overpriced? If the lot looks half empty, offer less than the daily rate. Planning to make a lot of phone calls? Some hotels offer a per-day flat fee for long-distance in the US and local calling—usually $9.95—but you must ask for it.

• **Rooms are available even when a hotel has no vacancies.** In any large hotel, a few rooms usually are listed as "out of order" at any given time. The problem might be something as simple as a stain on the carpet or a chair that has been sent out for repairs. If you're desperate for a last-minute room in a hotel that claims to have none available, tell the manager you are willing to take an out-of-order room that has only a minor problem. You might even be able to negotiate a better rate, since the room would otherwise sit empty.

• **"Guaranteed" rooms really aren't guaranteed.** When you make a hotel reservation, you often are asked to "guarantee" your room with a credit card—but there's still a chance that the hotel will give away your room if you arrive late. Providing a credit card number improves the odds that your room will be held—but it still pays to call to confirm that you're coming if you won't arrive until after 9 pm.

SAFEGUARDING VALUABLES

• **A thief takes one credit card, not your entire wallet.** It's no secret that crime is common in hotels. The new twist is that some hotel thieves now take just one credit card when they find an unguarded wallet in a room—and leave everything else untouched. Often, the victim doesn't notice the card is missing until the credit line is maxed out.

Travel only with the credit cards that you really need, and check your wallet carefully if you accidentally leave it unattended.

• **Your bags aren't safe with the bellhop.** Even in elite hotels, luggage can be stolen right off the luggage carts in the lobby. Though these bags theoretically are in the possession of the bellhop, the hotel assumes no legal responsibility for the loss.

If your bag is going to sit for more than a few minutes, ask that it be placed in a secure room. Keep valuable items in the hotel safe.

Helpful: High-end luggage might impress fellow travelers, but it also impresses thieves. The cheaper or uglier your luggage looks, the greater the odds that a thief will target someone else.

• **It pays to tip the housekeeper every day.** Exchange a few pleasant words with the housekeeper if you see him/her—and leave a $2 or $3 tip each day. You'll get better service—housekeepers are the most overworked, underpaid, underappreciated individuals in the hotel, so any gesture will be appreciated.

Knowing the housekeeper also reduces the chances that your room will be burglarized. Dishonest housekeepers are less likely to target guests they have met. If a thief enters your room while it is being cleaned and pretends to be you—a common ruse—the housekeeper will be able to spot the impostor.

MORE INSIDER SECRETS

• **Hotel rooms are infested with germs.** Certain items in hotel rooms never get cleaned. The biggest trouble spots include the TV remote control, telephone and clock/radio. Travel with a package of antibacterial wipes, and clean these items when you arrive.

Also, while reputable hotels provide fresh linens, bedspreads might be cleaned only once every few months. Remove them from the beds as soon as you check in. Ask for clean blankets as soon as you arrive.

• **Lost-and-found is a great resource for cell-phone users.** If you use a cell phone, odds are that someday you'll forget to bring your recharging cord or lose it in transit. If you're staying at a hotel, there's no need to buy a replacement. Recharging cords are the number-one item left behind in hotel rooms. Most hotels are willing to lend cords from their lost-and-found—but guests rarely ask.

• **Not all concierges are really concierges.** A true concierge is the most connected person in town. He/she can get tickets to sold-out events...reservations to popular restaurants... prescriptions filled in the middle of the night... even a new heel on a shoe by 8 am. (A tip of $10 to $20 usually is appropriate—more if the concierge really worked miracles.) But not all hotels that advertise "concierge service" truly offer it. Many simply assign a regular hotel employee the role each shift.

An elite concierge wears a gold key on his lapel. It's the symbol of Les Clefs d'Or—French for "Keys of Gold"—a prestigious international concierge organization.

Top Food Critic Tells How to Enjoy Restaurants Even More

Bryan Miller, former food critic of *The New York Times*, who used to dine out more than 450 times a year. He is author of several books on New York City eateries and coauthor of *Cooking Basics for Dummies* (Wiley).

Having a great time at a restaurant depends on many factors—the table, the service, the food, the ambiance, etc. With just a little advance planning, you can greatly improve the odds of enjoying your dining experience.

In the 13 years that I spent as a restaurant critic—mostly at *The New York Times*—and dining out more than 450 times a year, I picked up some inside moves that you can use...

• **Become a regular.** Restaurants are not democratic institutions. You can become an insider at the restaurants you like by going to them with some regularity, tipping well and chatting with the owner or maitre d' so he/she gets to know you.

• **Finding somewhere new.** There are more than 23,000 restaurants in New York City alone. Even the average avid diner's universe is rarely more than a dozen. So how can you find somewhere new?

Just walk in—even if you have no plans to eat there. It is amazing how much you can deduce about a restaurant just by spending a minute inside. Is the room lively? Romantic? Suitable for discreet business conversations? Are the patrons enjoying themselves? Is the menu appealing and original? Does the dining room smell good?

• **Getting a table at trendy restaurants.** That ultrahot, hard-to-get-into place-of-the-moment may not be all that hard to get into. Booked to the gills though they may be, great establishments also find themselves with empty tables on weekdays—and even on weekends—from "no-shows."

If you are willing to take a chance, you can walk in without a reservation at 8 p.m. or later. A restaurant generally holds a table for about 25 minutes, so by that time you may get the table from no-shows who had reserved for 7 p.m. or 7:30 p.m.

Note: When you have reservations and are going to be more than 15 minutes late, a phone call to the restaurant is greatly appreciated. Chances are you will be remembered as a considerate customer and the restaurant will respond in kind.

• **Practical tipping.** This is the most confusing aspect of eating out. Unless you wind up wearing half your meal or are ignored by the waiter, a standard 15% tip on the total pretax bill is expected. If service is exceptionally good, a tip of 20%—or more—is appropriate.

Payment for captains, who usually supervise teams of waiters, varies. In older and traditional establishments, captains often receive substantial salaries and keep all of their tips. In most new restaurants, captains earn only slightly more than waiters—and also depend on tips (which are often pooled) for much of their income.

The rule of thumb for restaurants with captains is 15% to 18% of the pretax total for waiters plus 5% for captains.

If, however, you want to single out a particular captain or waiter for extraordinary work, you can hand him cash upon leaving and say something like, *Thank you...this is for you.* The amount, usually $10 to $20, should be commensurate with the bill.

Maitre d's do not usually receive tips unless they have performed specific favors, such as finding you a table on a busy night. In that case a cash gratuity is warranted, usually from $10 to $20.

Finally, here is a tactic that is rarely employed but can be astoundingly effective in making points with your favorite dining spot. One evening about 12 years ago, I was working as a chef's assistant in a French restaurant when the owner came back and placed a bottle of champagne before us. The Smiths (I don't recall their real name) want to thank you for a great meal, he said.

You can imagine how we took care of the Smiths on their subsequent visits.

• **Strategic complaining.** Restaurant owners have an adage—A happy customer tells 10 friends...an unhappy one tells 20.

The last thing restaurateurs need is an ugly brouhaha in the dining room. They are more inclined to settle any reasonable complaint on the spot—that is, if they are approached with civility, not animosity.

Bring your complaint to an authority, either the manager or the owner. Waiters often have no authority to act above a certain level, so don't waste your time fighting with them.

A well-run establishment will try to make amends for long delays in seating (say, more than 20 minutes) by buying you drinks or perhaps offering a complimentary course or a bottle of wine.

If you do not get satisfaction on the spot, the best recourse is to write a calm, reasonable letter to the owner. Countless times I have seen owners respond with a phone call or a letter and an invitation to return for dinner on the house. This is good customer relations and good business.

• **Having it your way.** If you have a special request for a restaurant—say, a vegetarian meal—you should ask when you make the reservation, not when you show up. Doing that at the last minute on a busy night can test the patience of the most genial chef.

Occasionally you may crave a simple dish—perhaps a hamburger or pasta with only olive oil and garlic, neither of which is on the menu. In that case, it isn't out of line to ask on the spot if it can be done.

• **Getting a good table.** If you are ushered to a table you don't like—actually, there should not be any undesirable tables in good restaurants—politely ask the maitre d' if anything else is available.

Restaurants are more flexible in seating than they admit. You may have to wait a bit, but if it enhances your experience it is worth it.

• **Beyond Beaujolais.** Those who are uncomfortable choosing a wine should ask the waiter for his suggestion. Be careful to always specify the price range.

The standard markup for wine is twice what you would pay in a wine shop...about three times wholesale.

What if you do not like the bottle or the glass of wine that you selected?

If it is off, the restaurant must take it back. If the wine is perfectly fine but not to your liking, tell the waiter. If a restaurant has any class at all, it will replace the wine without comment.

The same applies to food. If you are unhappy with a dish—even if it is well-prepared—you should talk to the waiter or the manager.

As in the wine example, a professional restaurateur would never risk alienating a customer for the price of one dish.

• **Good eating on a budget.** Many restaurants today are offering remarkable bargains during the week with prix fixe lunches and dinners. Always ask if there is a special deal like that.

Even better bargains can be had by those who are willing to dine at off hours, say, before 8 p.m. or after 10 p.m. The special menus come and go, so it is always worthwhile for patrons to ask if any exist.

How to Avoid Lines At Theme Parks

When taking kids to a theme park, visit on a weekday— attendance will be lower. Always start at the back of the park when it opens and work toward the front—moving against the crowds. Plan to ride the popular attractions as soon as the park opens—or after 6 p.m., when crowds thin out.

Also helpful: Be sure to dress in comfortable cotton clothing that dries quickly after a water ride or rain shower.

Scott Ahlsmith, executive vice president, global technology, Virtuoso, a leisure travel network.

9

Train Your Brain To Thrive

Stop Saying "I'm Fine" When You Can Break Out and Be Great!

We are all guilty of it. Someone asks you the question "How are you doing?"—and you say, "I'm fine."

Here's the problem with saying you're "fine'"—it's probably not true. Right now, in these tough economic times, the majority of us are far from fine. Most of us are dissatisfied, frustrated and stressed out.

The problem for most of us is that while we may want to change something about our lives, the idea of change is just too daunting. It seems easier not to change, even if we are not truly content.

As we age, we are more likely to ignore the natural desire to change and grow. Our routines become increasingly ingrained, and we start to believe that the opportunity to make major changes has passed us by. If you say, "It is what it is" when you think about your life—consider this a wake-up call. You are destined for more.

The good news is that you don't have to take major action to feel a major impact on your happiness. In fact, if you can find something new and enjoyable to do with just 6% of your waking hours—that's around one hour per day or one afternoon per week—your entire life will be more satisfying.

Here's how you can go from saying you're "fine" to feeling absolutely great about your life.

ADMIT WHAT YOU WANT

Reflect on what you really want. We all know what we want. We just do a darn good job convincing ourselves that we can't have it. Blame your brain. It talks you out of doing

---

Mel Robbins, who stars in the new A&E television program *Monster In-Laws* and hosts the syndicated radio show *The Mel Robbins Show.* She is a lawyer turned life coach who trained under Lauren Zander, cofounder and chairman of The Handel Group (*www.HandelGroup.com*). Based in Sherborn, Massachusetts, Robbins is author of *Stop Saying You're Fine* (Crown Archetype). *www.MelRobbins.com*

anything that's different from your normal routine.

Have you ever driven your car to the store and thought, Oh my gosh, I don't remember driving here? Your brain was on autopilot.

Your brain loves autopilot because it doesn't have to work very hard. When you have an impulse to change or take new action, your brain will do anything to convince you not to do it and instead stay with your normal routine.

So the first step to combat your autopilot is to ask yourself, What do I really want?

Just pick the first thing that jumps into your head. Is it to lose 50 pounds? Start a nonprofit? Find love again? Repair a relationship with a sibling? Climb Mount Everest? I guarantee that there's at least one thing you would love to do.

But be on guard—as soon as you lock onto one idea, your brain will come up with all kinds of reasons to tell you that it's a horrible idea. Ignore your brain, and just stick with the first idea.

BE SPECIFIC

Now, make your goal as specific as possible so that it starts to feel more real and will be easier for you to accomplish. *Examples...*

I want to fit into pants with a 34-inch waist is more likely to lead to weight loss than I want to be in better shape.

I want to spend time each week helping children who don't have enough to eat is more likely to lead to volunteering with a charity than I want to do something that helps people.

MAP OUT A PLAN

The key to getting what you want is simply starting! Most people never even start. They think and think and just can't get out of their heads.

To help you get out of your head, you are going to create a map to show you the many actions that you could take to explore what you want. This map should be a page full of circles, each containing an action that would push the idea forward. *Here are some suggested actions...*

• **Approximate your dream.** Come up with smaller ways to simulate the bigger idea.

Example: If you want to open a catering business, start by making fancy cakes for your friends or getting a booth at the local farmers' markets. These experiences will serve as training for your larger dream.

• **Follow a path that is already blazed.** There are people in the world who have what you want and are telling their stories to the world. Follow them on Twitter...become their fans on Facebook...read their blogs and books...and follow what they did.

Example: If you aspire to start a business, pick up one of the several hundred books written by people who have done just that. One of my favorites is Kitchen Table Entrepreneurs (Basic Books).

• **Join a group.** Join and attend meetings of organizations related to what you desire. You will gain the contacts, ideas and inspiration that you need to keep taking action.

• **Get a PhD—but not literally.** I'm talking about educating yourself. Make yourself an expert on the topic of your interest. For anything you wish to do, there are books, blogs and online courses by credentialed experts on the subject. Even iTunes has an entire university of podcasts that you can tap into for free.

So if your goal is to write a book, your map should include such actions as join a writers' group...read about Stephen King...ask my friend who is published for advice...take a writing class...subscribe to a publishing industry magazine...set up a writing area in my home...write every day for 30 minutes.

THE BIGGEST OBSTACLE TO CHANGE IS YOU

Now that you know exactly what actions to take, the only thing standing in your way is you and your brain. *Keep in mind the following...*

1. You will never feel like doing what you need to do to have what you want. Your brain just doesn't work that way, so stop waiting to feel like it. Make a point to do what you do not feel like doing. Then you'll have everything you've ever wanted.

2. Your brain will kill any impulse to take action within five seconds. You must adopt the five-second rule. If you find yourself momentarily inspired to take action—I should call so-and-so...I should sign up for...I should read...—you must immediately take action. If you don't, your brain will kill the impulse to act.

3. Use process simulation. Scientists have proved that when you visualize yourself engaged in taking action, your brain will be tricked into doing it.

Examples: If you are thinking about exercising, visualize what you would see if you were running—the street, the trees, the birds. If you want to find love, visualize being out on that date—picture the table at a restaurant, what you are eating, the face of your partner.

The bottom line is that you deserve to have everything you desire. The only thing standing between you and what you desire is you. It's time to stop saying you're fine. It's time to get what you deserve.

Retrain Your Brain and Break Free from the Patterns That Are Holding You Back

Rebecca Gladding, MD, staff psychiatrist with the Veterans Administration California Healthcare System. She recently served as a clinical instructor and medical director of the UCLA Adult Inpatient Eating Disorders Program. She is coauthor of *You Are Not Your Brain: The 4-Step Solution for Changing Bad Habits, Ending Unhealthy Thinking, and Taking Control of Your Life* (Avery).

Habits are hard to break because of the way the brain is wired. Each time you repeat a harmful behavior—overeating, overspending, procrastinating or something else—the brain circuits involved in that action become stronger. The brain associates the action with the situation that gave rise to it, such as being under stress. Over time, the brain becomes hardwired to choose that behavior automatically any time a similar situation arises.

Example: If you reach for a sugary snack whenever you are worried about a project at work, after a while, you may crave sugar the moment that you start feeling anxious about anything anywhere.

That's the bad news. *The good news:* You can rewire your brain to choose constructive habits...

STEP 1: RELABEL

Negative habits are triggered by deceptive brain messages—thoughts, beliefs and impulses that run counter to your positive, healthy intentions. These thoughts and urges are accompanied by unpleasant emotions or physical sensations such as anger, sadness, anxiety or fatigue. Because the discomfort is so intense, you are driven to get rid of it as fast as you can, usually by indulging in an unhealthy habit. This brings temporary relief but in reality makes the situation worse—each time you give in, you further strengthen the brain pathways that connect the thought or urge with the bad habit.

Relabeling means recognizing your impulses and negative thoughts as deceptive brain messages and calling them what they are. It means simply noting to yourself what is happening, such as, *I am having a craving even though I just ate 30 minutes ago* or *My boss just yelled at me, and because of that, now I need some chocolate.* The more you are aware of these habits, the more opportunities you have to stop acting on them.

Becoming aware of these messages can be challenging at first. *To develop your ability to relabel...*

- **Practice making mental notes.** Any time you feel "off" or uneasy in some way, notice what is going on in your body or mind, and pick a simple word or phrase to describe it. For example, if you notice that you are thinking about a conversation with a friend that went awry—when you really need to be working—say to yourself, *Mind wandering.* If you are having physical symptoms, such as heart pounding, shakiness, feeling a pit in your stomach, note this as anxiety. The key is to snap yourself back into awareness—which is the first step toward doing something about the situation in a healthy, productive way.

• **Focus on your breathing.** One way to enhance your ability to notice what's happening in a moment-to-moment way is by focusing on your breath. For five minutes, sit in a quiet place, close your eyes and simply pay attention to your breath as you inhale and exhale. What you will find as you try to do this is that your brain is constantly running, thinking about plans for later in the week or stressing about what you have to do today. Whenever you realize that you have become lost in thought in these ways, say to yourself, *Thinking* or *Planning* or *Wandering*, then gently turn your focus back to your breathing.

Do this focused breathing exercise once a day, and gradually extend the length of time to 20 or 30 minutes.

STEP 2: REFRAME

As you become aware of deceptive brain messages, you can begin changing your perception of their importance. You do this by reframing—challenging your default response.

Reframing does not mean denying the existence of a thought or impulse or judging yourself for having it. Instead, you look at the thought from a new perspective and diminish its importance so that you do not automatically react in your habitual way.

Example: *I feel upset right now, but that doesn't mean I have to have a cigarette* (or that I am a bad person because I am craving one).

To change your perspective...

• **Use distancing phrases.** When you notice a deceptive brain message, say to yourself, *That's not me, it's just my brain*...or *Oh, that's just mental chatter*...or *I'm having a bad brain day.*

• **Look for thinking errors.** We often make inaccurate assumptions about difficult situations and painful feelings. To uncover these erroneous, unhelpful thoughts, ask yourself nonjudgmental questions, such as, *What is it about this situation that is upsetting me? What am I telling myself about what is happening? What are some other interpretations?*

Common thinking errors include...

All-or-nothing thinking: Seeing situations and people in extremes, such as perfect or hopeless, all good or all bad.

Worst-case thinking: Assuming that something terrible inevitably is going to happen.

Discounting the positive: Ignoring your good qualities and failing to notice or take seriously other people's positive reactions toward you.

• **Be compassionate with yourself.** Write down the deceptive brain message—the thought, sensation or impulse—that is bothering you. Then ask yourself what a kindhearted friend would advise or think.

• **Use the 15-minute rule.** When you experience an especially powerful impulse, try to wait 15 minutes before you act. Then if you still cannot resist the urge, slowly and mindfully engage in the activity that your deceptive brain message is insisting upon.

Important: Do not try to talk yourself out of an uncomfortable feeling. Simply examine it. You are training yourself to be less frightened of discomfort, to learn that it will pass and that it is not such a big deal.

STEP 3: REFOCUS

Once you have relabeled and reframed a deceptive brain message, you may find it surprisingly easy to actively shift your attention to a healthy, constructive activity—even as your deceptive thoughts are urging you to act in your old, habitual way. By refocusing repeatedly, you weaken the brain circuits associated with your cravings and retrain your brain to choose healthier responses when you are stressed or sad.

The best refocusing activities are ones that engage and interest you. If they require strategy or learning something new, they will be even more effective, but any wholesome activity that you enjoy is fine.

Examples: Do a crossword puzzle... read...exercise...call a friend...play with a pet...sing a song...pursue a hobby...cook a healthy recipe.

If you are at work, refocus on a task that you can accomplish quickly or that is less demanding.

What makes this step powerful is that you allow uncomfortable sensations and impulses to be present...but then you act constructively anyway. You are learning that the messages do not have to dominate your attention or control your actions. You are training your brain to create new associations between thoughts and healthy actions. This takes patience.

STEP 4: REVALUE

The final step is really about gaining perspective and the strength to believe in yourself. Each person gets there at his/her own pace, and when you do, you can look at the deceptive brain message and unhelpful impulses and simply say to yourself, *This is nothing more than the feeling of a deceptive brain message. I do not have to act on it, and it does not define me.* The more you are able to relabel, reframe and refocus, the more empowered you will be to dismiss those deceptive brain messages and move on with your life in a positive direction—one that you define. That's the essence of revalue and the goal of the four steps.

The Surprising Secret of Willpower

Roy F. Baumeister, PhD, professor at Florida State University, Tallahassee, and director of the school's social psychology department. The Institute for Scientific Information lists him among the most influential psychologists in the world. He is coauthor of *Willpower: Rediscovering the Greatest Human Strength* (Penguin).

Today, more than ever, we're bombarded with temptations. We can start to work on a project, but our attention can be diverted in an instant by our computers or smartphones. In a recent study, researchers found that people spend about four hours a day resisting desires—that's about one-quarter of their waking hours. Common desires include the desire for leisure, to eat and to sleep.

But resisting desire can be the key to success in life.

Example: In the 1960s, Stanford University psychologist Walter Mischel, PhD, tested preschoolers' ability to resist eating marshmallows. When Mischel and his colleagues tracked down those now-grown preschoolers decades later, they discovered that the kids who had the self-control to wait to eat their marshmallows grew into adults who earned higher salaries, had better relationships, were in better physical shape, had higher self-esteem and were less likely to be addicts than their peers who couldn't wait to eat the treat.

Most people associate the word willpower with the Victorian notion of denying oneself pleasure. What it actually means is having the strength to persevere in the face of challenges. It is all about self-control, whether it is controlling emotions or resisting the many temptations that cross our paths every day.

But everyone's willpower varies from day to day—and even over the course of a single day—often for reasons that are within our control. *And despite the importance of willpower to our lives, few people understand how it works and how it can be increased...*

LIMITED WILLPOWER RESERVES

We draw from a limited pool of willpower each time we force ourselves to resist temptation, control our emotions or focus our thoughts.

Example: A study by University of Toronto researchers found that test subjects who were instructed to control their emotions while viewing upsetting clips from documentaries had trouble controlling their reactions and making good decisions afterward. Test subjects who were not asked to control their emotions while watching the clips did not have this trouble.

It's important not to overtax your willpower reserves. The more things we attempt that require significant willpower, the greater the odds that we will run short of willpower and fail at all of them.

Example: If you made New Year's resolutions to quit smoking, lose weight and find another job, pick only one of these to pursue at a time.

THE POWER OF AUTOMATIC PILOT

Developing good habits is crucial to willpower. In 2011, Dutch researchers conducted an analysis of studies on people who had greater-than-normal self-control. They were surprised to discover that high-self-control individuals tended not to use large amounts of willpower to control their day-to-day behavior. Rather, these high-self-control individuals generally expended much of their willpower establishing positive habits. Once positive habits had become routine, they no longer needed to rely on their willpower to do the right thing—the habit essentially did the right thing for them.

Example: High-self-control employees generally excel at meeting deadlines because they have developed the habit of working productively even when deadline pressure is low.

GOOD HABITS

Four strategies to create autopilot habits and reduce the demands on your day-to-day willpower supplies...

• **Break unloved tasks into small components, and make them part of your daily routine.** Stop forcing yourself to spend hours at a time doing things you dislike, whether that's cleaning your house or searching for a better job. Instead, spend just 30 minutes on such tasks—but do so every single day and at the same time every day. Establishing this routine will require significant willpower, but once it is in place, it will become like brushing your teeth—something you just do without thinking very much about it.

• **Keep temptations out of sight and out of reach.** Every time we see a temptation, we must expend willpower to resist the urge to indulge. Conserve willpower by making a habit of positioning these temptations—or yourself—where you will see them less.

Example: If you're trying to drink less, find a new route home from the office that doesn't take you past your favorite bar.

• **Make automatic "precommitments."** Precommitments are steps taken now that reduce the need for willpower later.

Examples: Arrange to have a portion of your paycheck deposited directly into an investment account to avoid the temptation to spend that money. Sign a "commitment contract" with stickK (*www.StickK.com*), a free Web site founded by Yale economists. The Web site lets users set personal goals, name their own referees to monitor their progress, then choose the punishment they will incur if they fail—perhaps a financial contribution to a politician they dislike.

• **Create "implementation intention"**—that is, form precise plans for how you will handle specific temptations that might come up before they come up. Psychologists have found that avoiding temptation requires significantly less willpower when such plans are in place.

Example: Before going to a party while on a diet, tell yourself, *If there is food at this party, I will eat only vegetables.*

THE SURPRISING ROLE OF BLOOD SUGAR

Psychologists have found that when people's blood sugar levels fall, their willpower falls, too. Similarly, people who have *hypoglycemia*—the predisposition to low blood sugar—are predisposed to have chronically low willpower.

Example: A Finnish study found that prisoners' glucose (sugar) tolerance levels predicted with 80% accuracy whether the prisoners would commit violent crimes again after release.

Sugary foods provide a quick spike in blood sugar and willpower, but this soon wears off. To boost willpower over a longer term, regularly consume foods that are low on the Glycemic Index, such as vegetables, nuts, raw fruits, fish, lean meat and poultry. The Glycemic Index is available at *www.GlycemicIndex.com.*

• **Postpone difficult discussions and projects that require willpower until after a good meal.** Avoid the temptation to skip meals when you're busy. Any time that you save by not eating is likely to be more than offset by a reduced ability to make prudent decisions. *Also...*

• **Sleep or meditate.** A good night's sleep reduces the body's demands for glucose and improves its ability to make use of the glucose already in the bloodstream. There is some evidence that meditation can provide similar benefits.

• **When you're sick, postpone major decisions.** When you're sick, your immune system requires much of the glucose in your bloodstream. That leaves your brain deprived of glucose—and you with less willpower than usual.

Happiness Is About Choices

In a recent finding, people with the highest levels of well-being were those who, no matter how much money they made, were able to make choices, such as taking up a hobby, socializing with friends and family, and visiting new places.

Ronald Fischer, PhD, senior lecturer, School of Psychology, Victoria University of Wellington, New Zealand, and coauthor of a study of 420,599 people in 63 countries, published in *Journal of Personality and Social Psychology.*

Visualize to Memorize

Memory aid: Instead of trying to remember a specific thing that you have to do—such as repaying money borrowed from a coworker—visualize a scene in which you actually are doing it.

Example: Imagine taking the money out of your pocket or purse and handing it to the coworker at a specific location, such as the break room. Create the visualization before going to sleep—your brain will strengthen the image overnight, and you will be more likely to do the task the next day.

Mark McDaniel, PhD, professor of psychology, Washington University in St. Louis.

Love and Cancer

Did you know that married people are more likely to survive cancer than people who have never married? Never-married men were 35% more likely to die from their cancer between 2005 and 2007 (latest data available) than men who were married, divorced or widowed. Never-married women were 22% more likely to die from their cancer. The findings apply to 13 common cancers, including breast and prostate.

Astri Syse, PhD, researcher, Cancer Registry of Norway, Oslo, and leader of a study of more than 440,000 people from 1970 to 2007, published online in *BMC Public Health.*

10

Get the Best of Everything

How to Get Faster Emergency Medical Care

These days, most emergency rooms (ERs) are characterized by confusion and chaos. But inside knowledge of how the system works can get you better treatment.

First step: A triage ("sorting") nurse will assess the priority of your medical need. This person will look you over and then ask several questions. Be prepared to give your medical history succinctly and descriptively.

Planning: Before a medical emergency strikes, prepare a card that lists your medical history, including allergies or other chronic conditions, previous operations or serious illnesses, and the names and dosages of any medications you are currently taking. Keep it in your wallet or purse so you have it with you in case of an emergency.

Organize your thoughts so that you can clearly and accurately describe symptoms, time of onset and medications taken. Don't draw conclusions or give opinions unless you're a physician. And don't selectively omit information. If you have breathing or bleeding problems, indicate these first, firmly and clearly.

Reason: Life-threatening conditions are given priority.

After seeing the triage nurse—and sometimes even before—you must make arrangements for payment.

Helpful: On your medical history card, include information about your medical insurance coverage, date of birth, Social Security number and the name, address and phone number of your employer.

For complex conditions: Go to a large teaching hospital.

Advantage: University affiliation...best-trained staff...advanced technology that most other hospitals can't afford.

Harry Alberts, MSW, certified social worker, formerly with the New York State Department of Health.

Hospitals, including teaching hospitals, generally come in three varieties: Private for-profit, private not-for-profit and government-run public hospitals.

Myth: Public hospitals are the worst...some are, in fact, excellent.

Advantage of for-profit hospitals: They're usually less crowded because they generally turn away those who can't pay. Private not-for-profit hospitals, many of which receive funding that obligates them to serve the poor, and public hospitals tend to be crowded. If you're a high-priority case and your public hospital is a teaching hospital, you may get the best care there.

Important: Location of a hospital...and contracts that it may have to care for special groups. Hospitals that receive admissions from "combat zones" or are convenient to public transportation are likely to have a crowded emergency room. Hospitals that have a contract to treat emergency cases from a local mental hospital, center for the retarded, prison or shelter are also apt to be more crowded...often with high-priority cases. A low-priority case, such as a broken arm, might be treated faster at a walk-in emergency medical center—where it would be a high priority.

Hospitals that take Medicaid and Medicare (almost all) are always more crowded in areas where few doctors accept these types of insurance.

Reason: People simply go to the ER instead of a doctor's office.

Especially crowded time in all ERs: Saturday nights.

Inside information: If you arrive at a hospital by ambulance, you will usually receive a higher priority, even if you could have gotten to the hospital without the ambulance. If your condition is serious enough that taking an ambulance isn't frivolous, it's a good idea to call one.

Best: Arriving in the hospital's own ambulance, because you then automatically become one of the hospital's patients...and its patients receive priority.

Caution: If your insurance company determines that an ambulance was not medically necessary, you could be stuck with a huge bill.

For the same reason, the ambulance of a local volunteer unit or fire district is a good choice.

These people know the local ER personnel, and they are your neighbors. Contribute to their fund drives and post contribution stickers.

If your condition is very serious: Call the police—always dial 911. Police response with an ambulance—or transport by the police, if no ambulance is available—will facilitate matters at the hospital.

Helpful: Call the ambulance a bus, an inside term used by police. They may assume that you or a close relative is a cop and render service accordingly.

Get the Respect You Deserve in the Hospital

Charles B. Inlander, consumer advocate and health-care consultant based in Fogelsville, Pennsylvania. He was founding president of People's Medical Society, a consumer health advocacy group active in the 1980s and 1990s. He is the author of more than 20 books, including *Take This Book to the Hospital with You* (St. Martin's).

A hospital stay should be a time of healing. But all too often the experience erodes a patient's personal dignity.

Here's how to ensure that your needs are met and your dignity stays intact during hospitalization...

- **Ask about everything.** Let your doctors and nurses know that you plan to play a major role in your care. Ask about treatments and prognosis.

Don't worry that your doctor will think you lack confidence in him/her or that asking questions will cause resentment among the hospital staff, producing worse care.

Hospital patients who ask questions receive better and more respectful treatment, studies have shown. Questions encourage the medical staff to pay more attention to you. If medical personnel use jargon, ask them to explain it.

Always inquire about the medication you are given. If you receive a new drug, ask: "Why is this different from what I was getting before? Who ordered it?"

Asking questions also helps prevent medical mistakes.

• **Know who is treating you.** Hospital staffing levels have been drastically reduced. A person in a white uniform is not necessarily a doctor or nurse. In fact, it may be someone with almost no training, such as an orderly.

If you are concerned that the person is not fully trained in the procedure, refuse it. You'll be surprised at how quickly you receive treatment from someone more qualified.

• **Don't be shy about seeking help.** If no one responds to your call button within a few minutes, pick up the phone. Call the hospital operator and ask to be connected to the nursing station on your floor. When the phone is answered, say you need help in your room—immediately.

Important: If you have a complaint, you have the right to a response in a reasonable period of time. If you're not getting one, ask to see the hospital's "patient representative" or "ombudsman," who mediates between staff and patients.

If there is no patient representative or the representative isn't helpful, ask to see the medical director or the hospital administrator.

• **Have someone with you at all times.** If you are seriously ill or undergoing surgery, you probably won't have the energy or mobility to protect your rights. So have someone with you 24 hours a day. As long as your "advocate" is not interfering with the delivery of care, he/she has a right to be there.

• **Make sure the food is appetizing.** Notify the hospital dietician if fresh fruits and vegetables aren't served...the food doesn't arrive hot...the meals are served at unusual times for the convenience of the staff...or you lack sufficient time to eat.

Better: Have visitors bring food to supplement hospital meals. Make sure they are aware of any special dietary restrictions you have. Tell the doctor or nurse that this is what you intend to do.

• **Know your rights.** You have a right to say "no" to any medical procedure. You have the right to see your medical records. You have the right to check yourself out at any time, even against the advice of hospital personnel. You have the right to fire your doctor. You have the right not to be treated by a medical student, if you so choose.

The Best Cholesterol-Lowering Diet

John McDougall, MD, founder and medical director of the McDougall Wellness Center in Santa Rosa, California. *www.drmcdougall.com.* He is the author of many books, including *The McDougall Program for a Healthy Heart: A Lifesaving Approach to Preventing and Treating Heart Disease* (Plume).

The National Institutes of Health (NIH) has established guidelines calling for aggressive treatment for total cholesterol levels of 240 or higher.

The NIH also recommends aiming for a total cholesterol level of 200 or below.

With my patients, I go even further—I work with them to achieve and maintain a total cholesterol level *no higher than 150.* This is the point where heart disease stops progressing and begins to reverse itself. This is also a level of cholesterol where the risk of dying from heart disease is almost zero. If you settle for a total cholesterol of 200 instead, you still subject your arteries to toxins and plaque buildup—and risk a heart attack.

Here is how I helped my high-cholesterol patients get their levels under control...

CUT OUT ANIMAL PRODUCTS

The single most effective way to lower your blood cholesterol is to stop eating foods that contain cholesterol. In other words, avoid all animal products—red meat, poultry, shellfish, fish, eggs, dairy products and foods made with them.

As far as the health of your arteries is concerned, there is no "safe" amount in regard to the consumption of animal products.

Forbidden foods (many of which have long been perceived as permissible) include...

• **Fish and fowl.** These foods may raise cholesterol just as surely as beef or pork.

• **Low-fat or skim milk, cheese or other dairy products.** Even when the fat is taken out, the animal proteins in these foods can raise cholesterol levels and damage the artery walls.

• **"Free" fats such as margarine, corn oil, olive oil and canola oil.** These fats are easily oxidized in the bloodstream, making plaque likely to build up on artery walls.

If you follow a strict vegetarian diet for several months, you can lower your cholesterol levels by 25% or more. At the same time, blood levels of triglycerides, homocysteine, uric acid and other heart disease risk factors will also decline.

VEGETARIAN DELIGHTS

Giving up animal products does not mean you must eat poorly. The foods in my program are varied and delicious. They provide all needed nutrients in optimal amounts.

You can eat all you want of the following...

• **Whole grains,** including barley, brown rice, buckwheat, bulgur, corn, oatmeal and wheat, as well as noodles that are made from these sources.

• **Potatoes,** sweet potatoes and yams.

• **Root vegetables,** including beets, carrots and turnips.

• **Squashes,** such as acorn, butternut and zucchini squash.

• **Beans and peas,** including chickpeas, green peas, kidney beans, lentils and string beans.

• **Other vegetables,** such as broccoli, brussels sprouts, cabbage, celery, the darker lettuces, spinach, cucumbers, okra, onions, peppers and mushrooms.

• **Mild spices and cooking herbs.**

Eat only limited amounts of fruit and fruit juice (no more than three servings a day), sugar and other sweeteners, salt and fatty plant foods, such as peanut butter, seed spreads, avocados, olives and soybean products—including tofu. Simple sugars, even fruit and juice, raise cholesterol and triglycerides.

HEART-HEALTHY MENU PLAN

There are many excellent vegetarian cookbooks to choose from, but you don't have to be a gourmet to prepare heart-healthful meals. Start with potatoes, rice, beans or spaghetti, then add some low-fat, plant-based sauces and soups. Throw in a salad and bread, and you've got a meal. *Other tips...*

• **For breakfast,** toast, bagels, oatmeal, cereals, hash browns and pancakes (all made from the right ingredients) are all fine. Use rice milk or soy milk on cold cereal.

• **Sauté food in soy sauce,** wine or sherry, vinegar (rice or balsamic), vegetarian Worcestershire sauce, salsa, or lemon or lime juice.

• **Eat until you're satisfied...**and eat as often as you need to.

• **To boost feelings of fullness,** include more beans and peas in your meals.

CHOLESTEROL-LOWERING DRUGS

With a high-risk patient—someone who's had a heart attack or appears headed for a heart attack, coronary bypass or angioplasty—I would not wait several months to "see what happens." If his/her total cholesterol hasn't fallen to 150 after 10 days of healthful eating, I suggest supplementing the diet with drugs.

Between a vegetarian diet and cholesterol-lowering medication, virtually anyone's cholesterol can be brought down to 150.

First, try out some of these natural cholesterol-lowering "medications"...

• **Garlic** (up to 800 milligrams [mg], or one clove a day).

• **Oat bran** (two ounces a day) or oatmeal (three ounces, dry weight, a day).

• **Vitamin C** (2,000 mg a day).

• **Vitamin E** (dry form, 400 international units [IU] a day).

• **Beta-carotene** (25,000 IU a day).

• **Gugulipid.** Recently, I have been recommending this Indian herb (500 to 1,500 mg, three times a day).

• **Immediate-release niacin** is yet another potentially useful medication. But it can damage the liver, so it should be taken only under a doctor's supervision.

If the patient doesn't respond, I typically prescribe *simvastatin* (Zocor), *pravastatin* (Pravachol), *lovastatin* (Mevacor) or *fluvastatin* (Lescol). Since my patient may have to take this medication for years, it's important to match him/her with the drug that's most effective, but with the fewest side effects.

EXERCISE AND GOOD HABITS

While exercise isn't as crucial as diet, a brisk walk of at least 30 minutes each day will benefit your heart and arteries in many ways.

Exercise trains the heart to beat more efficiently...increases levels of HDL (good) cholesterol...lowers levels of triglycerides ...increases oxygen flow to your heart, brain, muscles and other tissues...and boosts the immune system.

As if you didn't know: Don't smoke. Limit your coffee consumption (both regular and decaffeinated raise cholesterol levels about 10%). Drink alcohol moderately if at all. Your arteries will thank you.

How to Cut Costs of Heart Disease, Cancer, Diabetes and Other Chronic Conditions

David Nganele, PhD, former president of DMN Healthcare Solutions, a health-education company based in New York City. He founded Harmony Health Communications, where he developed award-winning disease-management programs in cooperation with doctors, drug companies and community groups. He is author of several books, including The Best Healthcare for Less (Wiley).

A chronic disease can be financially devastating even for someone who has health insurance. Benefit limits are often reached before the condition is under control.

People without insurance may be forced to borrow money or sell assets when faced with such conditions as recurring cancers, heart disease, depression and diabetes.

Making lifestyle changes—quitting smoking, improving your diet and exercising—can reduce the need for medication for many conditions. In addition, sufferers can eliminate some costs entirely by understanding how hospitals, drug companies and doctors do business. *Most effective cost-saving strategies...*

AT-HOME CARE

• **Become an expert.** Learning all you can about your illness may help you discover lower-cost treatments and aspects of the condition that even your doctor may not know about. You'll also benefit psychologically from putting yourself in charge instead of relying solely on your doctor.

• **Contact associations specializing in your condition.** They can help you to locate low-cost treatment centers and suggest ways to prevent your condition from worsening.

Example: Adding supplemental chromium, magnesium and vanadium to your diet may help with diabetes.

Associations for several common illnesses...

• American Cancer Society. 800-227-2345, *www.cancer.org.*

• American Diabetes Association. 800-342-2383, *www.diabetes.org.*

• American Heart Association, 800-242-8721, *www.heart.org.*

• American Kidney Fund, 800-638-8299, *www.kidneyfund.org.*

• Depression and Bipolar Support Alliance. 800-826-3632, *www.dbsalliance.org.*

If you're unsure of the appropriate organization, contact the American Medical Association for a referral (800-621-8335, *www.ama-assn.org*).

• **Investigate alternative treatments, such as acupuncture and biofeedback.** Many now are covered by insurance. Even if they're not, they may cost less and be more effective than conventional treatments. For information, contact the federal government's National Center for Complementary and Alternative Medicine at 888-644-6226, *http://nccam.nih.gov.*

• **Buy drugs in large quantities to save on copayments.** Most insurers charge a copayment for each prescription, regardless of the drug's cost. Copayments today can be as high as $50.

Ask your doctor to write 90-day prescriptions, instead of 30-day. You will reduce your copayment by two-thirds.

Example: If you take eight prescription medicines—not unusual for someone with a chronic condition—and have a $30 copayment, your cost will fall by $1,920, or two-thirds—from $2,880 (8 x $30 x 12) to $960 (8 x $30 x 4).

If your insurance company won't allow more than a 30-day supply of a drug from a local pharmacy, ask your health insurer if it uses a mail-order drug service. They typically supply 90-day quantities. Most insurers prefer that you order by mail because it holds down their costs.

• **Ask your doctors for free samples.** Pharmaceutical companies give away billions of dollars worth of samples for doctors to pass on to patients. Don't be embarrassed to ask. If your doctor doesn't have samples, ask him to prescribe generic drugs. For all but a very small percentage of patients, generics are just as effective as brand-name drugs. If you do have insurance, you may have a smaller copayment for generic drugs.

Example: A patient who suffers from depression and doesn't have drug coverage typically pays about $800 for 90 tablets of Prozac in 40-milligram (mg) strength. The generic equivalent represents a saving of 30% or more.

• **Take part in a clinical trial.** Each year, thousands of people with chronic ailments receive free treatment by taking part in trials designed to assess new drugs and procedures. The drug industry or the National Library of Medicine–National Institutes of Health coordinates most of these trials. Contact 888-346-3656 or *www.clinicaltrials.gov* for more information.

Important: Participants are given a consent form explaining the trial. Read it, and ask questions before signing.

Some trials are *open*—all the participants are given the medicine being tested and are informed about the results of the trial at each stage.

Other trials are *double-blind*—the patients and the doctors aren't told who has received the drug and who has received the placebo. This prevents test results from being skewed by psychological factors.

Despite the risk that you won't receive any treatment, don't rule out a double-blind trial. If you take part in one, you have about a 50-50 chance of receiving cutting-edge medication.

Even if you get the placebo, doctors typically take you out of the trial if your condition worsens, so you can resume treatment on your own.

HOSPITAL-BASED CARE

• **When you are hospitalized, put your primary-care physician in charge.** Doctors who are unfamiliar with your health history might recommend costly, unnecessary procedures.

Primary physicians, as a rule, recommend fewer procedures than other doctors at a hospital. Your primary doctor is already familiar with your condition and may have tried a variety of treatments for you in the past.

You might even ask your primary physician to help check your hospital bill for inaccuracies. As a patient with a chronic illness, you need to be vigilant about not reaching insurance policy limits sooner than necessary.

• **Consider treatment at a teaching or government-run hospital or clinic.** These institutions usually charge patients according to their ability to pay. They can make sense for people with limited incomes, especially those who lack insurance or have passed their insurance limit.

Information: Health Resources and Services Administration, 888-275-4772. *www.hrsa.gov.*

• **Negotiate with the hospital and other providers.** Pay what you can now, and work out a payment plan for the rest. Or ask for a fee reduction. A hospital or doctor will nearly always compromise because reducing the bill may be cheaper than paying a collection agency or not collecting anything at all.

• **Get the opinion of more than one doctor before any procedure.** Second opinions increase your chances of finding less expensive—and perhaps more effective—treatment.

Example: Cancer treatments vary greatly in cost and outcome. Since few doctors are experts in all procedures, it's best to weigh the options with different specialists.

Many chronic disease sufferers don't get more than one opinion because they think that their insurance will not pay for a second opinion. In fact, most policies will pay for two or three consultations as long as the doctors are in the insurer's network of approved physicians.

Life Insurance Warning—Your Paid-Up Policy May Not Be Paid Up After All

Thomas J. Henske, CFP, CFS, a chartered life insurance underwriter, certified in long-term care, and a partner in the wealth-advisory firm Lenox Advisors, Inc., which has offices in New York, Chicago, San Francisco and Stamford, Connecticut. *www.LenoxAdvisors.com*

Today's low interest rates mean that many people who think they have fully paid-up whole and universal life insurance policies will one day receive some distressing news in the mail—there are insufficient funds in their accounts to keep their policies in effect.

When consumers purchase whole or universal life insurance, they typically are told that if they make payments of a certain size for a certain number of years, their policies will be fully paid up, with no additional payments required for a lifetime of coverage and death benefits for their heirs.

Trouble is, those payment schedules are not guarantees—they're just estimates based on the returns that insurance companies expect to earn by investing policyholders' payments in low-risk investments. The ultra-low interest rates paid by those low-risk investments in recent years have left many whole and universal policies that were written more than 10 years ago well short of their projected investment returns and therefore underfunded. (Less-than-stellar stock market returns mean many variable life policies written in the mid-to-late 1990s have fallen well short, too.) When that happens, any cash value that the policy has built up begins to erode—eaten away by the need to fund new premium payments.

Policyholders who receive notices of insufficient funds typically are given two options—make sizable additional payments or allow the policy to lapse, requiring no more payments but voiding the coverage. If a policy is allowed to lapse, the policyholder and beneficiaries will receive nothing despite all the money previously poured into the policy. Many of these policyholders now are retired and living on fixed incomes. The additional payments required to keep original coverage amounts can take a massive bite out of their nest eggs.

Example: A 72-year-old man who thought his $3 million universal life policy was completely paid up decades earlier, ensuring that his heirs would receive $3 million when he died, instead received a notice warning that he would have to pay an additional $50,000 per year for 10 years.

Helpful: There might be a third option—some policies allow policy- holders facing this situation to keep their policies in effect with a lower coverage amount. But insurance companies often do not mention this option unless policyholders know to ask.

What policyholders need to know now to protect their policies...

DON'T WAIT FOR NOTICE

Insurers typically send policyholders notices of insufficient funds only when their policies are on the verge of default. The companies have no incentive to send them out sooner—they would prefer that the policies lapse so that they never have to pay out the death benefits. The earlier that you identify such a problem, the smaller the annual payments required to keep your policy in effect.

What to do: Don't wait. Call or send a letter to your life insurance company's policyholder service department requesting your policy's "In Force Policy Pages." (A form or written request signed by the policy owner may be required.) You will receive paperwork projecting what the future looks like for your policy, including whether additional annual payments are likely to be required. Contact the agent who sold you your policy or the insurance company's policyholder service department for help interpreting this complex document.

MAKE AN INVESTMENT DECISION

If your paid-up status is in danger, you may feel angry about it, but resist the urge to allow the policy to lapse because of this anger. Instead, assuming that you can afford to make the additional payments, think of them as the cost of a new investment and the amount that the policy eventually will pay out as the investment's return. Compare that return to what you could earn from other safe investments. A financial planner can help with this analysis if necessary.

Example: If you must pay $40,000 a year for 10 years to keep a $1 million policy in effect, your $400,000 essentially is earning a 150% return ($600,000) over the remaining years of your life, which might be far better than you and your heirs could do with any other low-risk investment.

If you cannot afford to make the annual payments required, give your heirs the option of making them for you. As the beneficiaries of the policy, it might be in their financial interests to do so.

TRUSTEE TROUBLES

You are at risk if you are a trustee for a trust that contains an insufficiently funded life insurance policy. You could be sued if this policy lapses—even if you agreed to be a trustee only as a favor for a friend. Do not assume litigation is unthinkable because the trust belongs to a friend who would never sue you. You still could be sued by your friend's adult children, the future beneficiaries of the trust.

Bring the policy to a well-credentialed insurance expert, such as a Certified Life Underwriter (CLU), Chartered Financial Consultant (ChFC) or Certified Financial Planner (CFP), for review. Doing this should fulfill your fiduciary duty as trustee. This expert might charge $500 to $1,000 for his/her time—a fee that typically is paid by the trust—or he might audit the policy for free to build a relationship with a potential new client

Save Money on Almost Everything

Linda Bowman, author of the *Free Stuff & Good Deals* series of guides, including *Free Stuff & Good Deals for Your Kids and Free Stuff & Good Deals for Folks Over 50* (both from Santa Monica Press).

A few dollars saved here and there can add up very quickly. *Here are some resources that will help you cut costs without sacrificing...*

UTILITIES/ENERGY

- **For a free evaluation of your energy usage, call your local utilities company.** Many utilities also give away energy-saving devices, such as low-flow shower heads, water heater blankets and fluorescent bulbs.
- **Repair major appliances yourself.**

How: Contact customer service for instructions.

- General Electric, *www.geappliances.com*
- Whirlpool, *www.whirlpool.com*
- Electrolux, *www.electrolux.com*

- **Gather discounted (often free) firewood and Christmas trees from any of our 155 national forests.** Contact your regional office of the USDA Forest Service to find out the cost for a permit, which allows you up to 10 cords per household of downed or dead wood. At the going rate of about $150 a cord, this will save approximately $1,500. Go to *www.fs.fed.us*. Click on the state and forest near you, then "Passes & Permits."
- **Install a water restrictor for your shower.** It saves thousands of gallons of water a year. Check with your utility for a free restrictor.

HOME AND HEALTH-CARE PRODUCTS

- **Take advantage of refund/rebate offers.** Take the time to save UPC symbols, labels and receipts. The savings can easily reach hundreds of dollars a year.

Good source of offers: Supermarket and drugstore bulletin boards.

- **Ask for free samples at department store cosmetics counters.** Say you need to try products before you buy, and you'll receive handfuls of high-priced makeup, skin care products and fragrances.

Watch for: Fine print in magazine ads offering free samples of perfumes or moisturizers if you write or call an 800 number.

- **Have your hair cut, colored, permed or styled at a cosmetology school.** Students are closely supervised by expert instructors.

Savings: About 60% less than a salon. The average American woman spends approximately $400 a year at hair salons, so expect to save $240.

- **Get routine dental care at a dental school.** Services, including orthodontics, at the country's 56 dental school clinics are high quality and 60% less expensive than normal dentists' fees.
- **Ask your doctor for free samples of medications whenever you get a prescription.** Most doctors have plenty to give away.

HOME ENTERTAINMENT

- **Take advantage of free magazine offers.** Don't throw away subscription invitations from periodicals. Most publications will send you a free issue, and then begin your subscription unless you cancel.

Key: Write "cancel" on the invoice, and mail it back. The postage is almost always paid, and you owe nothing.

- **Use your public library** to borrow books, CDs, audiotapes, DVDs, even artwork.
- **Free publications from your favorite manufacturers.** Quite a few food companies offer free cookbooks, including Sargento Cheese, Jiffy Mix and Smuckers...as do trade organizations, such as the California Walnut Commissionand the Idaho Potato Commission.

Examples: Minwax Company of Upper Saddle River, New Jersey, offers free booklets on wood finishing...and United Van Lines of Fenton, Missouri, offers a free booklet called "Moving with Pets," as well as other brochures related to planning a move.

Check package labels for the location of company headquarters. Then contact the company's customer service department.

Simple Renovations that Can Transform Any Home

Jonathan and Drew Scott, hosts of *Property Brothers*, an HGTV program about renovating fixer-uppers, Wednesdays at 9:00 pm EST. Jonathan is a licensed contractor...his twin brother, Drew, a real estate agent. Together they own Scott Real Estate Inc., which has offices in Las Vegas and Vancouver and Calgary, Canada. *www.hgtv.com*

You might be surprised at how much you can change the character of your home—and make it much more attractive to potential buyers—without going broke doing it.

If you make changes that are popular with today's buyers, your renovation won't just provide you with a nicer home to live in—it will make the home easier to sell.

Here are eight renovations and modifications that you can enjoy now and that can help you sell your home in what remains very much a buyer's market...

- **Add a full glass wall.** Glass exterior walls provide three benefits that today's buyers love—they bring in massive amounts of natural light...make the home feel more connected to the outdoors...and make a small room feel bigger.

Replacing a 12-to-14-foot wall with floor-to-ceiling windows that slide open will cost around $15,000. Adding nice curtains or blinds sufficient to cover this window wall could add several hundred or more to the price, depending on the materials selected. Yes, that's a lot of money, but it really will turn the room into a distinctive selling point for the home.

Consider adding a patio and deck furniture right outside the sliding glass wall to create some outdoor living space. That's like adding a room to your home without the relatively high costs of an addition.

• **Remove interior walls in the main living space.** Today's home buyers like open floor plans with good sight lines. Ripping out some of the walls that separate the kitchen, dining area and living room could make an old, cramped home seem significantly more modern and spacious.

Costs will vary greatly depending mainly on whether the walls removed are load-bearing walls. Pulling down nonload-bearing walls and patching and repainting the resulting gaps in the drywall, ceiling and floor could cost as little as $500 to $1,000.

Removing a load-bearing wall could cost well into the thousands—perhaps as much as $10,000—depending on the size of the wall and the amount of structural work required.

Warning: Consult a contractor or residential structural engineer before removing any walls unless you have access to the blueprints and are absolutely certain that the wall is not load-bearing.

• **Combine two bedrooms of modest size into a master bedroom suite.** An impressive master bedroom suite featuring a big bedroom, spacious closets and a roomy master bath helps sell a home these days—more so than a large number of bedrooms. Perhaps that's because couples are marrying later and having fewer children.

It typically costs just a few thousand dollars to convert two small adjacent bedrooms into one big one. However, prices could climb into the low five figures if the project includes adding a new bathroom or completely remodeling an existing bathroom and/or if a load-bearing wall is removed.

• **Turn a dining room into an office.** Today's home buyers don't see much value in having multiple eating areas. If a home's kitchen is large enough for a full-sized table, consider alternative uses for the dining room.

It could become part of an open floor plan, as discussed earlier, but another option is to convert the dining room into an office. This might be as simple as framing a door into an open dining room entryway, which should cost well under $1,000.

Warning: Some people turn their dining room into an extra bedroom, but having a bedroom right next to the kitchen usually is an awkward configuration. An office is more appropriate in this location. Buyers with big families still can use the office as a bedroom if they like.

• **Add built-in storage.** Americans don't like stowing their stuff in dank basements or hard-to-access attics. That's one reason why many home buyers consider extensive built-in storage a big plus.

Woodworkers might charge tens of thousands of dollars to build custom cabinets, but there are more cost-effective options.

For example, Ikea's wardrobe systems are well-designed, stylish and affordable. On the Ikea Web site (*www.Ikea.com*), select "Bedroom," then "Bedroom storage" and finally "Wardrobes" to see the styles that are available. For a few thousand dollars, you can line an entire wall with these, then hire a drywall contractor for about $500 to add wallboard above and at the ends of the wardrobes so that they appear to be built-in components.

• **Add windows, skylights or solar light tubes** to bring more natural light into dark rooms. Older homes often have less sunlight than today's buyers like. Adding windows or skylights could be an option, depending on the layout of the home, but each one that you add could cost upward of $1,000, between the cost of the unit itself and the cost of professional installation.

Solar light tubes are a more affordable and versatile option. These use a small rooftop dome and reflective tube to pull a surprising amount of sunlight down into the house—even into interior rooms where adding windows and skylights is not feasible. From inside the room, these just look like overhead lights on the ceiling.

One light tube should be enough for a small room, though two or more might be needed in a large space. They can make a dark room sunny and bright for perhaps $500 or $600 apiece installed. Solatube is the nation's leading provider (888-765-2882, *www.Solatube.com*).

• **Replace your kitchen countertop.** Countertops are the single kitchen element most likely to influence a buyer's opinion of the room. Granite and quartz countertops convey a sense of high-end quality—even though they have come down significantly in price in recent years.

Shop carefully, and you now can find these for as little as $3,500, including installation, assuming that your kitchen is of average size.

Adding impressive new countertops above old, worn kitchen cabinets won't fool anyone, however. If your cabinets are showing some age but they still are in reasonable shape, you could paint them white and add attractive new hardware—big-box stores such as Walmart, Lowe's and The Home Depot sometimes sell bags of attractive brushed nickel cabinet hardware for as little as $1 per piece.

If your kitchen cabinets are beyond basic rehab, new prefab cabinets of reasonable quality can be found at big-box stores for as little as $3,000 to $4,000 for a complete kitchen update.

• **Replace old bathroom vanities.** The single most cost-effective way to make a bathroom seem more upscale is to install a vanity that has a granite or quartz top and dark-wood cabinets.

I've come across these for as little as $800 at Costco (*www.Costco.com*). Grab one if you see such a deal and the item seems right for your bathroom—that's less than you would normally pay for the granite top alone, and these vanities tend to sell out fast.

When It Pays to Pay More for a Camera... TV...Smartphone...

Rafe Needleman, editor at large at CNET, the leading technology news and reviews Web site. Based in San Francisco, Needleman has been a technology journalist for more than 20 years and previously served as manager of advanced technologies for ZD Labs and editor in chief of *Byte* magazine. He hosts CNET's weekly *Reporters' Roundtable* podcast about technology issues. *www.cnet.com*

The packaging of consumer electronics products often sports impressively long lists of the devices' features and functions. Product makers would like us to believe that it's worth paying extra for each of these. In reality, while some of the add-ons and abilities ballyhooed on electronics boxes are worth a higher price, others are just gimmicks that are worth next to nothing.

Here's how to spend your money wisely when shopping for five common consumer electronics products...

DIGITAL CAMERAS

• **Pay extra for a high-quality lens...but not for more megapixels.** Digital camera ads and packaging often trumpet a camera's impressively high number of megapixels. More megapixels means higher resolution, but unless you blow your pictures up to poster size, 10 megapixels is all the resolution that you really need—and the vast majority of cameras offer at least 10 megapixels these days.

Rather than put your money into additional resolution that you don't need, spend extra for a camera that features a faster lens, as measured by lens aperture, or "f-stop." The lower a lens' aperture, the better it gathers light, which means sharper and more natural pictures indoors and in low light.

Helpful: A camera's lens aperture often is expressed as a range, such as f/2.0–f/22. The number to compare is the lowest one mentioned, here f/2.0. That's the lens' largest, or "maximum," aperture, and remember, lower is better.

SMARTPHONES AND SMARTPHONE SERVICE PLANS

• **Pay extra for the smartphone with longer battery life...but not for the smartphone plan offering additional or unlimited data.** Smartphones can do lots of great things, but they can't do anything at all after their batteries die. And smartphones consume so much power that some can't even make it through a single day of heavy use, unlike conventional cell phones, which typically have enough battery life to last for a few days or longer on a single charge. The longer your smartphone's batteries last, the happier you are likely to be with your phone.

Examples: Smartphones that fared well in CNET's battery-life tests...

- Motorola Droid X2
- Samsung Infuse
- Motorola Atrix
- Apple iPhone 4
- Samsung Galaxy S 4G
- LG Optimus S.

Warning: As a rule of thumb, the battery-life estimate on a smartphone's packaging will overestimate its actual life by around three hours.

On the other hand, the vast majority of smartphone users find that their cellular-service provider's basic data plan—typically two gigabytes per month—more than meets their needs. You should pay extra for a data plan only if you intend to use your smartphone for large amounts of video streaming.

HDTV

• Pay extra for a larger HDTV or for one with a 120-hertz (Hz) refresh rate...but not for one too large for the room or for a refresh rate above 120 Hz. Bigger definitely is better when you're buying an HDTV—but only up to a point. A larger screen creates a more immersive viewing experience, but a large HDTV can be hard to watch in a small space.

To know how large a TV to buy: Measure the distance in inches from where the HDTV will be placed to where you will sit when watching. Divide this distance by 1.5 to find the largest diagonal screen size that you can comfortably watch there. (Divide by three, as well, to find the minimum screen size that will provide something approaching an immersive viewing experience.)

Also, consider an HDTV's refresh rate before buying. That's the number of times per second that the image on the screen is updated. It's worth paying extra to get a 120-Hz HDTV rather than a 60-Hz model, particularly if you watch sports. But don't pay any extra for a refresh rate above 120 Hz. Though manufacturers often trumpet higher figures, any improvement above 120 Hz is virtually imperceptible to human sight.

ENTERTAINMENT SYSTEMS

• Pay extra for audio and video components...not for the cables that connect them. A $400 audio or video component often is truly superior to a $200 one. But those $20 to $50 cables sold by electronics stores are no better than the cables available for $2 to $4 at Web sites such as Monoprice.com and Amazon.com.

These days, most audio and video components are connected by High-Definition Multimedia Interface (HDMI) cables—those cables that have flat metal ends that are inserted into slots on components. HDMI cables transmit digital signals. With digital, either the signal is transmitted or it isn't. There's no such thing as a staticky or low-quality connection, no matter what a salesperson might claim.

In other words, one HDMI cable essentially is just as good as the next regardless of the price you pay or where you buy it.

PERSONAL COMPUTERS

• Pay extra for additional memory...but not for an upgraded graphics or audio card. More storage memory will let you save more digital content such as photos and video on your computer, but another kind of memory—random access memory (RAM)—will boost the computer's speed and allow it to run more applications at the same time. How much RAM you need depends on how the computer will be used, but at the very least, upgrading from four to perhaps six or eight gigabytes of RAM is money very well-spent for most computer buyers.

The computer's performance will be significantly better, and the added cost is often as little as $20 to $30 for each gigabyte that you choose to add.

Another cheaper option is to buy aftermarket RAM from an independent Internet company, such as Crucial (*www.Crucial.com*). You then can install it yourself (or ask a tech-savvy friend or family member to help you with it).

On the other hand, the graphics and audio that come standard in computers these days usually are sufficient for most uses. Unless you play lots of graphically intense video games, it's probably not worth investing the $50 to $200 or more that upgrades tend to cost.

Get Your Hotel Room Upgraded for Free

Look up a specific high-end room prior to checking in, and then ask to be upgraded to that room by name, such as the honeymoon suite. Make the front desk clerk's job easier by being specific about the type of room you want, such as one with a pool view, instead of just asking for a better room. If there are problems with your room, ask to be upgraded because of the inconvenience. If it's a special occasion such as a birthday or anniversary, tell the front desk clerk.

Men's Health Magazine. www.MensHealth.com

How to See the Concerts And Shows That You Want To See Without Paying Scalpers' Prices

Angie Diehl-Jacobs, former executive of a California–based tour and concert promotion company for many of entertainment's top acts. She was head of marketing for one of California's largest music retailers, which operates ticket centers in many locations.

You don't have to spend a fortune or be buddies with an industry VIP to get great tickets to great shows and concerts. *Here's how to avoid paying scalpers' prices...*

• **Call out-of-town ticket centers.** Your calls will likely go through more quickly, since phone lines in cities other than where the concert is to be held won't be as tied up the moment tickets for an event go on sale.

In the ticket business, "subregions" are often linked to a larger region's ticket database, so your selection is the same as the person calling from the town of the event. Tickets on phone orders are typically mailed to you, so leave yourself enough time.

Example: If you're trying to get seats to a performance in Los Angeles, call the ticket company's phone line in San Diego, Las Vegas or even Phoenix.

Helpful: Call the ticket center before the on-sale date and ask whether it will have tickets on sale in the outer markets and which ones (they vary each time).

• **Go to a ticket center with the smallest lines.** Some ticket centers do massive business, while others have hardly anyone waiting.

helpful: A few days before your selected event goes on sale, stop by your local ticket center outlet. Ask a seasoned employee how many people are anticipated for that event's initial lineup.

Ask how long a line they've had for similar shows. Then ask if there's another store or outlet in their chain that may be less busy for that event.

Example: One record store may get long lines for country artists but few people for rock or pop.

Double-check that the store's ticket counter will be open at the designated sale time. Some stores may open their doors but not their ticket counters at that hour. Always stop by or call in advance to ask someone who knows—the ticket manager or store manager.

• **Go to the box office of the arena or theater an hour before show time.** Frequently, tickets that were on hold for VIPs, celebrities and industry executives aren't claimed by curtain time.

The remainder of unused tickets are returned to the box office for sale at the last minute. Unpaid COD or "will-call" tickets may also be released just after the show begins.

Be calm and clear when dealing with box office personnel. Many patrons turn into absolute maniacs at box office windows and are turned down.

If you're remotely pleasant and a genuine fan, you might get great seats—but you may miss a few bars of the opening act.

• **Buy season tickets.** While prices like $1,500 to $3,000 a seat may seem high for 25 or 30 shows per season, it's a lot cheaper if you take on partners.

Combine funds with a few friends or co-workers, then split up the shows on the schedule. The perks for season ticket holders are advance mailings and notifications, discount offers and more.

At some arenas, season ticket holders even have the option of reserving additional tickets before they go on sale to the general public. Other arenas offer preferred patrons exclusive parking, hospitality privileges or parties as part of the season ticket package.

• **Buy group tickets** if you're only interested in one event.

Helpful: Call the arena or theater, and ask to speak to the group sales or sponsorship director as far in advance of the ticket sale as possible.

Some arenas consider 20 tickets a "group sale." If you represent a number of people at your company, school or organization who would like to buy tickets to a single event, you may be able to place your order ahead of time, get a group discount or both.

You'll have to play collection agent and gather the funds, but it may be well worth the effort to see your favorite performer in a decent seat for a face-value ticket and a nominal service charge.

How to Get Free Admission to Concerts And Shows

Volunteer as an usher at concerts and plays. Ushers seat the audience before the show and after intermission, then help sweep up. You must arrive a little early and stay a bit late, but you are pretty much free to enjoy yourself during the performance. There often is an open seat. Promoters' names and phone numbers are generally listed on advertising posters. Call as far in advance as possible to ask if volunteer ushers are needed.

Shel Horowitz, Hadley, Massachusetts–based author of the electronic book *The Penny-Pinching Hedonist*, available from the Web site *www.frugalfun.com.*

Get Good Seats to Sold-Out Events

Dale Ratermann, former executive director of the Indiana Pacers Foundation, and Mark Andrew Zwartynski, former vice president of ticket sales for the NBA's Dallas Mavericks. They are coauthors of *Two on the Aisle: How to Get Tickets to Any Event, Anytime, Anywhere* (Masters Press).

The best seats to most events—whether it's a Broadway show, a major concert or a professional sports event—often go to corporate clients or friends of the performers.

But there are ways that anyone can get great seats—even when the box office tells you the event is sold out.

• **Invest in a package deal.** Choice seats in most stadiums, arenas and concert halls often go to subscribers or season ticket holders. Buying a package also guarantees the holder an opportunity to buy tickets for special events, such as postseason play-off games.

Most people aren't aware that they don't have to commit to the *maximum* number of home games or all of the concert season's Friday nights. A partial package will likely get you most of the same benefits.

One way to cut the cost of a limited ticket package is to share the cost with friends.

Helpful: Organize your own lottery for special events with names drawn out of a hat to avoid disagreements.

• **Buy tickets at the last minute.** When a computerized seller, such as Ticketmaster, tells you over the phone that a show or game is sold out, do not despair. Even the hottest events release tickets on the day of the performance, frequently with choice seat locations. These tickets may have been held for performers who could not use them...are season ticket returns...or bad credit card orders.

These late-released tickets for sporting events and large-scale concerts usually go back into the inventories of computerized ticket sellers. For theater and opera, you may need to go directly to the box office.

Helpful: Check three hours before the performance to see if any tickets have been released. Then check again one hour before...

and again at show time. It is not unheard of for tickets to be released a few minutes after a performance has begun.

Broadway strategy: Pick three sold-out Broadway shows that you would like to see. Then make the rounds to all three box offices on the same day of the performances...and do it again and again in the hours leading up to show time.

• **Be willing to sit by yourself.** Long after pairs of tickets are sold out, single seats are often still available.

Important: When the only seats that are next to each other are in terrible locations, you usually can do much better by buying separate seats.

Catch up with your partner during intermissions and after the final curtain. After all, you don't communicate much during performances anyway.

• **Beat the crowds.** When tickets to a hot event go on sale through a computerized ticket vendor, the phone lines get swamped. To avoid an endless busy signal, start calling an hour earlier than the listed time. If the salespeople are ready to work, they may be willing to take your order.

Helpful: Try the local number for the vendor in case the 800 number is busy. It also takes less time to redial seven numbers locally than the 11 needed in the 800 number.

• **Try ticket vendors' off-site locations,** which are usually located inside record, department and souvenir stores. Although you may have to pay a small charge, the crowds are likely to be smaller than at the box office.

Unlike the box office, off-site outlets generally accept only cash, not credit cards. That means faster lines.

• **Attack on two fronts.** While waiting in line at a ticket outlet, use a cell-phone to reach the outlet's operators. If you get through before reaching the head of the line, you'll have reserved better seats than everyone else standing in front of you.

• **Order tickets through the Internet.** While using your computer won't allow you to reach a computerized vendor faster than by calling, you will be better prepared to buy the seats you want.

At vendor Web sites you will be able to access starting times...price ranges...and maps that show seat locations—information that a telephone seller may be too busy to provide.

When buying from a ticket broker, hold out for the best possible deal. For especially tough tickets, like the Super Bowl or the NBA Finals, ticket brokers in the city of the event may demand five to 10 times the face value of the tickets.

Good news: Their asking prices are often negotiable or may even drop due to sluggish last-minute demand.

Helpful: Call three brokers. If all of the prices quoted seem too high, be patient—check back...and back again

---

How to Get Anyone to Like You in Two Minutes Or Less

Leil Lowndes, communications consultant and corporate trainer based in New York City, whose clients have included The Walt Disney Company, Kodak and the US Peace Corps. She is author of *How to Instantly Connect with Anyone* (McGraw-Hill). *www.lowndes.com*

If you want to make new friends or land new clients or a new job, you need to make a great first impression—fast. People form permanent opinions of those they meet within just a few minutes of setting eyes upon them.

A study published in *Journal of Experimental Psychology: General* reported that the first impression someone has of a new acquaintance is likely to always dominate the way he/she views this acquaintance. Any later evidence that this first impression might have been erroneous tends to be dismissed as nothing more than an exception to the rule.

The trouble is, making a good first impression can be tricky. Our words, actions, facial expressions and body language all send subtle messages, often without our even realizing that we are doing it.

Below are 11 tricks for making a great first impression. Pick just one or two to try at a time, and add more when those become second nature.

YOUR BODY AND FACE

Facial expression and body position can make you seem more likable to those you meet...

1. Use a slow-flooding smile. Obviously it's a good idea to smile when you meet someone, but instantly switching on a 100-watt smile can make you seem phony. Instead, let your smile build slowly when you make eye contact. This sends the message that there is something about this person in particular that you like.

2. Have "sticky" eyes. People are inclined to like and trust those who make strong eye contact. If you are not a natural at maintaining eye contact, make it a habit to note specific characteristics about new acquaintances' eyes—what color are they...what shape...how far apart...how long are their lashes...how often do they blink...how often do they look away while talking to you? Answering these questions will force you to make strong eye contact with the other person.

Do break eye contact occasionally—staring too intently can make people uncomfortable—but don't do it abruptly. Break eye contact slowly, as if your gaze were stuck on this person and you find it difficult to pull it away.

3. Select an open, welcoming body position. Arrange yourself so that your torso is mostly but not completely facing the person whom you just met. During the first minute of conversation, very slowly and slightly rotate your body to completely face this person.

Exception: A man meeting a woman for the first time should stop a few degrees short of angling his upper body directly toward hers. That seems overly aggressive to some women.

If you are holding a drink or plate of hors d'oeuvres, either find a spot to set it down or hold it down by your side. If you hold it up in front of your chest, your arm will block off your body, making you seem less open. If you are self-conscious about what to do with your hands, use gestures when you talk or even put your hands in your pockets—just don't cross your arms across your chest, which makes you seem closed off.

4. Stand with one foot a few inches forward of the other. Put most of your weight on the forward foot. This stance suggests that you're an energetic person and are interested in the person with whom you are speaking.

YOUR ACTIONS

Even seemingly inconsequential actions can affect how you are viewed during an initial meeting...

5. Find your conversation partner's personal-space comfort zone. Stand too close to a new acquaintance, and you will make him feel uncomfortable. Stand too far away, and the odds increase that he will not feel a connection with you. What's the proper distance? For the average American, it's around 24 inches. Trouble is, that's just an average—everyone is a little different.

The best strategy is to start a conversation with a new acquaintance by placing yourself 26 to 28 inches away. Move toward this person imperceptibly slowly until you see discomfort in his eyes. Then ease back very slightly until that discomfort disappears.

6. When you shake hands, very gently touch your forefinger to the other person's wrist. Aim for the spot on the underside of the wrist where you would take a pulse. This is a very sensitive spot, and gently touching it tends to foster a feeling of warmth and closeness, even though your light contact might not be consciously noticed by the other person. Attempting this wrist touch also forces a deep handshake, which encourages a sense of closeness, too.

7. Treat business cards with respect. A business card symbolizes someone's professional accomplishments. Showing respect for the card shows respect for the person. When you are handed a card, imagine that it is a delicate and precious gift. Hold it gently in your hands. Pause to read it, then carefully place it into your briefcase or purse or, at the very least, your wallet. Never just jam a card into a pocket.

YOUR WORDS

A few tips for an initial conversation...

8. Begin with a conversation starter question or two. Questions that make great icebreakers include, "What do you do?" followed by "How did you decide that you wanted to do that?"...Or (to couples) "How did you two meet?"

9. Slowly nod while people speak. This sends a message of acceptance and encouragement, which makes people feel more in sync with us.

Important: Be aware that men and women can have different interpretations of nodding. Do not nod if a man is saying something with which you completely disagree. Your nodding might be interpreted as agreement. Women, however, tend to interpret nodding as meaning, "I understand," not "I agree."

10. Listen for words that suggest people's interests. The words that people use and the topics that they reference, even in passing, often provide hints at their true areas of interest. If you can spot these words and topics, you can redirect dull, forgettable small-talk conversations toward things that people actually want to talk about.

Examples: If the small talk is about the weather and someone says, "At least the rain is good for my plants," seize on the word plants and ask, "Do you have a garden?" If someone says, "It's been too hot to walk my dogs," seize on the word dogs and ask "What kind of dogs do you have?"

11. Use the same terms as your conversation partner. This is particularly important when discussing topics that tend to matter to a lot of people, such as their families or careers.

Examples: If a parent refers to her "child," you should ask about her "child" as well, not her "little one" or "baby." If someone refers to his "profession," you should refer to it as his "profession," not his "job" or "career."

People tend to use the terms that their family members or closest friends use. If you use the same terms, it increases the odds that this person will feel comfortable with you.

Bottom Line's How to Prosper During the Great Middle-Class Squeeze

Second Printing

281 Tresser Boulevard, Stamford, CT 06901

www.bottomlinepublications.com

Bottom Line Books® is an imprint of Boardroom® Inc., publisher of print periodicals, e-letters and books. We are dedicated to bringing you the best information from the most knowledgeable sources in the world. Our goal is to help you gain greater wealth, better health, more wisdom, extra time and increased happiness.

Printed in the United States of America

BLP/am

Index